BRITISH MOTHS
AND BUTTERFLIES

A photographic guide

Chris Manley

Foreword by Alan Titchmarsh

A&C Black • London

'The wildlife of today is not ours to dispose of as we please.
We have it in trust.
We must account for it to those who come after.'

King George VI

Dedication

To Eve, who is hoping to see a bit more of me now.

Published in the United Kingdom in 2008 by A & C Black Publishers Ltd,
36 Soho Square, London W1D 3QY

Reprinted with corrections 2009, 2010

www.acblack.com

A CIP catalogue record for this book is available from the British Library

ISBN 978-0-7136-8636-4

Commissioning editor: Nigel Redman
Edited and designed by D & N Publishing, Baydon, Wiltshire

Photographs opposite page: Yellow Shell, CMM (top); Poplar Hawk-moth RW (bottom
left); Swallowtail PE (bottom right)

Printed in China
Lion Productions Ltd

10 9 8 7 6 5 4 3

CONTENTS

FOREWORD

I have always been fascinated by butterflies and moths. It was an interest that began during a childhood in the Yorkshire Dales when, as the youngest member of the Wharfedale Naturalists' Society, I was intrigued by that category of wildlife known by the mysterious name of 'Lepidoptera'. It sounded like something to do with dinosaurs. But I quickly discovered the truth, and my interest in butterflies and moths has continued to grow ever since. Perhaps it's because they have such a close association with plants, even though that association means they will often eat my treasures! But I have come to value their presence in the garden every bit as much as the wild flowers and cultivated plants on which they feed. 'Animated flowers', the Prince of Wales calls them, and our landscape – cultivated or wild – would be a poorer place without them.

Their fragility makes them good indicators of a healthy environment. But this means that when pollution threatens they are the first things to suffer, so it is even more important that we know as much as possible about them so that we can safeguard their future.

That knowledge begins with their identification, and this is where Chris Manley's photographic guide comes in. It is, quite simply, sensational. I cannot imagine that such a comprehensive and lavish undertaking has ever been made before, and anyone seriously or even marginally interested in the butterflies and moths that make their homes within our islands should be proud to own a copy.

Butterflies are widely appreciated; moths less so, perhaps because of their mainly nocturnal habits and often duller colours. But this guide shows that they can be every bit as spectacular as their butterfly counterparts and are equally important in terms of their preservation and our need to understand them.

Chris's achievement in putting together this tour de force deserves the support of anyone claiming to be interested in nature, and I'm delighted to recommend it wholeheartedly. I also can't wait to put it to good use!

Alan Titchmarsh
Vice President of Butterfly Conservation

Swallowtail butterfly nectaring on Lavender.
CMM

INTRODUCTION

This book came about after a chance remark by Dave Green following a moth-watching trip to Hungary in 2006. Commenting on the huge number of species that we had seen in a week, he said that with a list like that it might almost be possible to photograph all the British species, which started me thinking. A few weeks later, a chance meeting with Cheryle Sifontes at the British Birdwatching Fair in Rutland resulted in finding an enthusiastic publisher who wanted to publish a comprehensive book on British moths.

In July 2006 I had published a small book about moths in Dorset with 500 species illustrated using my own photographs. The idea of 'doing the job properly' to illustrate the whole British list seemed like an interesting and very worthwhile challenge, though not something I would be able to achieve using only my own photographs. There are already guides available on the market illustrated with excellent artwork, and others with photographs of dead specimens, so I decided that the book would show only photographs of living insects. Although butterflies are well covered photographically in other books, I felt it worthwhile to include them again here as an important, though small, group of lepidopteran families.

The initial plan was to cover just the Macro moths and butterflies, but so many photographers kindly offered to contribute a multitude of additional superb images of Micros and larvae that it would have been foolish not to include them. As a result, not only are over 850 Macros and 74 butterflies illustrated, including several that are extinct or very rare migrants to this country, but also 314 species of larvae, pupae and eggs, and almost 500 Micros. The caterpillars and Micros included are not a comprehensive collection but will hopefully provide much useful information nevertheless.

This book aims to convey the beauty and fascination of moths to a new audience of both adults and children. The photographs are not only there to aid identification, but are also portraits of live moths in the wild and in natural poses. As well as showcasing the wealth and variety of moths to be found in Britain, it is hoped that the book will also provide a useful reference for those already interested in these wonderful insects.

Chris Manley

Slender Scotch Burnet nectaring on Nettle-leaved Bellflower. CMM

ACKNOWLEDGEMENTS

This book could not have been produced without the generous contributions from the photographers listed in the Photo Credits, who kindly entrusted me with so many superb images. I am deeply grateful to every one of them.

Special thanks are due to Phil Sterling and Roy Leverton who, in addition to lending slides, also gave up their time to check over the images for any identification errors. The Macro Moth and Butterfly Larval Foodplants list is largely based on the work of Tony Pritchard, for which many thanks. I would also like to thank Mark Parsons at Butterfly Conservation, Martin Honey at the Natural History Museum in London, Mark Tunmore at Atropos and Ian Kimber at UK Moths for their invaluable assistance, and Alan Titchmarsh for his kind comments in the foreword.

I would like to thank my editor, Nigel Redman, for not only persuading the publishers A & C Black that this was a worthwhile project, but also for guiding me through how the book should look. David and Namrita Price-Goodfellow and their team at D & N Publishing have done a brilliant job on the design and layout of the pages, and special thanks to Sarah Church for all her work on the layouts, and for somehow managing to incorporate all my last-minute additions and alterations.

My sincere thanks go to everyone involved in this enterprise for their help and input. It has been much appreciated.

PHOTO CREDITS

Photographers are credited at the end of the species descriptions using their initials as below. If a species is illustrated by more than one photo, initials are listed for each photograph, in the order that they appear (reading from left to right).

MB:	Mike Bailey
JSB:	Jon Baker
CB:	Chris Bentley
PB:	Paul Butter
MC:	Martin Cade
AC:	Andrew Charlton
SC:	Sarah Church
PGC:	Patrick Clement
ARC:	Andy Collins
GAC:	Graham Collins
PAD:	Peter Davey
TD:	Tony Davison
MD:	Matthew Deans
RDJ:	Rob De Jong
KDR:	Kevin Du Rose
PE:	Pete Eeles
DE:	David Element
GF:	Gianpiero Ferrari
DF:	Dave Foot
MF:	Mark Forster
AF:	Andy Foster
AMF:	Anne & Mat Frijsinger
JG:	Jan Gaisler
JEG:	Janet Graham
DGG:	Dave Green
LG:	Lee Gregory
MJH:	Michael J Hammett

BH:	Brian Hancock
SH:	Steve Hatch
JBH:	Jeff Higgott
RH:	Robin Howard
MJ:	Michael Jones
IK:	Ian Kimber
RL:	Roy Leverton
AM:	Andy Mackay
CMM:	Chris Manley
DM:	Daniel Morel
SN:	Steve Nash
TJN:	Tim Norriss
NO:	Nir Ofir, Wikimedia
DJP:	David Painter
MSP:	Mark Parsons/Butterfly Conservation
SP:	Sarah Patton
RPJ:	Rob Petley-Jones
JPo:	Jim Porter
KP-G:	Kai Price-Goodfellow
SR:	Stuart Read
NS:	Neil Sherman
CS:	Chris Steeman
PHS:	Phil Sterling
BS:	Barry Stewart
CJS:	Caron Stubbs
SS:	Safian Szabolcs
KT:	Keith Tailby
TT:	Tom Tams
IT:	Ian Tillotson
BU:	Bill Urwin
JV:	Jeroen Voogd
RW:	Rosemary Winnall
BY:	Barry Yates

HOW TO USE THIS BOOK

OBJECTIVES

The first aim of this book is to provide sufficient information to be able to identify almost any Macro moth or butterfly recorded in Britain, using a combination of photographs of the live insect and textual information. The 'almost' acknowledges that there can be local variations, melanic (dark or black) examples, aberrations, or simply very worn individuals whose identity will be cause for discussion. The identification information provides guidance on where to look for target species. Additionally, there are photographs of a significant number of Micro moths and caterpillars, which should enable positive identification in a great many cases.

The book also aims to be visually stimulating and to celebrate, and raise awareness of, the stunning beauty and diversity of the Lepidoptera in all their forms and life stages.

LOG NUMBERS

The layout of this book is based on the Bradley *Checklist of Lepidoptera Recorded from the British Isles* (Bradley 2000), which assigns a number to each species, beginning with the most primitive moths. Some of these primitive moths do not have a proboscis to suck nectar but have mandibles to eat pollen instead.

The Bradley list includes all Lepidoptera that have been recorded in Britain, even records from perhaps 200 years ago that were possibly fraudulent, or species that have only been imported once accidentally.

The list is continually updated as new arrivals appear, either as migrants in hot summers or imports with exotic plants or foods. When a moth or butterfly new to Britain is confirmed, its position on the list is determined by experts at the Natural History Museum and a number is assigned. These late additions account for the numbers being suffixed with 'a' or 'b' or even 'c'.

THE PLATES

The photographic plates follow the Bradley order, with brief notes summarising each family. However, there are a few exceptions. Some of the most primitive moths are relatively large, such as the Swifts, Leopards and Goat, Festoon and Triangle, Foresters and Burnets, and Clearwings. Although they appear early on in the checklist they are given honorary 'Macro' status so are included here with these as is customary.

The emphasis in the pictures is on clearly illustrating the insect. The photographs are not laid out to any particular scale, but a wingspan in millimetres is given in the species accounts for comparative purposes. An accurate and consistent scale would not really work as picture sizes would be so variable and individual insects can vary greatly in size. Life size could be useful but larger than life shows far more detail, which is more interesting and also aids identification.

In general the layouts are roughly relative to the size of insect. There are exceptions throughout, usually simply because a picture merits display status, such as Scarce Merveille du Jour or Swallowtail Butterfly. Occasionally, more than one picture is shown for aesthetic purposes, such as for Black-veined Moth, even though it is not strictly necessary purely for identification.

THE PHOTOGRAPHS

Each photograph shows the log number (*see* above) with the relevant text included on the same spread. Where appropriate the symbols ♂ (male) or ♀ (female) are shown, and also 'aberration' or form names.

SPECIES ACCOUNTS

Apart from studying the photographs, other facts should be considered:
Flight period, e.g. a spring-flyer like Pine Beauty cannot be seen in autumn.
Distribution, e.g. Scotch Annulet only occurs in northern Scotland or western Ireland, so a similar moth elsewhere in Britain must be the Annulet.
Habitat, e.g. Dark Crimson Underwing is found only in ancient oak woods in the New Forest, whereas Red Underwing could appear almost anywhere in southern Britain.

The descriptions in the species accounts give the following information:
1. **Bradley 2000 Checklist number** as described above in Log Numbers.
2. **English (vernacular) name**. Generally used for Macros, and for some of the larger, most common or most important Micros. Names are often descriptive of looks (Leopard Moth has spots), feeding habits

(Larch Pug feeds on Larch tree needles), or perhaps the name of first recorder (Sarah Patton caught the first British example of Patton's Tiger).

3. **Scientific name**, in italics. This is the name used worldwide regardless of local names and language and is either Latin, Greek or a mixture of both. These names are often descriptive: for example, White Plume Moth is *Pterophorus pentadactyla* – *pentadactyla* means five fingers in Greek, resembling the wing shape of the moth. Similarly, the Lappet is *Gastropacha quercifolia* – *quercifolia* is the Latin for 'oak leaf', which the moth resembles in coloration and outline.

4. **Wingspan**. An average wingspan (in mm) is given for comparative purposes.

5. **Scarcity**. The status of each species is allocated by the Joint Nature Conservation Committee, the statutory body that advises the government on conservation issues.
RDB stands for Red Data Book, followed by a number: 1 is the rarest, with the moth occurring in five or fewer 10km squares in Britain, 2 occurs in six to ten 10km squares, 3 in 11–15 10km squares. The letter p before RDB indicates provisional, i.e. the moth fits the criteria but has not yet been listed.
Na is Nationally Scarce A: recorded in 16–30 10km squares since 1980.
Nb is Nationally Scarce B: recorded from 31–100 10km squares since 1980. This is only about 3.5% of the land area of Britain.
Local. Recorded from 101–300 10km squares since 1960.
Common. Recorded from over 300 10km squares since 1960.
Migrant. Regularly, though not necessarily often, recorded in Britain but originating from another country. These lepidopterans do not overwinter in this country. Very few of the migrants, except Red Admiral butterfly, deliberately travel to and from Britain. They nearly all arrive when the wind and weather conditions are right to carry them across the Channel, the North Sea or even the Atlantic Ocean.
Vagrant/Accidental. Origin uncertain, dubious or just a very rare stray.
Import. Brought to Britain from overseas with timber, vegetables, flowers, etc .
Synanthropic. Ecologically associated with humans, in flour mills, etc .
Naturalised. Formerly migrant or import, now established and resident.

6. **Flight Period**. Approximate months that the insect may be on the wing. Weather conditions can have a significant effect on emergence dates. Some lepidopterans have a second brood, or may hibernate and re-appear in spring, so more than one flight period may be shown.

7. **Adult Identification, Distribution, Habitat**. Descriptions and distinctive features are given if similar species cause confusion. Distribution and habitat are important aids to identification (*see* above introduction to Species Accounts), and provide clues as to where to search for a species. They are not in themselves diagnostic, as moths of course can fly and may occasionally turn up a long way from their breeding place.

8. **FP – Larval Foodplant**. An important clue to identity or to knowing where to look for a moth is the distribution of the foodplant. If the foodplant does not occur in the area, that can preclude some species. For example, the common and widespread Frosted Orange has a wide range of foodplants, whereas the similar Fisher's Estuarine Moth, which flies at the same time of year, feeds only on Hogs Fennel. Notes are also given on which parts of the host plant are eaten, for example some Micros mine leaves, some larvae eat flowers, or leaves, or live underground in roots, or inside plant stems or perhaps in wood.

9. **Photographer**. Initials are of the photographer(s), *see* 'Photo Credits', p.6.

In the caterpillar section just the Bradley 2000 Checklist number, English name, scientific name, approximate maximum length, photographer's initials, and a page cross reference to the adult insect are given.

LARVAL FOODPLANTS (see p.328)

This list has been largely compiled by Tony Pritchard from the foodplant information included in Jim Porter's invaluable *Colour Identification Guide to Caterpillars of the British Isles* (1997), and contains the following information:

- The English (vernacular) name.
- Scientific name in italics.
- The species of Macro moth in alphabetical order that feed on the foodplant.
- The species of butterflies, if any, that feed on the foodplant.

Many moths appear more than once in the list, as many species feed on several different host plants.

Although the foodplant is given in the Species Accounts, this does not necessarily help if an unknown caterpillar is found in the wild. Identifying the plant that the larva is on means that the choice of possible Macro moth or butterfly can be narrowed down by using this list. In some cases of common plants or trees (oak, birch, Beech, grasses, etc .) there will be a large number of prospective species of moth, but often the choice will be very limited. Studying the details of the species will further narrow down the options, and there may well be a photograph in the Caterpillar section to go with the description.

Conversely, if a new or unusual plant is found it is possible to see what might feed on it and when, and decide whether to look for larvae at a suitable time.

HOW TO SEE MOTHS AND BUTTERFLIES

Small Tortoiseshells, a honey bee and a hoverfly enjoying an Ice Plant. CMM

Moths and butterflies exploit almost every habitat, so it follows that they can be found almost anywhere and in several different ways. Sometimes they can be found casually in a garden, resting on a wall by a light or flying by when you are out for a walk, but other times only as a result of determined, targeted searching in a specific habitat.

Butterflies, of course, generally fly in daylight, usually preferring sunshine, so this is the time to search or look out for them. There are more species of day-flying moths in Britain than there are butterflies, so moths may turn up at the same time. Most gardens and parks will have flowers that will produce nectar on which insects can feed. Buddleia is always popular and is not known as the Butterfly Bush for nothing! Ice plants, *Sedum*, also attract plenty of butterflies (as shown right) and Tobacco flowers, *Nicotiana*, are irresistible to some moths and butterflies.

Most moths are attracted to light, though it is unclear why. However, attracted they are and probably many people will have seen their first moth on the outside of a lighted window at night. Placing a clean glass over the moth and sliding a piece of card between the window and the glass will catch the moth unharmed so it can be brought indoors to be studied. Once identified and admired it can then be released back outside.

This attraction to light is exploited with mercury-vapour (mv) lamps. These are very bright and produce ultra-violet light, which has been found to be the most attractive to moths and other insects. Ultra-violet is also produced by actinic lights, which are the blue ones in food shops used in fly killers. Actinic lamps are not very bright but will still attract plenty of moths. Moth traps operating with mv or actinic bulbs are by far the easiest method of attracting and seeing large numbers of moths of many different species. Mv lamps are very bright and may not be popular with neighbours, but actinics are good in the garden or on a balcony or patio and will not dazzle anyone else, though catches will be smaller than with mv bulbs.

Moths will come to a light and then either rest nearby or dive down below the bulb to hide. Traps exploit this by giving moths somewhere to go, usually a few egg boxes in the trap with the lamp above. It can be very exciting sitting around a trap on a warm summer evening watching moths appear out of the darkness heading for the lamp. It helps to have a supply of clear plastic pots to contain individual moths once they have settled. Once safely 'potted' the moth can be studied at leisure, identified, recorded, passed around to other 'mothers', compared to other potted insects, etc., before being released unharmed or retained temporarily for breeding or further study.

Inevitably, as the interest in moths grows, the new moth recorder will want to search further afield. Fortunately, lightweight portable generators are readily available. These can easily be carried in a car or wheelbarrow and provide power for an mv light trap in locations far from mains electricity. This will mean that new habitats can be explored and targeted searches made in suitable country for a specific moth. The picture shows the Dorset coastline several kilometres from the nearest road or electricity supply. The white-

The Dorset coast, near Swanage, is an exciting trap site. CMM

flowered plant in the foreground is Nottingham Catchfly, the rare foodplant for the Red Data Book species White Spot. Running the light here overnight attracted several of these beautiful moths.

Many moths and, of course, butterflies can be seen flying during the day, or at least persuaded to fly if their habitat is disturbed. Carrying a hand net will give a chance to capture the flying insect unharmed. It can either then be inspected in the net or harmlessly 'potted' for positive identification. It is extremely difficult in many cases to be certain of the identity of a small flying insect without 'potting' and impossible to show it to anyone else for confirmation.

Dusk and soon afterwards on a warm summer evening can be a very rewarding moth-hunting time. Carrying a net and a few pots, as well as wearing a head torch, will mean that many moths can be caught and identified by taking a stroll along a quiet hedgerow, woodland ride or open field whilst it is still not really dark enough for moths to come to the mv trap.

Later in the evening nectar sources can attract many moths. In the spring sallow blossom can be especially productive as other food sources are scarce; ivy flowers are popular in autumn. Artificial nectar sources can be prepared. All that is required is sugar dissolved in water, perhaps with molasses, beer or rum added and painted onto a tree or post, or something similar.

Pheromones are the sexually attractive scents given off by virgin female moths advertising that they are available to mate. Male moths smell these with their antennae, sometimes from several hundred metres away, and fly towards the source. If a female Emperor Moth is bred from a pupa and placed outside in sunshine in early May it is astonishing how males can appear from nowhere within minutes. The female in the photo was bred from eggs laid the previous year, the darker, smaller male is wild and quickly appeared in my garden. The feathery antennae of some males such as Emperors provide a larger surface area to smell with than the simple antennae of females.

Mating Emperor moths, female above, male below. CMM

Artificial pheromones are available for some species. These have been developed commercially for controlling pest species, but pheromone lures have been found to work very well for Clearwing moths. These are available from the equipment suppliers listed on p.342, with notes on which moths to use them for. Since Clearwings are day-flying moths that do not come to light, they used to be thought rather scarce, but using pheromones has shown that, in some cases, they can be quite common.

Five male Welsh Clearwings attracted to a pheromone lure. DGG

Finally, studying lepidopterans has to include their caterpillars, pupae and even eggs. All of these may be encountered casually in the field but they can also be actively sought out. Sweeping a net through vegetation for insects will often collect caterpillars as well, and this can be more productive at night. Many species hide from predators by day, so torchlight can show up feeding larvae. Holding a tray or upturned umbrella under a branch and tapping it sharply (known as 'beating') will often dislodge lots of caterpillars. Checking with the foodplant list and illustrations should provide identification. Rearing caterpillars through to adulthood can be exciting and rewarding and provide confirmation of identity.

HOW TO PHOTOGRAPH MOTHS AND BUTTERFLIES

The author having vital fluids drained by a Lesser Purple Emperor in Josvafo National Park, Hungary. ARC

Photography is an important recording tool. Clear pictures of an insect will provide positive identification and confirmation of records long after the insect has flown away.

Digital cameras have revolutionised moth watching. Many are able to focus very close to their subject, ideal for small moths, and also have a built-in flash, which means that pictures can be taken at night when moths are coming to a trap (although sometimes the scales on the insect can produce reflections from the flash). A camera on automatic will probably use flash, which will produce a sharp image, but may produce stark reflections and shadows. I prefer to use natural light without flash, but it is essential to put the camera on a tripod, ideally with a remote shutter release, or the photo may well be disappointingly blurred when viewed on a computer.

If possible, the camera should be set to Aperture Priority with a large 'f' number. This will give good 'depth of field', so that as much of the moth as possible is sharply in focus, but will mean that the exposure time is longer – hence the need for a stable tripod to avoid blurred pictures. If you have a telephoto lens with your camera this can be a big help, enabling photos to be taken several metres away. Looming over a butterfly to get a close-up shot with a macro lens may well disturb the subject!

When trapping moths at night, my preference is to leave the light running all night. This can frequently involve sleeping in the back of the car but pays dividends for photography in the early morning. Apart from being a wonderful time of day to be outside anyway, there are fewer biting insects about, and often some stunning views if the trap is sited away from civilisation.

Moths tend to be fairly docile around dawn when it is relatively cool and not bright enough for them to feel exposed and try to hide. This makes it easier to go through the trap and record the contents. Moths tapped off onto surrounding vegetation or a tree trunk will often sit quietly where they land. This is the ideal opportunity to take a picture.

Moths can be taken home in plastic pots (one per pot) for later photography, or even photographed in the pot through the plastic for a simple 'record' shot. They can be kept unharmed in the cool of the fridge and brought out one by one to be photographed in controlled conditions, from where hopefully they will not escape. They will be relatively docile, being cool, but may well appreciate a small drip of weak sugar and water solution to drink, applied to whatever they are on for the picture with a small artists brush. Many of my pictures are taken in the kitchen near the window, but not in direct sun.

Butterflies outside in the open rarely sit still for long and may be difficult to approach closely. Patience, and some suitable nectar-producing flowers, will generally provide the best photo-opportunities. They may also be seen soaking up the sun on a warm wall, and occasionally they will congregate around damp ground to take up minerals. The picture above shows minerals in sweat being taken up on a hot day. Ripe fruit will also attract butterflies.

As with all photography, the trick is to take plenty of shots and discard most of them, which, of course, is one of the advantages of digital photography. With moths and butterflies it is also worth taking a shot or two as soon as possible in case the insect flies away. If it doesn't, there is the opportunity to take a better picture and possibly move in a lot closer for the intimate portrait that reveals the details rarely seen in the field. After your first successes, there will probably be no stopping you!

The Six-spot Burnet is a common day-flying grassland species. PB

CLASSIFICATION AND DISTINGUISHING FEATURES

Moths and butterflies (Lepidoptera) are scientifically classified as members of the CLASS Insecta, insects, of which there have been some 20,000 species recorded in Britain. Insects are divided into 29 ORDERS, of which Lepidoptera is one.

Lepidoptera are members of the SUBCLASS Endopterygota, which contains nine orders. The Endopterygota develop wings internally, and these cannot be seen in the early larval stages. This is unlike the Exopterygota, such as grasshoppers, dragonflies or mayflies, whose young stages, known as nymphs, resemble adults with visible but under-developed wings. Endopterygota are winged insects whose life involves a complex metamorphosis. The life cycle is split into three parts: the egg hatches as a larva (caterpillar), which bears no resemblance to the adult; during this stage eating and growth takes place. This is followed by a sessile pupal stage, during which the insect undergoes a dramatic transformation before emergence as a mature, fully developed adult ready to breed.

Moths and butterflies are members of the ORDER Lepidoptera (Greek: *lepidos* = scale, pteron = *wing*), which have coloured scales on their wings, laid out like tiles on a roof as shown in the photograph below of a Swallowtail butterfly hind wing. These scales are loosely attached to the wings and are easily worn off, which causes no harm to the insect, though it can make identification more tricky! Lepidoptera have three main body parts (as do all insects): head, thorax and abdomen.

The *head* has one pair of eyes, mouthparts (usually a coiled proboscis, a hollow feeding tube for sucking nectar) and one pair of antennae. Male moths often have feathery antennae for better detection of the scent (pheromones) of females (e.g. Plumed Prominent or Reed Tussock), whereas females' antennae are plain.

The *thorax* has six legs, as have all insects, and two pairs of wings (if present). Some females may have only vestigial wings and be flightless, such as the Vapourer.

The *abdomen* (hind body) stores food if the adult is able to feed, or energy reserves provided by the larva in the case of non-feeding moths. The sex organs are also located in the abdomen. Females appear very plump before eggs are laid, males are slim with a pair of claspers at the tip of the abdomen for gripping the female during copulation.

About 2,500 species of Lepidoptera have been recorded in Britain. These are split into around 50 FAMILIES, usually with SUB-FAMILIES grouped within these. There is still discussion, and probably always will be, regarding these family splits, as well as their individual members in the light of current research and the latest discoveries.

The 50 families are commonly split into 25 Micros, 19 Macros and 6 (now 5) Butterflies. The terms Micro, Macro and butterfly are fairly artificial and are mainly based on common usage. Micros in general are small, primitive moths. However, some are large but primitive and so are included in Macros (*see* 'Micro Moths' introduction, p.15). Many members of the Pyralidae, a Micro moth family, are easily large enough to be studied and mistaken for Macros. The small group of Butterfly families fits between the Micros and Macros (*see* 'Butterflies' introduction, p.75).

Within the sub-families are the individual SPECIES. Members of a species are recognised as being able to interbreed and exchange genetic information. By definition, separate species cannot interbreed. Closely related species are grouped into GENERA (singular, GENUS).

FORMS are insects that may look different but are actually the same species and can breed together. Several moths have a melanic (very dark) form, such as Peppered Moth; some have different forms that occur equally frequently in the same population, such as Burnished Brass. Garden Tigers are so variable that no two individuals are identical but there are also two rare but recognised forms. The prize for 'most variable moth' has to go to the Micro *Acleris cristana* (*see* p.43), with 137 described and named forms!

ABERRATIONS are unusual examples of moths or butterflies (*see* Scalloped Oak p.154). They do not occur regularly like the forms. Occasionally aberrations occur showing both male and female characteristics, known as gynandromorphs, though these are extremely rare.

Hind wing of Swallowtail butterfly, showing scales. PE

LEPIDOPTERAN ANATOMY, CATERPILLAR

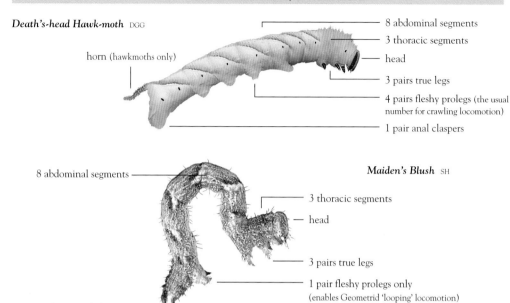

Death's-head Hawk-moth DGG

horn (hawkmoths only)

8 abdominal segments
3 thoracic segments
head
3 pairs true legs
4 pairs fleshy prolegs (the usual number for crawling locomotion)
1 pair anal claspers

8 abdominal segments

Maiden's Blush SH

3 thoracic segments
head

3 pairs true legs
1 pair fleshy prolegs only (enables Geometrid 'looping' locomotion)

1 pair anal claspers

LEPIDOPTERAN ANATOMY, ADULT

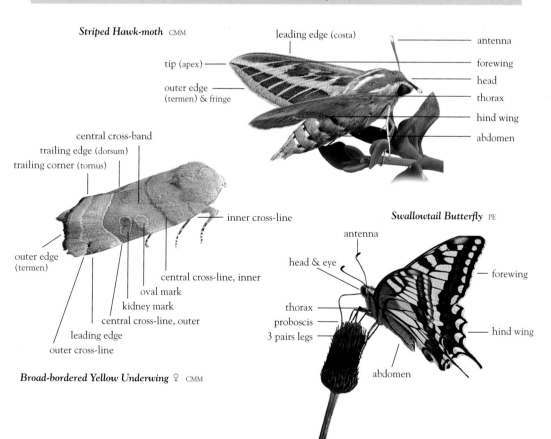

Striped Hawk-moth CMM

leading edge (costa)
antenna
forewing
head
thorax
hind wing
abdomen

tip (apex)
outer edge (termen) & fringe

central cross-band
trailing edge (dorsum)
trailing corner (tornus)

inner cross-line

outer edge (termen)

central cross-line, inner
oval mark
kidney mark
central cross-line, outer
leading edge
outer cross-line

Swallowtail Butterfly PE

antenna
head & eye
forewing
thorax
proboscis
3 pairs legs
hind wing
abdomen

Broad-bordered Yellow Underwing ♀ CMM

LIFE CYCLE OF A TYPICAL LEPIDOPTERAN

These photographs of White Admiral illustrate the stages of the complex metamorphosis in the lepidopteran life cycle, which is identical for moths and butterflies. Early larval stages are completely different from the adult. In simple metamorphosis, as exhibited by dragonflies for example, early stages resemble the adult and are known as nymphs.

The adult insect splits open the pupa to crawl out. The wings are soft and crumpled but are pumped up through the veins and harden in a few hours. Males seek out a mate, females seek suitable habitats to lay eggs, often travelling considerable distances. Some adults do not feed at all, using energy supplies stored as a caterpillar; others feed through their proboscis on nectar, sap runs or juicy ripe fruit and live as adults for a few weeks. Some adults hibernate over winter, usually in caves or hollow trees where the temperature is more stable. Many species have two or more generations each year, so first brood larvae will develop into adults within a few weeks of hatching from the egg; second broods may well overwinter either as a larva or pupa.

Eggs are laid by the adult insect, usually on the foodplant, sometimes in batches, sometimes singly. Some moths scatter their eggs in flight over suitable habitat. Eggs can hatch within a few days or overwinter to hatch next spring.

White Admiral life stages PE

By the time the caterpillar is fully grown, it will have consumed all the food reserves needed to produce a full-sized adult. It then enters a resting stage as a pupa, also known as a chrysalis, with a hard outer shell. This may be attached to foliage, amongst leaves on the ground or hidden in a silk cocoon underground. In this state, outlines of adult features such as wings and head can be seen. The pupa may develop in weeks, or overwinter to hatch the following year.

Caterpillars, also known as larvae, usually hatch from the eggs after a few days of development. They feed and grow, changing their skin, and often their appearance, as they do so. These stages, usually four, are known as instars. Some will be fully grown in a few weeks; others may overwinter to finish development in spring, and some may take 2 or 3 years.

MICRO MOTHS

The Micros are a far larger group of moths than the Macros, with around 1,500 species on the British list.

Generally speaking, the Micros are small moths, but as the taxonomic classification places the most primitive moths at the beginning, and some of these happen to be large moths, such as the swifts and Goat Moth, the split between Macro and Micro is a matter of convenience. The swifts, Goat Moth, clearwings, burnets, etc. are generally given 'honorary' Macro status owing to their size and are accordingly placed with the other Macros here as is usual.

One of the smallest moths in the world is found in Britain, with a wingspan of a mere 3–4mm: *Enteucha acetosae* is very local, and is usually found as a larva that mines the leaves of sorrel, often turning them red (*see* photos right).

A very large moth with a 100mm wingspan that is still technically a 'Micro' is the Surreptitious, *Paysandisia archon* (*see* below). The example illustrated is one of only two British records, almost certainly imported as eggs or larvae in ornamental palms. This moth is native to South America but has also been found on palms imported to southern France and Spain. The caterpillars bore into stems and can cause considerable damage to, and even kill, the host tree.

The caterpillars of most Micros can wriggle backwards, unlike most Macros.

118 *Enteucha acetosae* 3–4mm Nb. Apr–Sep. World's smallest moth. In south-east England and north Wales. **FP** Mines in leaves of Sheep's & Common Sorrel, turning them red. JEG

384a *Paysandisia archon* **Surreptitious** 100mm Migrant/Import. Unmistakable. Originally from South America. Two British records almost certainly imported in ornamental palm trees. Now resident in south of France. **FP** Bores inside palm trees. SP

MICROPTERIGIDAE

These are very primitive moths, which evolved with flowering plants 100 million years ago. The adults feed on pollen; the larvae of some species are unknown.

1 Micropterix tunbergella 10mm Common. Jun–Jul. Day-flying, feeds on pollen, in woods. Not found in Scotland. CMM
4 Micropterix aruncella 7mm Common. May–Aug.

Wood margins and pasture, throughout Britain. Adult feeds on plant pollen. SR
5 Micropterix calthella 9mm Common. May–Jun. Abundant throughout, feeds on grass pollen. NS, PGC

ERIOCRANIIDAE

These are primitive micros. The adults do not feed, whereas the larvae feed in mines in leaves of birch and other trees.

6 Eriocrania subpurpurella 12mm Common. Apr–May. Metallic gold with tiny purple spots. In every oak wood throughout Britain. Flies in sunshine or at night. **FP** Mines in oak leaves. CMM
8 Eriocrania unimaculella 10mm Common. Mar–Apr. Flies in sunshine in birch. Throughout Britain. **FP** Mines in birch leaves. NS
9 Eriocrania sparrmannella 12mm Local. Apr–May. Day flying in sunshine amongst birch. Golden, often

with purple markings. **FP** Mines in birch leaves. CMM
12 Eriocrania sangii 12mm Local. Mar–Apr. Widespread. Flies in sunshine amongst birch. Often similar to *E. semipurpurella* below. Genitalia examination required for confirmation. **FP** Mine as blotch in birch leaf. CMM
13 Eriocrania semipurpurella 14mm Common. Mar–Apr. Widespread throughout, in birch woods. Flies in sunshine. **FP** On birch. NS

NEPTICULIDAE

There are around 100 moths in this group, many of which are very similar. All are tiny and feed from mines in leaves. For positive identification, they are either bred from larvae or the genitalia examined.

50 Stigmella aurella 6mm Common. May, Aug–Sep. Abundant throughout most of Britain except northern Scotland. Leaf mines visible wherever foodplant grows. **FP** Bramble. PHS, CMM
54 Stigmella auromarginella 5mm pRDB1. May, Aug–Sep. Very similar to *S. aurella* but head less golden. Only found in Weymouth, Dorset and Burren, Ireland.

Leaf mine is edged with reddish purple as shown. **FP** Bramble. PHS
77 Stigmella tityrella Common. Apr–May, Jul–Aug. Throughout Britain. Leaf mine is distinctive, on underside of leaf always between ribs, not crossing ribs. **FP** Beech. PHS

INCURVARIIDAE

Includes two species with comb-like (pectinate) antennae and the moths known as 'longhorns', due to their very long but smooth antennae. Most fly by day, but some also come to light.

130 Incurvaria masculella 14mm Common. May. Male has comb-like (pectinate) antennae. Throughout in woods, scrubland. **FP** Hawthorn and other bushes. CMM

131 Incurvaria oehlmanniella 14mm Local. Jun–Jul. Similar to above but with creamy mark on forewing leading edge. In woods in south but open moors up to 1,000m in Wales and Scotland. **FP** On Bilberry and Cloudberry. CMM

LONGHORNS: ADELIDAE

Longhorns have distinctive, very long, antennae, with the males possessing the longest.

140 *Nematopogon swammerdamella* 20mm Common. May–Jun. Britain's largest Longhorn. Widespread in woodland throughout. **FP** Dead leaves. CMM

144 *Nemophora fasciella* Horehound Longhorn Moth 15mm Nb. Jul. Male has much longer antennae than female. Very local in south and south-east England, Yorkshire and Lancashire. Flies in sunshine. **FP** Black Horehound. NS

147 *Nemophora scabiosella* 20mm Local. Jun–Jul. Mainly in central southern England. **FP** Seeds and leaves of scabious. PAD

148 *Nemophora degeerella* 20mm Common. May–Jun. Flies at dusk in damp woodland in England and Wales. **FP** Dead leaves, often amongst Bluebells. CMM

150 *Adela reaumurella* 15mm Common. May–Jun. Throughout, but local in Scotland. Flies by day, males in swarms at tree tops. **FP** On oak and leaf litter in portable case. SH, NS

151 *Adela croesella* 13mm Local. Jun. Scattered through England and Wales, Perthshire in Scotland. Flies in sun. **FP** Sea Buckthorn, Wild Privet. NS

152 *Adela rufimitrella* 11mm Common. May–Jun. Throughout, common in south. Flies in sun. **FP** Leaves of Cuckoo Flower, Garlic Mustard. SR

153 *Adela fibulella* 9mm Common. Jun. Throughout Britain. Smallest Longhorn. Flies in sunshine, visits flowers of foodplant. **FP** Germander Speedwell seeds, leaves. NS

CASE-BEARERS: PSYCHIDAE

The 21 British species are known as case-bearers. Larvae construct a protective case from debris, which they carry with them, like a hermit crab. Females of some species are self-fertile (parthenogenic), and some do not fly. Adults do not feed.

181 *Taleporia tubulosa* 18mm Common. May–Jun. Throughout Britain to southern Scotland. Larva lives in case attached to tree trunks, walls, etc. **FP** Eats lichens, decaying plants. TJN, NS

185 *Luffia ferchaultella* 6mm Common. Jul. Abundant in south Britain on tree trunks in damp woods. Female form only. Larva lives in case attached to tree trunk. **FP** Eats lichens. CMM

191 *Acanthopsyche atra* 20mm Nb. May–Jun. Heaths and moors of southern England, north Wales, Pennines, Scottish Highlands. Female flightless. Eggs can be distributed by birds after female is eaten. Larva lives in case. **FP** Feeds on grasses, sallows. PHS, PHS

192 *Pachythelia villosella* 30mm RDB2. Jun–Aug. Only on heaths of New Forest, Hampshire and Dorset. Female flightless. Male similar to above, but larger. Larva lives in case (illustrated) made from heather. CMM

140

144

147

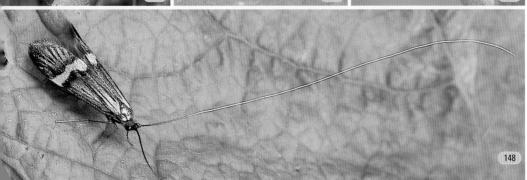
148

150 ♂

150 ♀

151 ♀

152 ♂

153

larva 181

181 ♂

larva 185

♀ emerging from case 191

191 ♂

larva 192

TINEIDAE

There are over 50 British species, including clothes moths. They are usually scavengers of dead plant and animal matter, fungi and rotten wood. They rest with their wings held in a tent-like aspect, and sometimes run rather than fly when disturbed.

196 *Morophaga choragella* 30mm Local. Jun–Aug. In woods in south-east England. **FP** Bracket fungi. NS
220 *Nemapogon clematella* 14mm Nb. Jun–Aug. Widespread in England and Wales in woods, hedgerows. **FP** In rotten wood and fungi, especially on dead hazel. PHS
224 *Triaxomera parasitella* 20mm Common. May–Jul. Widespread through most of southern Britain. **FP** Bracket fungi, rotten wood. NS
228 *Monopis weaverella* 12mm Local. May–Aug. Widespread throughout but local. **FP** Scavenger in fox faeces, rabbit and fox carcasses. NS
229 *Monopis obviella* 12mm Common. May–Oct. Mainly in southern Britain. **FP** Scavenger in birds' nests and wool. CMM
232 *Monopis monachella* 18mm Local. May–Sep. In fens of East Anglia. **FP** Scavenger in owl pellets, birds' nests, animal carcasses. NS

246 *Tinea semifulvella* 20mm Common. May–Sep. Abundant throughout in birds' nests. **FP** Scavenger in nests. CMM
247 *Tinea trinotella* 15mm Common. May–Aug. Abundant throughout in birds' nests. **FP** Scavenger in nests, feeding from a portable case. SR
263 *Lyonetia clerkella* Apple Leaf Miner 8mm Common. Jun–Oct, Apr. Throughout in fruit trees. Adult overwinters. **FP** Mine in leaf of Apple, etc. CMM
274 *Bucculatrix ulmella* 8mm Common. Apr–Jun, Aug. Throughout Britain. **FP** Mines in oak leaves. SR

GRACILLARIIDAE

There are 87 British representatives of this family. The early instars of the larvae drink sap from leaves or tender bark, before developing mouth parts to actually eat leaves. The study of larval leaf-mines is key to identification.

281 *Caloptilia populetorum* 12mm Local. Aug–Sep, Apr–May. Widespread on heathland, moors and open woods throughout. Hibernates. **FP** Mines in birch leaves. NS

282 *Caloptilia elongella* 15mm Common. Jun, Sep, Mar–Apr. Two broods, second of which hibernates. Found throughout Britain. Hind leg is same colour as wings. **FP** Mines in Alder leaves. CMM

283 *Caloptilia betulicola* 15mm Common. Jun, Sep, Mar–Apr. Two broods, second of which hibernates. Found throughout Britain. Similar to above, but hind leg is conspicuously whitish. **FP** Mines in birch leaves. NS

286 *Caloptilia alchimiella* 11mm Common. May–July. Throughout in oak woodland. **FP** Mines in oak leaves. NS

287 *Caloptilia robustella* 11mm Common. Apr–May, Aug. Throughout in oak woodland. Very similar to C.

alchimiella above, but colour towards wingtip sharply defined, not diffused. **FP** Mines in oak leaves. TJN

288 *Caloptilia stigmatella* 13mm Common. Apr–May. Hibernates. Found in woods throughout. **FP** Mines in leaves of sallows and other willows, Aspen and other poplars. NS

292 *Caloptilia leucapennella* 12mm Local. Sep–Oct, Mar–May. Hibernates. Two forms, one much paler than shown. In woods throughout. **FP** Mines in Evergreen Oak leaves. NS

293 *Caloptilia syringella* 12mm Common. Apr–May, Jul. Can be abundant, in woods and gardens throughout. **FP** Mines in leaves of Lilac, Privet. NS

294 *Aspilapteryx tringipennella* 12mm Common. May, Aug. Widespread on downs, rough grass, verges. Flies in afternoon sun. **FP** Mines in Ribwort Plantain leaves. blotches. CMM

GRACILLARIIDAE (cont.)

296 *Calybites phasianipennella* 10mm Local. Sep–Oct, Apr–May. Hibernates. Widespread in England in damp woods and fens, not found in Wales and scarce in Scotland. Two forms (dimorphic). **FP** Mines in leaves of Water-pepper, Redshank, Black Bindweed, sorrel, dock, Yellow Loosestrife. NS, CMM

332a *Phyllonorycter leucographella* Firethorn Leaf Miner 8mm Naturalised, alien host. May–Oct. First discovered Essex 1989. Can be abundant on Pyracantha bushes, in almost every leaf. Spreading rapidly northwards. **FP** Mine is a blotch in Firethorn leaf. PJC

342 *Phyllonorycter coryli* Nut Leaf Blister Moth 8mm Common. May, Aug. Throughout. Should be bred for identification, as similar to some other *Phyllonorycter* species. **FP** Mine in hazel leaves. CMM

351 *Phyllonorycter lautella* 6mm Common. May, Aug. Throughout Britain. **FP** Mines in leaves of oak seedlings or saplings. NS

353 *Phyllonorycter ulmifoliella* 8mm Common. May, Aug. Throughout Britain. **FP** Mines in birch leaves. NS

364 *Phyllonorycter geniculella* 8mm Common. May, Aug. Throughout Britain. Similar to other *Phyllonorycter* species. Should be bred from foodplant to be certain. **FP** Mine in Sycamore leaf. NS

366a *Cameraria ohridella* Horse Chestnut Leaf-miner 8mm Naturalised. May–Oct. First discovered in Wimbledon, London, 2002. Can seriously damage host tree owing to sheer numbers. **FP** Mines in Horse Chestnut leaves, several per leaf, causing brown blotches. SR

296 | quadruplella | 296 | 332a
342 | 364 | 366a
351 | 353

CHOREUTIDAE

Only six species are found in Britain. They are mainly day-fliers.

385 *Anthophila fabriciana* **Nettle-tap** 14mm Common. May–Oct. Abundant throughout Britain. Flies by day. **FP** Nettle. CMM

386 *Tebenna micalis* 15mm Vagrant/Accidental. Scarce migrant, occasional resident in southern England. **FP** Common Fleabane. PHS

388 *Prochoreutis myllerana* 14mm May–Aug in overlapping generations. Local but widespread throughout Britain. **FP** Skullcap. CMM

389 *Choreutis pariana* **Apple Leaf Skeletoniser** 15mm Local. Jul, Sep. Widespread, locally common, can overwinter. Larvae strip leaves, leaving ribs like skeleton. **FP** Crab-apple and other roseaceous trees. CMM

GLYPHIPTERIGIDAE

Tiny moths whose larvae nearly all feed on grasses and sedges.

391 *Glyphipterix simpliciella* **Cocksfoot Moth** 6mm Common. May–Jul. Tiny, adults often abundant on buttercup flowers, throughout Britain. **FP** Cocksfoot, Tall Fescue. SR

397 *Glyphipterix thrasonella* 14mm Common. May–Aug. Abundant in bogs and marsh amongst rushes throughout Britain. Silver-bronze forewing, with outer edge notched. **FP** Rushes. CMM

YPONOMEUTIDAE, ARGYRESTHIINAE

This family consists of 77 species in seven subfamilies. It includes moths usually known as ermines, as the adults resemble a Stoat in its winter coat, being white with black marks. Larvae often form a communal web and can be pests.

409a *Argyresthia trifasciata* 7mm Vagrant/Accidental. May–Jun. Tiny, imported on foodplant. First seen 1982. **FP** Juniper, cypress. SR

410 *Argyresthia brockeella* 12mm Common. Jun–Jul. Throughout. Flies in afternoon sun and at night. Distinctive 'head down' resting posture. **FP** Birch or Alder catkins. NS, CMM

411 *Argyresthia goedartella* 12mm Common. Jun–Aug. Throughout. Flies by day or night. Y-shaped dark mark on forewing can help distinguish this from other *Argyresthia* species, but marks are variable. White can also be golden. **FP** Birch catkins. CMM

385 386 388
389 391 397
409a aberration 410 410 411

YPONOMEUTIDAE, ARGYRESTHIINAE (cont.)

414 *Argyresthia curvella* 10mm Common. Jun–Jul. Widespread throughout in gardens and orchards. **FP** Apple, in flowering shoot. NS

415 *Argyresthia retinella* 10mm Common. Jun–Jul. Widespread throughout. Flies in afternoon sun and at night. **FP** Birch shoots or catkins. NS

YPONOMEUTIDAE, YPONOMEUTINAE

424 *Yponomeuta evonymella* Bird-cherry Ermine 22mm Common. Jul–Aug. Widespread throughout, especially in the north. **FP** Bird Cherry. CMM

425 *Yponomeuta padella* Orchard Ermine 20mm Common. Jul–Aug. Widespread throughout. Very similar to Apple Ermine. Breed from foodplant to be certain. **FP** Blackthorn, Hawthorn, Plum, Cherry. CMM

426 *Yponomeuta malinellus* Apple Ermine 20mm Common. Jul–Aug. Widespread throughout, but *see* above. Ground colour of wing usually whiter than padella. **FP** Apple on 2–4-year-old shoots. CMM

427 *Yponomeuta cagnagella* Spindle Ermine 25mm Common. Jul–Aug. Widespread throughout on calcareous soils. Fringe at outer edge is white, not grey as in two species above. **FP** Spindle. NS

428 *Yponomeuta rorrella* Willow Ermine 20mm pRDB3. Jul–Aug. Local from Devon to Northumberland, mostly near east coasts. Forewing suffused grey, but pale patch near tip on leading edge. **FP** White and Grey Willow. NS

435 *Zelleria hepariella* 12mm Local. Jul–Apr. Hibernates. Throughout Britain, mainly on calcareous soils. **FP** Ash. CMM, NS

436 *Pseudoswammerdamia combinella* 15mm Common. May–Jun. Widespread throughout. Thorax white, with orange patch at outer edge of forewing. **FP** Blackthorn. CMM

438 *Swammerdamia pyrella* 12mm Common. May, Aug. Widespread throughout. Similar to *Pseudoswammerdamia combinella* but thorax dark, outer fringe coppery. **FP** Apple, Pear, Hawthorn. CMM

441 *Paraswammerdamia lutarea* 13mm Common. Jul. Widespread throughout. **FP** Hawthorn, Rowan, Rose, Cotoneaster. PGC
442 *Cedestis gysseleniella* 12mm Common. Jun–Jul. Widespread throughout. **FP** Scots and Lodgepole Pine. NS

449 *Prays fraxinella* Ash Bud Moth 16mm Common. Jun–Jul. Widespread throughout, wherever foodplant grows. Plain dark form also occurs. **FP** Ash. CMM
450 *Scythropia crataegella* Hawthorn Moth 14mm Local. Jul. Common in southern Britain. **FP** Hawthorn, Blackthorn. NS

YPONOMEUTIDAE, YPSOLOPHINAE

451 *Ypsolopha mucronella* 30mm Local. Aug–Apr. Hibernates, but flies on mild nights in November. Elongated wingtips are distinctive. In woods in England on calcareous soils from the Midlands southwards. **FP** Spindle. CMM
452 *Ypsolopha nemorella* 24mm Local. Jul–Aug. In woodland throughout. **FP** Honeysuckle. CMM
453 *Ypsolopha dentella* Honeysuckle Moth 22mm

Common. Jul–Aug. In woodland and gardens throughout. **FP** Honeysuckle. NS
455 *Ypsolopha scabrella* 22mm Local. Jul–Aug. In open woods and gardens in England and Wales. **FP** Hawthorn, Apple. CMM
458 *Ypsolopha alpella* 16mm Local. Aug. In oak woods in England and Wales from Yorkshire southwards. **FP** Oak. CMM

YPONOMEUTIDAE, YPSOLOPHINAE (cont.)

459 *Ypsolopha sylvella* 20mm Local. Aug–Sep. In oak woods in Wales and England, north to Yorkshire. **FP** Oak. NS
460 *Ypsolopha parenthesella* 20mm Common. Aug–Sep. Widespread in woods throughout. Darker and lighter forms than shown occur. **FP** Oak, Hornbeam, hazel, birch. NS
461 *Ypsolopha ustella* 18mm Common. Aug–Apr.

Hibernates. Very variable. Flies and comes to light in winter. In oak woods throughout. **FP** Oak. NS, CMM
462 *Ypsolopha sequella* 20mm Local. Aug–Sep. Widespread in south in woods and gardens. **FP** Acers, including Field Maple and Sycamore. CMM
463 *Ypsolopha vittella* 18mm Common. Jul–Aug. Widespread throughout, in woods or isolated trees. **FP** Elm, Beech. NS

YPONOMEUTIDAE, PLUTELLINAE

464 *Plutella xylostella* Diamond-back Moth 14mm Migrant. May, Jul–Sep. Breeding migrant that can be abundant. **FP** Brassicas. CMM
465 *Plutella porrectella* 17mm Local. May, Jul–Aug. Throughout. Comes to light, can be disturbed from foodplant in day. **FP** Dame's Violet. CMM

YPONOMEUTIDAE, ACROLEPIINAE

473 *Acrolepiopsis assectella* **Leek Moth** 12mm pRDB3.
Oct–Apr, Jun–Jul. South-east England, mainly coastal.
FP Leek, Onion, Garlic. NS

475 *Acrolepiopsis marcidella* 13mm pRDB1. Jun–Jul.
Very local in southern England. Adults can be found
by torchlight at dusk, flying within foodplant bush.
FP Butcher's Broom. CMM

EPERMENIIDAE

There are eight British species from about 100 worldwide. They have narrow, pointed (lanceolate) wings, often with
raised tufts of scales. Some feed on umbellifers.

481 *Epermenia falciformis* 12mm Local. Jun–Sep. In
damp woods and marshes from Midlands southwards. **FP**
Wild Angelica, Ground-elder. NS

483 *Epermenia chaerophyllella* 13mm Common.
Oct–May, Jul–Aug. Throughout Britain. Several
generations, can overwinter. Visible raised scale tufts.
FP Hogweed, Parsnip, Cow Parsley, Angelica. SR

COLEOPHORIDAE

There are over 100 British species from over 1,000 worldwide. Larvae are case-bearing. Adults of different species
are often similar in appearance, with long, slender wings; many are pale and plain-looking. They are best bred or
their genitalia dissected for certain identification.

518 *Coleophora mayrella* 11mm Common. Jun–Jul. Throughout on rough ground, grassland, road verges. Flies by day
or night. **FP** White Clover flowers and seeds. NS
531 *Coleophora ochrea* 17mm pRDB3. Jul–Aug. Chalk and limestone downs of south-east England, Cotswolds, Dorset,
Isle of Wight, Gower in south Wales. **FP** Common Rock-rose. Mines leaves, joins leaves together diagonally. PHS, PHS
541 *Coleophora pyrrhulipennella* 10mm Common. May–Aug. Widespread on heaths, moors, bogs. Feeds from
distinctive case. **FP** Ling, Bell Heather, leaves and flowers. CMM
544 *Coleophora albicosta* 14mm Common. May–Jun. Common throughout
wherever foodplant grows. Flies mainly at dusk. White leading edge to wing is
distinctive, but easily confused with other similar *Coleophora*. Breeding and
genitalia examination required for certainty. **FP** Gorse flowers and seed pods. CMM
553 *Coleophora striatipennella* 12mm Common. May–Aug. Throughout Britain
in damp woods, grassland, marshes. Very similar to other *Coleophora* so breeding
and genitalia examination required for certainty. **FP** Flowers of Lesser Stitchwort,
Chickweed, Common Mouse-ear. CMM

473

475 | 481 | 483
518 | 531 | larval feeding case 531
larval feeding case 541 | 544 | 553

ELACHISTIDAE

Small moths, mostly coloured with combinations of brown and/or white. Many larvae feed on grasses.

597 *Elachista atricomella* 12mm Common. May–Sep. Throughout on wood edges, grassland, verges. **FP** Mine in leaf and stem of Cock's-foot. SR
608 *Elachista rufocinerea* 10mm Common. Apr–Jun. Throughout in grassland, bogs, heaths. **FP** Mine in leaf of Creeping Soft-grass, False Oat-grass, etc. CMM

609 *Elachista maculicerusella* 10mm Local. May–Aug. Throughout in marshes, along river banks, wet ditches. **FP** Mines in stems of Reed Canary-grass, Common Reed. CMM
610 *Elachista argentella* 11mm Common. May–Aug. Throughout in grassland, including salt marshes. **FP** Mines leaves of many grasses. CMM

OECOPHORIDAE

A large and diverse family with 4,000 species worldwide, half in Australia. In Europe, there are 305 species, of which 85 are found in Britain, split into four sub-families. The family includes some of the most colourful micros (*see also* p.34).

640 *Batia lunaris* 9mm Common. Jul–Aug. Throughout England in woodland. Similar to *B. lambdella* but smaller. **FP** Under tree bark, on decaying wood. SR
641 *Batia lambdella* 15mm Common. Jul–Aug. Throughout Britain, especially Gorse. NS
642 *Batia unitella* 15mm Local. Jun–Aug. Southern Britain, north to Yorkshire, in woodland. **FP** Under tree bark, on decaying wood. SR
646 *Telechrysis tripuncta* 12mm Local. Jun–Aug. Hedgerows, scrub, woods. **FP** In dead stems of Bramble. NS
647 *Hofmannophila pseudospretella* **Brown House Moth** 20mm Common. Any month. Throughout Britain, often indoors. Often hops or runs when disturbed, rather than fly. **FP** Dead plant and animal matter, including old wool, leather. CMM
648 *Endrosis sarcitrella* **White-shouldered House Moth** 20mm Common. Any month. Throughout Britain, often indoors. **FP** Dead plant and animal matter. CMM
649 *Esperia sulphurella* 15mm Common. May–Jun. Day-flying in woods. **FP** Dead wood. SR
651 *Oecophora bractella* 15mm pRDB3. May–Jul. In ancient woods in Midlands and southern England, south Wales. **FP** Dead wood, fungi. PGC
652 *Alabonia geoffrella* 20mm Common. May–Jun.

Woods and marshes in southern Britain. **FP** Under bark of dead wood. CMM
654 *Pleurota bicostella* 24mm Local. Jun–Jul. Widely distributed on heaths and moors. Huge labial palps are distinctive. **FP** Heathers. CMM
656 *Tachystola acroxantha* 18mm pRDB3. May–Sep. First recorded 1908, originally from Australia. Now found as far north as Lancashire. **FP** Leaf litter. PHS
657 *Hypercallia citrinalis* 20mm RDB1. Jun–Jul. Formerly in Kent on chalk downs, but not seen since 1975. Resident in Burren, Ireland. **FP** Milkworts. CMM
658 *Carcina quercana* 20mm Common. Jul–Aug. Throughout in woodland. **FP** Oak, Beech. CMM
663 *Diurnea fagella* 25mm Common. Mar–May. In woods throughout in spring. Two colour forms. **FP** Deciduous trees. CMM
664 *Diurnea lipsiella* 23mm Local. Oct–Nov. Widespread in woodland. **FP** Oak, Bilberry. CMM
665 *Dasystoma salicella* 20mm (♂), female wingless Local. Apr. Widespread but scarce, in woodland, scrub, heaths. Female is flightless. **FP** Leaves sewn together of sallows, Blackthorn, Bog Myrtle. PHS, PHS
667 *Semioscopis steinkellneriana* 22mm Local. Apr. Scrub and hedgerows. **FP** Blackthorn, Hawthorn. CMM

OECOPHORIDAE (cont.)

668 *Luquetia lobella* 19mm Nb. Jun. Southern England in woods and scrub. **FP** Blackthorn. NS

672 *Depressaria pastinacella* **Parsnip Moth** 25mm Common. Sep, May. Hibernates. Found in dry pastures. **FP** Flowers and seeds of Wild Parsnip, Hogweed. Pupates in stem. CMM

688 *Agonopterix heracliana* 21mm Common. Sep–Apr. Throughout. **FP** Umbelliferous plants. CMM

689 *Agonopterix ciliella* 22mm Common. Aug–May. Throughout. Similar to above, but hind-wing fringe has five lines instead of one. **FP** Umbelliferous plants. NS

692 *Agonopterix subpropinquella* 20mm Common. Aug–May. Throughout. Similar to other *Agonopterix*. Needs genitalia examined and breeding to be certain. **FP** Knapweed, thistles. NS

695 *Agonopterix alstromeriana* 18mm Common. Aug–Apr. Throughout. **FP** Hemlock. NS

698 *Agonopterix kaekeritziana* 20mm Common. Jul–Sep. Widespread. Does not come to light. Pale, but with slight sandy marks. **FP** Rolled leaves of Knapweed. NS

700 *Agonopterix pallorella* 20mm Nb. Aug–Apr. In southern Britain only. **FP** Rolled leaves of Knapweed, Saw Wort. CMM

701 *Agonopterix ocellana* 20mm Common. Sep–Apr. Throughout. **FP** Leaves of willows spun together. NS

704 *Agonopterix scopariella* 20mm Local. Aug–Apr. Widespread, usually near foodplant. Similar to other *Agonopterix*. Needs genitalia examined and breeding to be certain. **FP** Spun shoots of Broom. NS

705 *Agonopterix umbellana* 21mm Common. Aug–Apr. Widespread, especially near coasts. Row of dark dots at outer edge is distinctive, *see below*. **FP** Spun shoots of gorse, Greenweed. CMM

706 *Agonopterix nervosa* 20mm Common. Aug–Apr. Throughout Britain. No dark dots around outer edge, *see above*. **FP** Spun shoots of gorse, Broom, Dyer's Greenweed, Petty Whin, Tree Lupin. CMM

ETHMIIDAE

A small family with six species on the British list, one of which is extinct. Adults are mostly black and white.

718 *Ethmia dodecea* 20mm Nb. May–Jul. Scattered throughout England on scrubby chalk downland. Similar to Ermines but spots fewer and larger. **FP** Common Gromwell. CMM
719 *Ethmia quadrillella* 17mm pRDB3. May–Jul.

South-east England. **FP** Larvae in silk web on leaves of Comfrey, Lungwort. SR, SR
720 *Ethmia bipunctella* 25mm pRDB1. May–Jun. On coastal shingle in south-east England only. **FP** Viper's Bugloss. NS

GELECHIIDAE

This family is represented by around 4,000 species worldwide, of which 600 are found in Europe, and 150 in Britain, divided into six subfamilies. Adults rest with wings folded flat or rolled around the abdomen, with the front end of the body often raised; the antennae lie on top of the forewings.

724 *Metzneria lappella* 18mm Common. Jun–Jul. Common in southern Britain, local in Scotland. **FP** Buck's-horn Plantain, Greater Burdock on seeds. NS
726 *Metzneria metzneriella* 18mm Common. Jun–Aug. Dry pastures and downland. **FP** Seeds and seedheads of

Saw-wort, Common Knapweed. CMM
727a *Metzneria aprilella* 17mm Na. May–Aug. Grassy chalk and limestone downs in southern England. First recognised in 1981. **FP** Seeds and seedheads of Greater Knapweed. CMM

GELECHIIDAE (cont.)

728 Monochroa cytisella 11mm Common. Jul. Throughout England and Wales amongst bracken in warm, sunny areas. **FP** Inside gall in stem of Bracken. NS

729 Isophrictis striatella 12mm Local. Jul–Aug. South-east England, including Dorset. **FP** Inside seedheads of Tansy, Sneezewort. CMM

733 Eulamprotes wilkella 9mm Nb. Jun, Aug. Throughout but generally coastal, on sandy or shingle areas. **FP** Common Mouse-ear. SR

737 Monochroa palustrella 18mm Local. Jun–Aug. South-east England in sandy areas. **FP** In roots and stems of Curled Dock. SR

752 Aristotelia ericinella 12mm Common. Jul–Aug. Throughout on heaths and moors. Flies in afternoon and at night. **FP** Heather. NS

756 Parachronistis albiceps 10mm Local. Jun–Jul. In woods in southern Britain as far north as Yorkshire. **FP** Hazel. NS

758 Recurvaria leucatella 14mm Nb. Jun–Jul. Scattered throughout England and Wales. **FP** Spun leaves of Hawthorn, Apple. NS

762 Athrips mouffetella 15mm Local. Jul–Sep. In southern Britain in woods, gardens. **FP** Honeysuckle, Snowberry. NS

764 Pseudotelphusa scalella 12mm Nb. May–Jun. In woodland in central southern England. **FP** Lichens and moss on oak. NS

765 Teleiodes vulgella 12mm Common. Jun–Jul. Throughout. Pale raised scale tufts beside dark dots are distinctive. **FP** Hawthorn, Blackthorn. SR

771 Carpatolechia alburnella 13mm Common. Jun–Aug. May be found on trunk of host tree throughout Britain. **FP** Birch. NS

779 Bryotropha affinis 12mm Common. Jun–Jul. Throughout. Comes to light. **FP** Mosses. NS

792 Mirificarma mulinella 13mm Common. Jul–Sep. Throughout on heathland and waste ground. Two distinctive dark stripes down forewing. **FP** Gorse, Broom, Lupin. NS

796 Aroga velocella 15mm Local. May–Aug. Mainly in eastern central and southern England in heathland and breckland. **FP** Sheep's Sorrel. SR

797 Neofaculta ericetella 17mm Common. Apr–Jun. Throughout Britain, wherever foodplant grows. **FP** Flowers and shoots of heather. CMM

812 Scrobipalpa instabilella 12mm Common. Jun–Sep. Abundant on salt marshes in England and Wales. Very similar to some other Scrobipalpa in same habitats. Need to be bred from foodplant or genitalia examined to be certain. **FP** Sea Purslane. CMM

819 Scrobipalpa costella 18mm Common. Sep–Apr. In damp woods throughout. **FP** Bittersweet. CMM

840 Thiotricha subocellea 10mm Local. Jul–Aug. Scattered throughout. Larva feeds from inside a case made of calyxes. **FP** Wild Marjoram. NS

854 Anacampsis blattariella 17mm Local. Jul–Sep. Central and southern England in mature birch woods. **FP** Rolled leaves of birch. CMM

856 Anarsia spartiella 14mm Local. Jun–Aug. Scattered throughout England, mainly coastal in Wales and Scotland. **FP** Spun shoots of Gorse, Broom, Dyer's Greenweed. NS

862 Dichomeris marginella Juniper Webber 16mm Local. Jul–Aug. In chalk and limestone areas of England as well as gardens where foodplant is grown. Looks similar to a Crambid. **FP** Juniper, including cultivated varieties. NS

867 Brachmia inornatella 14mm Nb. Jun–Jul. Only in fens and marshes of East Anglia and south-east England. **FP** Probably in Common Reed stems. SR

868 Helcystogramma rufescens 14mm Common. Jun–Aug. In England and Wales. **FP** Wood Small-reed, False Brome. SR

869 Helcystogramma lutatella 14mm pRDB1. Jun. On sea cliffs and landslips in Dorset. **FP** False Brome, Cock's-foot. PHS

BLASTOBASIDAE

Another small family. Adults are generally drab and not well studied.

873 Blastobasis lignea 18mm Aug–Sep. Naturalised adventive. Common throughout Britain. **FP** Withered and decaying vegetable matter. CMM
874 Blastobasis decolorella 20mm Common. May–Jun, Sep. First recorded in Britain in Kent 1946, now naturalised throughout. From Madeira. **FP** Fresh or dead plants, fruit, dead insects, bird droppings. CMM

OECOPHORIDAE, STATHMOPODINAE

877 Stathmopoda pedella 12mm Local. Jul. In alder carr in East Anglia. **FP** Alder, feeding in cones. PHS, PHS

877

larval frass on Alder cone   877

873

874

MOMPHIDAE

Represented by 15 British species, although the number of subfamilies and their status has been the subject of much debate and their classification could well change again.

883 Mompha raschkiella 9mm Common. May–Oct. Throughout, in heathland, brecks, road verges, waste ground. **FP** Rosebay Willowherb. NS
888 Mompha propinquella 12mm Local. Jun–Sep. Scarce, in open woods, waste ground, gardens. **FP** Willowherbs. SR

891 Mompha sturnipennella 16mm Nb. Apr–May, Jul–Aug. On dry heaths, waste ground. **FP** In stems of Rosebay Willowherb. NS
892 Mompha subbistrigella 10mm Common. Apr–May, Jul–Aug. In damp woods, ditches, on stream banks. **FP** Unripe seeds of various willowherbs. PGC

883

888

891

892

COSMOPTERIGIDAE

Previously treated as a sub-family of the Momphidae. There are 17 British species, mostly scarce, from 1,500 worldwide.

896a *Cosmopterix pulchrimella* 9mm
Vagrant/Accidental. Apr–Aug. First recorded in Britain in Dorset 2001. Breeds on south-west coasts. **FP** Mines in Pellitory-of-the-Wall leaves. SH
898 *Limnaecia phragmitella* 20mm Common.
Jun–Aug. In streams, ponds, fens, marshes, wherever foodplant grows. **FP** Seedheads of bulrushes. SR
905 *Blastodacna hellerella* 11mm Common. Jun–Jul.
Throughout Britain, wherever foodplant grows.
FP Hawthorn. NS
907 *Dystebenna stephensi* 10mm pRDB3. Jun. Open woods and parks with mature oaks. **FP** Oak. NS

SCYTHRIDIDAE

There are 12, mostly rare, British species. The wings are slightly curved, like a scythe. They live in dry, open habitats with low-growing plants. They are rarely seen as they tend to hop through the vegetation rather than fly.

917 *Scythris empetrella* 7mm pRDB1. May–Jun. Very local on southern sandy heaths and dunes. Scythe-shaped wings aid tiny adult to hop through heather rather than fly. **FP** Heather, feeding from a protective tube of sand grains. CMM, CMM

larval feeding tube

TORTRICIDAE

This is the largest and most diverse group, with some 350 species in Britain from over 6,000 worldwide. The caterpillars spin silk webs, drawing leaves or flowers into a rolled-up covering around themselves.

921 *Phtheochroa inopiana* 20mm Common. Jun–Aug. Damp meadows and woodland edges in England and Wales. **FP** Common Fleabane. CMM

926 *Phalonidia manniana* 12mm Nb. May–Jun. Widespread from Europe to eastern Russia, China and Asia. **FP** Mint. NS

932 *Phalonidia affinitana* 12mm Local. Jun–Aug. On salt marshes in England and Wales. **FP** Sea Aster flowers, overwinters in root. NS

936 *Cochylimorpha straminea* 15mm Common. May–Jun, Aug–Sep. Widespread throughout. **FP** Seedheads of Common Knapweed. CMM

938 *Agapeta zoegana* 20mm Common. May–Aug. Throughout Britain. **FP** Common Knapweed. NS

939 *Aethes tesserana* 15mm Jun–Aug. Local in England and Wales from Yorkshire southwards. Variable markings. **FP** In roots of ox-tongue, hawkweed, hawk's-beard. CMM

942 *Aethes piercei* 20mm Jun–Jul. Nb. Local throughout Britain in damp meadows. **FP** Roots of Devil's-bit Scabious. CMM

945 *Aethes cnicana* 15mm Common. Jun–Jul. Throughout Britain. **FP** Thistle seedheads, pupating in stem. NS

946 *Aethes rubigana* 18mm Local. Jun–Aug. Widespread in dry, open areas. **FP** Seedheads of Burdock. NS

947 *Aethes smeathmanniana* 18mm Local. May–Aug. Throughout Britain. **FP** Seedheads of Yarrow, knapweeds, etc. NS

950 *Aethes francillana* 16mm Local. Jun–Sep. A southern species of chalk downs and limestone coasts. **FP** Wild Carrot. CMM

954 *Eupoecilia angustana* 12mm Common. Jun–Sep. Throughout in meadows, woodland edges, heathland. **FP** Various plants, including plantains, Yarrow, heather. NS

956 *Cochylidia implicitana* 12mm Local. May–Aug. Southen England on open rough ground, verges, field edges. **FP** Flowers, seeds, stems of Goldenrod, Mayweed, etc. NS

962 *Cochylis roseana* 15mm Common. May–Aug. Mainly in southern Britain wherever foodplant is profuse. **FP** Inside seedheads of Teasel. NS

963 *Cochylis flaviciliana* 16mm Nb. May–Aug. Similar to *C. roseana* above but striking cream and pink and different foodplant. **FP** Field Scabious. PHS

964 *Cochylis dubitana* 13mm Common. May–Jun, Jul–Aug. Widespread but mostly in southern Britain. Has white head with dark thorax. **FP** Inside flowers and seedheads of Compositae, including Ragwort, Sow-thistle, Goldenrod, Hawkweed. NS

964a *Cochylis molliculana* 12mm Local. May–Jun, Jul. Similar to *C. hybridella* below, but dark thorax. **FP** Unknown. TJN

965 *Cochylis hybridella* 15mm Local. Jul–Aug. On chalk and limestone ground in southern Britain. **FP** Seedheads of Ox-tongue, Hawk's-beard. NS, CMM

966 *Cochylis atricapitana* 15mm Common. May–Jun, Aug. Throughout, particularly on chalk coasts. Has dark head and thorax. **FP** Common Ragwort flowers, stems, roots. NS

968 *Cochylis nana* 11mm Common. Jun. Widespread throughout in birch woodland. **FP** In catkins of birch. NS

TORTRICIDAE (cont.)

969 *Pandemis corylana* **Chequered Fruit-tree Tortrix** 20mm Common. Jul–Aug. Throughout Britain in woodland. **FP** In rolled leaves of deciduous trees. CMM, CMM

970 *Pandemis cerasana* **Barred Fruit-tree Tortrix** 20mm Common. Jun–Aug. Throughout Britain in woodland. Similar to *P. corylana* above, but softer brown with less well-defined markings. **FP** In rolled leaves of deciduous trees, especially fruit. NS

971 *Pandemis cinnamomeana* 20mm Local. Jun–Jul. In woodland in southern Britain. Male has white forehead and gingery colour. **FP** Leaves of deciduous trees. CMM

972 *Pandemis heparana* **Dark Fruit-tree Tortrix** 20mm Common. Jun–Aug. Throughout in woodland. **FP** In rolled leaves of deciduous trees, especially fruit. JSB

974 *Argyrotaenia ljungiana* 15mm Common. Apr–May, Jun–Jul. Throughout Britain on heaths and moorland. **FP** Bog Myrtle, heather, Marsh Gentian. NS

976 *Archips oporana* 18mm (♂), 25mm (♀) pRDB1. Jun–Jul. In pinewoods in south and south-east England. Population is increasing. Sexually dimorphic species. **FP** Feeds between spun needles of pines, especially Scots Pine. PHS, CMM

977 *Archips podana* **Large Fruit-tree Tortrix** 18mm (♂), 25mm (♀) Common. May–Sep. In low-lying areas in most of Britain. Pronounced sexual dimorphism: both bell-shaped, but males smaller and darker. **FP** Foliage, flowers, fruit of various deciduous trees including Blackthorn, Cherry, Apple. CMM, CMM

979 *Archips crataegana* 20mm Local. Jun–Aug. Widespread but not common in woodland. Males have a fold along front edge of forewing. **FP** Rolled leaves of various trees including oak, elm, ash, sallows. CMM

980 *Archips xylosteana* **Variegated Golden Tortrix** 20mm Common. Jul–Aug. Throughout in wooded areas. **FP** Leaves of deciduous trees and shrubs. NS

985 *Cacoecimorpha pronubana* **Carnation Tortrix** 20mm Common. May–Jun, Aug–Sep. First recorded in Britain around 1900, now widespread. Orange hind wings. **FP** Many foodplants. SR

986 *Syndemis musculana* 20mm Common. May–Jun. Throughout in various habitats. **FP** Polyphagous, including Bramble, birch, oak, grasses, shrubs. CMM

988 *Aphelia viburnana* **Bilberry Tortrix** 20mm Common. Jul–Aug. Throughout in various habitats. **FP** Polyphagous, inc Bilberry, Bog Myrtle, pines, etc. NS

989 *Aphelia paleana* **Timothy Tortrix** 20mm Common. Jun–Aug. Inhabits damp, rough ground. Plain but with yellowish look. **FP** Herbaceous plants. CMM, SR

993 *Clepsis spectrana* **Cyclamen Tortrix** 20mm Common. May–Sep. Throughout in damp marsh, bogs, estuaries, woodland. Very variable. **FP** Polyphagous. CMM, CMM

994 *Clepsis consimilana* 17mm Common. Jun–Sep. A rather plain Tortrix, with two dark marks on trailing edge of forewing. **FP** Polyphagous, but especially dead leaves of Lilac, Privet. SR

976 ♀

977 ♂

977 ♀

979

980

985

986

988

989

993

993

989

994

TORTRICIDAE (cont.)

998 *Epiphyas postvittana* **Light Brown Apple Moth** 20mm Common. May–Oct. Naturalised Australian moth, first recorded 1911, now abundant in south, spreading north. Extremely variable. **FP** Polyphagous. Eats any greenery. CMM (all 6 photos)

1000 *Ptycholoma lecheana* 18mm Common. Jun–Jul. Throughout, but local in Scotland. **FP** Inside rolled leaves of various trees and shrubs. NS

1001 *Lozotaeniodes formosanus* 25mm Local. Jun–Aug. In pine woods in southern Britain. First recorded around 1945 in Surrey. **FP** Scots Pine. CMM

1002 *Lozotaenia forsterana* 28mm Common. Jun–Jul. The largest Tortrix, very grey. In suburban parks, gardens, woods. **FP** Trees and shrubs, especially Ivy. CMM

1006 *Epagoge grotiana* 15mm Common. Jun–Jul. Widespread in woodland. **FP** Leaves of oak, Hawthorn, Bramble. NS

1010 *Ditula angustiorana* **Red-barred Tortrix** 15mm Common. Jun–Jul. Throughout in woodland. **FP** Leaves and fruits of various trees and shrubs. CMM

1011 *Pseudargyrotoza conwagana* 13mm Common. May–Jul. Small but colourful, with central yellow blotch. Found in woodland. **FP** Mainly ash, also Privet. NS

1013 *Olindia schumacherana* 14mm Local. Jun–Jul. Distinctive but markings can vary. Damp meadows. **FP** Herbaceous plants especially in folded leaf of Lesser Celandine. CMM, NS

1015 *Eulia ministrana* 25mm Common. May–Jun. Very striking; in woodland. **FP** Various trees and shrubs. CMM

1016 *Cnephasia longana* 18mm Common. May–Aug. Throughout Britain. Eggs laid in batch of 100 or so, larvae disperse in wind on silk threads. **FP** Polyphagous on low herbaceous plants. SR

1020 *Cnephasia stephensiana* **Grey Tortrix** 20mm Common. Jul–Aug. Throughout. Very similar to C. *incertana*, dissection required for firm identification. **FP** Polyphagous on 120 plant species. NS

1024 *Cnephasia incertana* **Light Grey Tortrix** 16mm Common. Jun–Jul. Throughout. Very similar to C. *stephensiana*, dissection required for firm identification. **FP** Leaves of plants and shrubs, including plantain, sorrel, vines. NS

1025 *Tortricodes alternella* 21mm Common. Feb–Apr. Can be abundant very early in the year in woodland. **FP** Leaves spun together of oak, Hornbeam, etc. NS, CMM

1026 *Exapate congelatella* 20mm Local. Oct–Dec. Male has narrow wings, female is flightless. Widespread, in hedgerows in south, moorland in north. **FP** Spun leaves of Hawthorn, oak, sallows, Apple, etc. RPJ

1032 *Aleimma loeflingiana* 17mm Common. Jul–Aug. Throughout Britain in woodland. **FP** Oak. NS

998 | 998 | 998
998 | 998 | 998

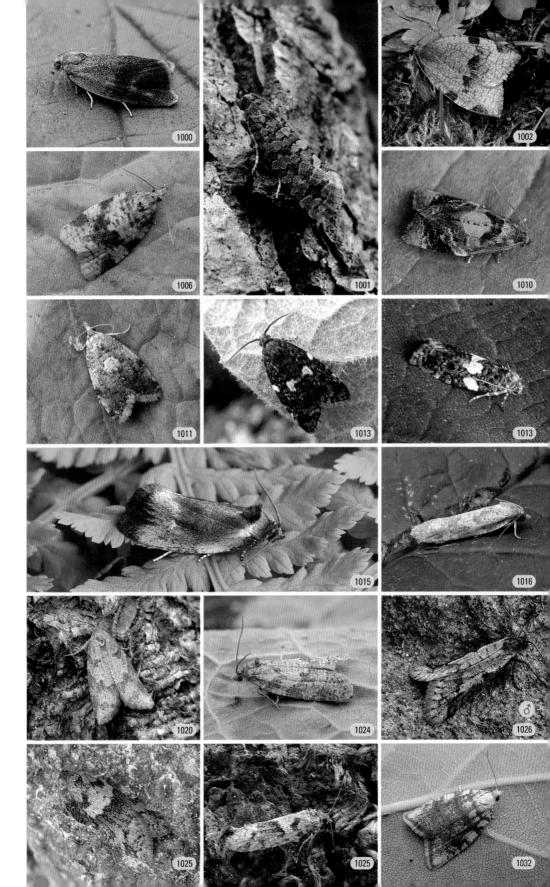

TORTRICIDAE (cont.)

1033 *Tortrix viridana* **Green Oak Tortrix** 20mm
Common. May–Jun. Throughout Britain in woodland.
Can be abundant to pest level, larvae can completely
defoliate trees. **FP** Mainly oak. NS

1034 *Spatalistis bifasciana* 13mm Nb. May–Jun. In
southern Britain in scrub and wood margins. **FP** Inside
fruits of Buckthorn, Dogwood. NS

1036 *Acleris forsskaleana* 15mm Common. Jul–Aug. In
woods and gardens throughout. Striking and
unmistakable. **FP** Field Maple, Sycamore. NS

1037 *Acleris holmiana* 13mm Common. Jul–Aug.
Widespread in open woods and scrub. White markings
distinctive even when worn, like the example shown. **FP**
Trees and shrubs, including Apple, Hawthorn, Rose. SR

1039 *Acleris comariana* **Strawberry Tortrix** 20mm
Common. Jun–Jul, Aug–Nov. In Strawberry beds.
Variable but usually with dark bar behind thorax.
FP Strawberry. CMM

1041 *Acleris sparsana* 20mm Common. Aug–Oct.
Throughout Britain in woodland. **FP** Beech, Sycamore,
Field Maple. SR

1042 *Acleris rhombana* **Rhomboid Tortrix** 18mm
Common. Aug–Oct. Throughout Britain in woodland,
hedgerows, gardens. Hooked wingtips and netted
pattern aid identification. **FP** Polyphagous on trees and
shrubs, including Hawthorn. NS

1044 *Acleris ferrugana* 17mm Common. Jul, Sep–Apr.
Very variable. Very similar to *A. notana*. Often has dark
scale tuft quarter way along wing. Should be bred from
foodplant or genitalia examined for confirmation. In
woods throughout. **FP** Rolled leaves of oak, Goat
Willow. CMM

1045 *Acleris notana* 17mm Common. Jul, Sep–Apr.
Very variable, can look very similar to *A. ferrugana*.
Dark scale tuft faint or absent. Should be bred from
foodplant or genitalia examined for confirmation. In
woods throughout. **FP** Folded leaves of Birch, Alder,
Bog Myrtle. CMM

1048 *Acleris variegana* **Garden Rose Tortrix** 16mm
Common. Jul–Sep. Variable. Throughout on rose bushes
and other shrubs. **FP** Roses, etc. CMM, CMM

1033 1034 1036 1037 1039 1041 1042 1045 1044 1048 1048

1051 *Acleris logiana* 20mm Nb. Sep–Apr. Formerly in Scotland only. Recorded in Hampshire Jan 2003. **FP** Birch. NS

1053 *Acleris hastiana* 20mm Common. Jun–Jul, Aug–Apr. Throughout in damp scrub. Very variable, similar to *A. cristana* but forewing less concave and without scale tufts. **FP** Spun leaves of small-leaved willows. CMM

1054 *Acleris cristana* 20mm Local. Aug–Apr. Mainly in mature Blackthorn thickets in southern England. Very variable and similar to *A. hastiana*. Often with distinctive raised scale tufts (button) in centre of concave-edged forewing. Over 120 named forms. **FP** Blackthorn, occasionally Hawthorn. CMM, NS, CMM

1055 *Acleris hyemana* 18mm Common. Sep–Apr. Throughout on heaths and moorland. **FP** Spun shoots of heather, Heath. CMM

1061 *Acleris literana* 20mm Local. Aug–May. Hibernates. In southern Britain occurs in oak woods. Variable, but always a combination of green and black markings. **FP** Mainly oaks, also birch, maple, etc. CMM, CMM

1062 *Acleris emargana* 20mm Common. Jul–Sep. In woods, hedgerows, marshland most commonly in southern Britain. Indented margins and pointed tips to wings are distinctive, but markings variable. *See also A. effractana* below. **FP** Sallows, poplar, birch. CMM, NS

1062a *Acleris effractana* 20mm This has recently (2004) been separated from *A. emargana* by genitalia examination. Markings of *A. effractana* generally similar to example shown, but dissection required for certainty. **FP** Probably as above. RPJ

1063 *Celypha striana* 20mm Common. Jun–Aug. In grasslands and open ground, mainly southern Britain. **FP** Dandelion roots. NS

TORTRICIDAE (cont.)

1064 *Celypha rosaceana* 18mm Local. Jun–Jul. Rough pastures in southern Britain. Pink when fresh, soon fades to dull brown. **FP** Roots of Dandelion, Sow Thistle. SR
1067 *Celypha cespitana* 17mm Local. Jun–Aug. Mainly on limestone or chalk coasts. Flies by day. **FP** Herbaceous plants, especially Thyme, Sea Lavender. NS
1076 *Celypha lacunana* 17mm Common. May–Aug. Very common throughout Britain along hedgerows, wood edges, rough ground. **FP** Various herbaceous plants. SR
1079 *Piniphila bifasciana* 15mm Local. Jun–Jul. Scattered in pine woods. **FP** Young shoots and male flowers of Scots Pine, Maritime Pine. NS
1080 *Olethreutes arcuella* 16mm Nb. May–Aug. Scattered through England and Wales in woods and heaths. Very distinctive. **FP** In leaf litter and withered leaves of low plants. CMM
1082 *Hedya pruniana* **Plum Tortrix** 17mm Common. May–Jul. Throughout in woods, gardens, hedgerows. Similar to other species that resemble bird droppings but outer edge darker than others. **FP** Prunus, including Blackthorn, Plum. CMM
1084 *Hedya ochroleucana* 19mm Common. Jun–Jul. Outer pale section of wing only lightly marked, black central dot merges with main dark band. Mainly in southern Britain. **FP** Spun leaves of Rose, Apple. SR
1085 *Metendothenia atropunctana* 15mm Local. May–Jun. Mainly northern Britain on damp heaths. Black central dot distinct. **FP** Spun terminal shoots of willow, Bog Myrtle. NS
1086 *Hedya salicella* 23mm Common. Jun–Aug. Well distributed in England and Wales. **FP** Spun leaves of sallows, poplar. NS
1087 *Orthotaenia undulana* 18mm Common. May–Jul. Widespread throughout in woods, moors, on dunes. **FP** Polyphagus on plants, bushes and trees, including Bog Myrtle, Bilberry, pines, birch, nettle, Bramble. NS
1092 *Apotomis turbidana* 20mm Common. Jun–Jul. Throughout Britain in birch woods. **FP** Spun leaves of birch. CMM

1093 *Apotomis betuletana* 18mm Common. Jul–Sep. Throughout Britain in birch woods. **FP** Spun leaves of birch. NS
1094 *Apotomis capreana* 20mm Local. Jun–Aug. Mainly in southern Britain. **FP** Spun leaves of Goat Willow. NS
1097 *Endothenia gentianaeana* 18mm Common. Jun–Jul. Commonly flying around Teasels after emergence. Can be in every seedhead. **FP** Inside seedheads of Teazel. CMM
1103 *Endothenia ericetana* 18mm Local. Jul–Aug. In meadows, farmland, open hedgerows. **FP** Stems and roots of Marsh Woundwort, Corn-mint. NS
1104 *Endothenia quadrimaculana* 20mm Local. Jul–Sep. In damp meadows, hedgerows, river banks. Similar to above but larger, paler and more strongly marked. **FP** Stems and roots of Marsh Woundwort. NS
1106 *Lobesia reliquana* 12mm Common. May–Jun. Mainly in southern Britain, in woodland. Flies in sun or at night. **FP** Spun leaves of oak, birch, Blackthorn. CMM
1108 *Lobesia abscisana* 12mm Local. May, Jul–Aug. Mainly in south and east England, as far north as Yorkshire. **FP** Creeping Thistle. NS
1109 *Lobesia littoralis* 14mm Common. Jun–Jul, Sep. Mostly coastal where the foodplant grows, but also in gardens on cultivated Thrift. **FP** Flowers of Thrift, Bird's-foot Trefoil. NS
1113 *Eudemis profundana* 18mm Local. Jul–Aug. In oak woods in England and Wales. **FP** In rolled oak leaves. NS
1115 *Ancylis achatana* 16mm Common. Jun–Jul. Southern Britain as far north as Yorkshire. In hedges, scrub. **FP** Rolled leaves of Blackthorn, Hawthorn. SR
1117 *Ancylis unguicella* 15mm Common. May–Jul. More common in northern and upland regions. **FP** Heather, Bell Heather. SR
1120 *Ancylis mitterbacheriana* 14mm Common. May–Jun. In woodland in southern Britain. **FP** Oak, Beech. CMM

1064 1067 1076 1079 1080

TORTRICIDAE (cont.)

1123 *Ancylis laetana* 15mm Local. May–Jun. Mainly in south-east England, scattered northwards. **FP** Aspen, Black Poplar. NS

1127 *Ancylis paludana* 13mm pRDB3. May–Jun, Jul–Aug. Found only in wetlands of East Anglia. **FP** Marsh Pea. SR

1129 *Ancylis apicella* 15mm Local. May–Jun, Jul–Aug. In damp woods, fens, etc. in south-west Britain. **FP** Folded and spun leaves of Buckthorn, Alder Buckthorn. CMM

1133 *Epinotia bilunana* 15mm Common. Jun–Jul. Throughout, in birch woods. Distinctive dark crescent seen from above. **FP** Catkins of birch. CMM, SR

1135 *Epinotia demarniana* 14mm Nb. Jun–Jul. In fens, bogs, damp heaths and woods in south-east England. **FP** Catkins of birch, Alder, Goat Willow. NS

1136 *Epinotia immundana* 13mm Common. Apr–Jun, Aug–Sep. Throughout, in fens, bogs, damp heaths, river banks and woods. **FP** Catkins of birch, Alder. NS

1138 *Epinotia nisella* 15mm Common. Jul–Aug. Throughout Britain. Very variable. **FP** Willow, poplar. NS, SR

1139 *Epinotia tenerana* **Nut Bud Moth** 15mm Common. Jul–Oct. Widespread in damp woodland areas. **FP** Catkins and leaf buds of hazel, Alder. NS

1146 *Epinotia rubiginosana* 14mm Common. Jun. Throughout in pine woods. Flies in sun and at night. **FP** Scots Pine, Stone Pine. NS

1147 *Epinotia cruciana* **Willow Tortrix** 14mm Common. Jun–Aug. Throughout. Can be disturbed from foodplant in daytime. **FP** Spun leaves of sallows and other willows, especially Creeping Willow. SR

1150 *Epinotia abbreviana* 14mm Common. Jun–Jul. In lowland wooded areas throughout Britain. **FP** Buds and leaves of elm, Field Maple. NS

1154 *Epinotia caprana* 15mm Local. Jul–Aug. Damp heathland. **FP** Spun leaves on shoots of willows, Bog Myrtle. CMM

1155 *Epinotia brunnichana* 20mm Common. Jul–Aug. Throughout, but more common in north. **FP** Inside rolled leaf of birch, hazel, sallows. NS, NS

1156 *Epinotia solandriana* 20mm Common. Jul–Aug. Throughout in woods and scrubland. Very variable. **FP** Inside rolled leaf of birch, hazel, sallows. NS

1159 *Rhopobota naevana* **Holly Tortrix** 14mm Common. Jul–Sep. Throughout in many habitats. **FP** Polyphagous on trees and shrubs, especially Holly. NS

1165 *Zeiraphera isertana* 17mm Common. Jul–Aug. Throughout in oak woodland. Rather variable, often with distinct pale dorsal blotch, olive tinged. **FP** Rolled leaf of oak. NS

1167 *Gypsonoma aceriana* 14mm Local. Jul. Southern Britain as far north as Yorkshire. **FP** Shoots, buds and leaf stems of poplar. NS

1168 *Gypsonoma sociana* Local. Jul–Aug. Throughout Britain. Diamond-shaped dorsal mark is distinctive, forehead is white. **FP** Twig and leaf buds of poplar, sallows. NS

1169 *Gypsonoma dealbana* 13mm Common. Jul–Aug. Widespread. Forehead is cream coloured. **FP** Leaves, buds, catkins of various trees and shrubs. NS

1170 *Gypsonoma oppressana* 14mm Local. Jun–Jul. Scattered. **FP** Leaves then buds of poplar. NS

1171 *Gypsonoma minutana* 14mm Nb. Jul. South-east England. **FP** Spun leaves of poplars, especially Aspen. NS

decorana 1138

1136

1138

1139

1146

1147

1150

1154

brunneodorsana 1155

1155

1156

1159

1165

1167

1168

1169

1170

1171

TORTRICIDAE (cont.)

1174 *Epiblema cynosbatella* 20mm Common May–Jul. Throughout Britain. Yellow labial palps are distinctive. **FP** Wild and cultivated rose. CMM, RPJ

1175 *Epiblema uddmanniana* Bramble Shoot Moth 18mm Common. Jun–Jul. Throughout Britain wherever foodplant grows. Dark dorsal blotch is distinctive. **FP** Bramble. NS, CMM

1176 *Epiblema trimaculana* 16mm Common. Jun–Jul. Throughout in woods, scrub, hedgerows. Tawny outer corner of wing aids identificaton. **FP** Hawthorn. CMM

1179 *Epiblema incarnatana* 17mm Nb. Jun–Sep. Coastal on limestone and sand, sometimes inland on chalk. Usually tinged pink when fresh. **FP** Rose, especially Burnet Rose. JSB

1183 *Epiblema foenella* 24mm Local. Jun–Aug. Mainly south and west Britain. Flies at dusk and at night. **FP** Root and lower stem of Mugwort. NS

1184 *Epiblema scutulana* 21mm Common. May–Jun. On rough ground throughout Britain. **FP** Stems and roots of Spear and Musk Thistles. NS

1192 *Eucosma conterminana* 18mm Nb. Jul–Aug. Dry chalk and limestone areas of south-east England. Creamy dorsal blotch is distinctive. **FP** Lettuce, including cultivated. CMM

1193 *Eucosma tripoliana* 17mm Local. Jul–Aug. Coastal salt marshes. **FP** Sea Aster. NS

1195 Eucosma lacteana 16mm pRDB3. Jul–Aug. Coastal salt marshes. **FP** Spun flowers and unripe seeds of Sea Wormwood. NS

1197 Eucosma campoliliana 18mm Common. Jun–Jul. Mainly on dry coastal areas. Distinctive white head. **FP** Seeds and stems of Ragwort. NS

1200 Eucosma hohenwartiana 20mm Common. Jun–Aug. Throughout most of Britain in dry, open grassland. **FP** Inside flower heads of Saw-wort, Knapweed. NS

1201 Eucosma cana 20mm Common. Jun–Aug. Throughout most of Britain in dry, open grassland. Flies in afternoon and at night. **FP** Flower heads of thistles, Black Knapweed. SR, CMM

1202 Eucosma obumbratana 17mm Local. Jul–Aug. Rough ground, field margins, etc. **FP** Seedheads of Sow-thistle. SR

1205 Spilonota ocellana Bud Moth 15mm Common. Jul–Aug. In woods, scrub, hedgerows; more common in the south. **FP** Buds of various trees and shrubs. SR

1207 Clavigesta purdeyi Pine Leaf-mining Moth 12mm Common. Jul–Sep. In pine woods in England and Wales. **FP** Inside needles of pines. NS

1208 Pseudococcyx posticana 14mm Common. May–Jun. Coniferous woods and heathland. **FP** Shoots of Scots Pine. NS

1209 Pseudococcyx turionella Pine Bud Moth 20mm Common. May–Jun. Coniferous woods and heathland. **FP** Inside buds and shoots of Scots Pine. CMM

1210 Rhyacionia buoliana Pine Shoot Moth 22mm Common. Jun–Aug. Coniferous woods. Can be similar to *R. pinicolana* below. Dissection required to be certain. **FP** Inside buds and shoots of Scots Pine. PGC

TORTRICIDAE (cont.)

1211 *Rhyacionia pinicolana* 22mm Common. Jul–Aug. Coniferous woods, mostly in England. **FP** Inside buds and shoots of Scots Pine. NS

1212 *Rhyacionia pinivorana* **Spotted Shoot Moth** 18mm Common. May–Jul. Coniferous woods throughout. **FP** Inside buds and shoots of Scots Pine. NS

1216 *Enarmonia formosana* **Cherry Bark Moth** 17mm Common. Jun–Jul. Throughout Britain, in gardens, orchards, parks. **FP** Bark of Apple, Cherry, including ornamental, etc. NS

1217 *Eucosmomorpha albersana* 14mm Nb. May–Jun. In southern England in woods and hedges. **FP** Honeysuckle leaves spun together. CMM

1219 *Lathronympha strigana* 16mm Local. Jun–Jul, Aug–Sep. Can be locally common in southern Britain in open woodland. **FP** Spun leaves of St John's Wort. JSB

1227 *Pammene giganteana* 16mm Local. Mar–Apr. In oak woods. **FP** In galls on oak. NS

1231 *Pammene spiniana* 12mm Local. Aug–Sep. Scrub and commons. **FP** Spun leaves and flowers of Blackthorn, Hawthorn. JSB

1233 *Pammene aurita* 15mm Common. Jul–Aug. First noted in Kent 1943, now expanding northwards through much of England and Wales. **FP** Seeds of Sycamore. CMM, JSB

1234 *Pammene regiana* 15mm Common. May–Jul. Throughout. **FP** Seeds of Sycamore. NS

1236 *Pammene fasciana* 16mm Nb. Jun–Jul. Mainly in southern Britain, in woodland. Flies at dawn and dusk, as well as at night. **FP** Inside oak acorns, nuts of Sweet Chestnut. NS

1237 *Pammene germmana* 12mm Nb. May–Jun. Scattered distribution in England, mostly southern. **FP** Twigs and fruits of Plum, twigs of oak, Hawthorn. JSB

1239 *Pammene rhediella* **Fruitlet Mining Tortrix** 11mm Common. May–Jun. Most common in southern Britain. Flies in sun around host trees. **FP** Flowers and fruits of Hawthorn, Apple, Pear. JSB

1241 *Grapholita compositella* 10mm Common. May–Jun, Aug. Small but striking. Scattered throughout Britain in meadows with low vegetation. Flies by day.

FP Spun leaves of clover. SR

1242 *Grapholita internana* 10mm Local. Apr–Jun. Scattered throughout. Flies around gorse by day. Similar to G. *compositella* but two dorsal bars only. **FP** Inside seedpods of Gorse. NS

1245 *Grapholita janthinana* 10mm Local. Jul–Aug. In southern half of Britain. Flies in afternoon. **FP** In berries of Hawthorn, spun together. JSB

1250 *Grapholita lathyrana* 10mm pRDB3. Apr. Scarce in Britain and throughout Europe. **FP** Dyer's Greenweed, Gorse, in spun leaves, then in roots. PHS

1251 *Grapholita jungiella* 12mm Common. Apr–May, Jul–Aug. Throughout Britain. Flies in sun over foodplants. **FP** Spun leaves and seedpods of Bitter Vetch, Bush Vetch. JSB

1255 *Cydia succedana* 14mm Common. May, Jul–Sep. Males fly around gorse in sun. Throughout Britain, on heath and moorland. **FP** Inside seedpods of Gorse, Broom. CMM, CMM

1257 *Cydia nigricana* **Pea Moth** 14mm Common. May–Aug. Throughout Britain. Can be pest of garden crops. **FP** Inside pods, in Pea seeds. JSB

1259 *Cydia fagiglandana* 17mm Common. Jun–Jul. In Beech woods throughout Britain. **FP** Inside Beech nuts. JSB

1260 *Cydia splendana* 15mm Common. Jul–Aug. Throughout, in woodland. **FP** Inside oak acorns, nuts of Sweet Chestnut. NS, JSB

1261 *Cydia pomonella* **Codling Moth** 20mm Common. Jul–Aug, Sep–Oct. Throughout in gardens, orchards, woodland. **FP** Inside fruits of Apple, Pear, etc. SR, JSB

TORTRICIDAE (cont.)

1262 Cydia amplana 20mm Migrant. Jun–Aug. In woodland. **FP** Inside oak acorns, also nuts of hazel, Sweet Chestnut. CMM

1267 Cydia cosmophorana 12mm Local. Apr–Jun. In pine woods. **FP** Under bark of Scots Pine. NS

1268 Cydia coniferana 12mm Nb. Apr–Jun. In pine woods. **FP** Under bark or in twigs of Scots and other pines. NS

1269 Cydia conicolana 12mm Local. May–Jun. South and south-east England in pine woods. Flies by day and at dusk. **FP** Inside pine cones, especially Scots Pine. NS

1272 Pammene aurana 11mm Local. Jun–Jul. Widespread on rough, open ground. Very distinctive. **FP** Seeds of Hogweed spun together. JSB

1273 Dichrorampha petiverella 12mm Common. Jun–Aug. Widespread in meadows and rough places. Flies in afternoon and evening. **FP** Roots of Yarrow, Tansy. CMM

1274 Dichrorampha alpinana 14mm Common. Jun–Aug. Widespread in meadows and rough places. Flies in afternoon and evening over Ox-eye Daisy. **FP** Roots of Ox-eye Daisy. JSB

1279 Dichrorampha acuminatana 12mm Common. Apr–May, Aug–Sep. Generally a grey moth but has fine chestnut markings. Throughout Britain, in meadows. **FP** Roots of Ox-eye Daisy, Tansy. SR

1285 Dichrorampha plumbana 13mm Common. May–Jun. Throughout Britain, in meadows and rough ground. **FP** Roots of Ox-eye Daisy, Yarrow. SR

ALUCITIDAE

The Twenty-plume Moth is the only member of this family in Britain.

1288 Alucita hexadactyla Twenty-plume Moth 15mm Common. Any month. Throughout Britain, throughout the year. Each wing is split into six plumes, hence the scientific name. **FP** Honeysuckle. CMM

PYRALES: PYRALIDAE

There are over 200 Pyrales on the British list, divided into 12 sub-families. Approximately 140 are native species, living out of doors, while about 30, though resident, are indoor pests of stored food or have been imported with plant material. Around 30 more species are migrants, some seen at almost any time of year, some very rarely. Pyrales generally rest with their antennae swept back over the wings.

Many Pyrales are larger than other Micros and could be thought to be Macros. Some of these are given vernacular names, such as Mother of Pearl, *Pleuroptya ruralis*.

1289 Euchromius ocellea 25mm Migrant. Scarce migrant, usually in south in spring or autumn. White border with black spots on outer edge is distinctive. **FP** Grain. SP

1290 Chilo phragmitella 30mm (♂), 35mm (♀) Common. Jun–Jul. In reed-beds in southern Britain. Sexually dimorphic, female is larger and paler than male. Both have very long labial palps. **FP** Inside stems of Common Reed, Reed Sweet-grass. NS, JSB

1292 Calamotropha paludella 30mm (♂), 34mm (♀) Nb. Jul–Aug. In reed-beds in south-east Britain from East Anglia to Dorset. Sexually dimorphic, female is larger and paler than male. **FP** Inside stems of bulrush. JSB, CMM

1293 Chrysoteuchia culmella Garden Grass-veneer 22mm Common. Jun–Jul. Abundant in grassland throughout Britain. Flies in day or at night. **FP** At base of grass stems. CMM

1294 Crambus pascuella 23mm Common. Jun–Aug. Throughout Britain, in grassy areas. **FP** Fescues, Moor-grass. SH

1296 Crambus silvella 24mm pRDB3. Jul–Aug. On wet heaths in south-east England. Similar to C. *pascuella* but white blotch at end of streak is oval. **FP** On sedges, in spinning. SR

1289 · 1290 ♀ · 1290 ♂ · 1294 · 1292 ♂ · 1292 ♀ · 1293 · 1296

PYRALES: PYRALIDAE (cont.)

1298 *Crambus ericella* 23mm Nb. Jul–Aug. On moorland in northern England and Scotland. **FP** Unknown. RPJ

1299 *Crambus hamella* 27mm Nb. Jul–Aug. On dry heaths throughout. Broad white streak has distinctive angled spike. **FP** Possibly on Wavy Hair-grass. CMM

1301 *Crambus lathoniellus* 21mm Common. May–Aug. In grassy areas throughout, resting head down on stems. **FP** Grass roots. JSB, RW

1302 *Crambus perlella* 30mm Common. Jul–Aug. In any grassy habitat, often abundant. Pearly form is most common but form *warringtonellus* occurs in all populations. **FP** Bases of grass stems. CMM, CMM

1303 *Agriphila selasella* 26mm Local. Jul–Aug. Coastal species. Similar to more common *A. tristella* but white streak is longer and brighter. **FP** Common Saltmarsh-grass, Sheep's Fescue. JSB

1304 *Agriphila straminella* 20mm Common. Jun–Aug. Abundant throughout in grassy habitats. **FP** In stems of grasses, especially Sheep's Fescue. JSB

1305 *Agriphila tristella* 30mm Common. Jul–Sep. Can be abundant in tall grasses throughout. White streak splits into 'fingers'. **FP** In silken galleries amongst bases of grass stems. JSB, CMM

1306 *Agriphila inquinatella* 24mm Common. Jul–Sep. In dry short grass in most of Britain. **FP** In silken galleries amongst bases of grass stems, especially Sheep's Fescue. NS, JSB

1307 *Agriphila latistria* 28mm Local. Jul–Aug. On dry heaths and coastal sand dunes, mainly in southern Britain, but scattered in Scotland also. Single white streak extends full length of wing. **FP** Roots of grasses, especially Brome Grass. CMM

1309 *Agriphila geniculea* 22mm Common. Jul–Oct. Throughout in dry meadows and coastal sandhills. Can be abundant. **FP** Short grasses, especially fescues. CMM, CMM

1310 *Catoptria permutatella* 25mm Na. Jul–Aug. Found only in Scotland. Hides amongst pine needles by day. Distinguished from commoner *C. pinella* by third outer white band. **FP** Mosses. CMM

1313 *Catoptria pinella* 24mm Local. Jul–Aug. Widespread but not common, on wooded heaths and bogs. Hides amongst pine needles by day. **FP** In silk tube amongst grasses, especially Cottongrass, Tufted Hair-grass. PGC

1314 *Catoptria margaritella* **Pearl-band Grass Veneer** 24mm Local. Jul–Aug. Locally common on boggy moors and heaths in northern Britain, Norfolk and south-west England. **FP** Unknown. JSB

1316 *Catoptria falsella* 20mm Local. Jul–Aug. Widespread, mainly southern. **FP** In moss on walls. CMM

1319 *Chrysocrambus linetella* 25mm Vagrant/Accidental. Rare migrant. Kent 1879, Surrey 1896, Sussex 1997. RPJ

1320 *Chrysocrambus craterella* 25mm Vagrant/Accidental. Jun–Jul. Rare European migrant. CMM

1298

1299

1301

1301

warringtonellus

1302

1302

1303

PYRALES: PYRALIDAE (cont.)

1321 Thisanotia chrysonuchella 25mm Nb. May–Jun. In brecks of East Anglia, coastal sandhills and chalk downs of south-east England. **FP** Stem bases of grasses, especially Sheep's Fescue, meadow-grass. NS, TJN

1323 Pediasia contaminella 28mm Nb. Jul–Aug. Usually paler than the example shown. On dry grassland, golf courses, etc., in south-east England. **FP** Grasses, especially Sheep's Fescue. NS

1324 Pediasia aridella 26mm Nb. Jun–Aug. On dry salt-marsh margins of south and east England. **FP** In silken gallery on stem bases of Common Saltmarsh Grass. NS

1325 Platytes alpinella 22mm pRDB3. Jul–Aug. On coastal sandhills and shingle, from Yorkshire south round to Devon. **FP** Possibly on moss. SR

1326 Platytes cerussella 15mm Local. Jun–Jul. Brecks of East Anglia southwards on shingle or sandy coasts. Female is smaller and paler than male. **FP** In roots of short grasses, Sand Sedge. NS

1327 Ancylolomia tentaculella 30mm Migrant. Jun–Jul. Very rare migrant from southern Europe. Two British records from Kent in 1935, 1952. **FP** Stems of Cock's-foot Grass. RPJ

1328 Schoenobius gigantella 30mm Nb. Jul. In large, coastal reed-beds in southern England. Sexually dimorphic, female is nearly 50% larger than male, illustrated. **FP** Inside stem of Common Reed, Reed Sweet-grass. Larva makes a raft to float to a new stem. SR

1329 Donacaula forficella 30mm Common. Jun–Jul. In ditches, marshes, fens, bogs, ponds in Britain from Yorkshire southwards. **FP** Inside stem of Common Reed, Reed Sweet-grass. Larva makes a raft to float to a new stem. JSB, NS, CMM

1331 Acentria ephemerella Water Veneer 18mm Common. Jun–Aug. Throughout in ponds, slow streams, etc. Female is usually wingless and remains under water after emergence, mating at the surface with winged male. **FP** As much as 2m under water in spinnings on Canadian Waterweed, pondweeds, algae. CMM

1332 Scoparia subfusca 25mm Common. Jun–Aug. Throughout Britain. May be found by day on rocks, stone walls, tree trunks. **FP** Roots of Ox-tongue, Colt's-foot. JSB

1333 Scoparia pyralella 20mm Common. Jun. Throughout Britain, mainly on chalk and limestone downs, especially near sea. **FP** Decaying plant material and roots of Common Ragwort. JSB, CMM

1334 Scoparia ambigualis 22mm Common. May–Jun. Throughout Britain. In woodland in south, moors in north. **FP** Feeds under moss. CMM

1336 Eudonia pallida 16mm Common. Jun–Jul. Throughout in marshes and bogs. **FP** Probably on mosses. NS, CMM

1337 Eudonia alpina 25mm Na. Jun–Jul. High mountains of Scotland, easily disturbed from mossy turf. **FP** Probably on mosses. SR

1338 Dipleurina lacustrata 18mm Common. Jun–Jul. Throughout. Prefers open country. **FP** Mosses on walls and tree trunks. JSB

1340 Eudonia truncicolella 22mm Common. Jul–Aug. In woodland throughout. **FP** Moss. NS

1341 Eudonia lineola 20mm Nb. Jul–Aug. Widespread, mainly coastal. **FP** Lichens. SH

1321

1323

1324

1321

1325

1326

PYRALES: PYRALIDAE (cont.)

1342 *Eudonia angustea* 16mm Local. Jul–Oct. Widespread, often coastal. **FP** Moss on walls and sand dunes. NS

1343 *Eudonia delunella* 18mm Nb. Jul–Aug. Widespread in woodland. May be found by day on tree trunks of oak, ash, etc. **FP** Lichens and moss on tree trunks. JSB, CMM

1344 *Eudonia mercurella* 18mm Common. Jun–Sep. Throughout Britain. Easily disturbed by day from rocks, walls, tree trunks. **FP** Moss on tree trunks, walls, etc. JSB

1345 *Elophila nymphaeata* Brown China-mark 30mm Common. Jun–Aug. Throughout in ponds, canals, slow rivers, etc. A smaller, darker, form occurs in New Forest and Dorset bogs. **FP** Larva is entirely aquatic on pondweeds, Frogbit, Bur-reeds. JSB, CMM

1348 *Parapoynx stratiotata* Ringed China-mark 24mm (♂), 32mm (♀) Local. Jun–Aug. Sexually dimorphic. Female is 30% larger and also browner than male. Found near ponds, lakes, canals, etc., from Yorkshire southwards. **FP** Larva is entirely aquatic on pondweeds, Canadian Waterweed, etc. CMM, CMM, JSB

1350 *Nymphula stagnata* Beautiful China-mark 22mm Common. Jul–Aug. Margins of ponds, lakes, streams throughout. **FP** Aquatic larva on Bur-reeds, Yellow Water-lily, etc. CMM

1354 *Cataclysta lemnata* Small China-mark 18mm (♂), 22mm (♀) Common. Jun–Aug. Throughout in ditches, ponds, canals. Hind-wing margin, black with blue spots, is distinctive. **FP** Duckweed. NS, JSB

1342 — 1343 — 1343
1344 — 1345 — 1345
1348 ♂ — 1348 ♂ — 1348 ♀
1350 — 1354 ♀ — 1354 ♂

1356 *Evergestis forficalis* Garden Pebble 30mm
Common. May–Jun, Aug–Sep. Throughout Britain in
gardens and allotments. **FP** Crucifers, especially
Cabbage, Turnip, Horseradish. CMM
1356a *Evergestis limbata* 25mm Migrant. Jul–Aug.
Rare and very distinctive migrant, usually along south
coast. **FP** Garlic and Hedge Mustard. DF
1357 *Evergestis extimalis* 30mm Nb. Jun–Jul. On chalk
downs of south-east England and brecks of East Anglia.
FP Seedheads of crucifers, especially Perennial Wall-
rocket, Charlock. SR, SR
1358 *Evergestis pallidata* 30mm Local. Jun–Aug.

In damp, open woods in southern England and south
Scotland. **FP** Crucifers, especially Winter-cress. JSB
1359 *Cynaeda dentalis* 30mm pRDB3. Jul. On coasts of
southern England. **FP** Inside stems of Viper's Bugloss.
CMM, NS
1360 Old World Webworm *Hellula undalis* 16mm
Migrant. Sep–Oct. Scarce migrant from tropics. NS
1361 *Pyrausta aurata* 18mm Common. May–Jun, Jul–
Aug. On chalk downs, beside rivers, in gardens. Similar to
P. purpuralis below but only single gold mark. Flies in sun
and at night. **FP** Leaves and flowers of mint, including
garden varieties, Dead-nettle, Marjoram, etc. RW, SR

PYRALES: PYRALIDAE (cont.)

1362 Pyrausta purpuralis 22mm Common. May–Jun, Jul–Aug. On chalk downs, beside rivers, in gardens. Similar to *P. aurata* above but gold mark usually split into three, spread across wing. Flies in sun and at night. **FP** Leaves and flowers of mint, including garden varieties, Corn Mint, Thyme. CMM, CMM

1363 Pyrausta ostrinalis 18mm Local. May–Jun, Jul–Aug. Similar in looks, habits and distribution to *P. purpuralis* above. **FP** Unknown, but probably similar to above. JSB

1364 Pyrausta sanguinalis Scarce Crimson and Gold 18mm pRDB1. Jun, Aug. Formerly in coastal sandhills in north Wales and Lancashire, now restricted to Isle of Man, Northern Ireland and the Burren in Ireland. **FP** Thyme flowers. MF

1365 Pyrausta despicata 18mm Common. May–Jun, Jul–Aug. Throughout on dry calcareous soils, cliffs, downs. Flies in sun and at night. **FP** Gregarious on leaves of Greater and Ribwort Plantain. NS

1366 Pyrausta nigrata 14mm Local. Jun–Jul. Sep–Oct. On rough downland in southern England, also limestone pavements of Cumberland and Westmorland. Flies by day. **FP** Leaves of Thyme, Marjoram, Corn Mint, Woodruff. DE

1367 Pyrausta cingulata 20mm Local. May–Jun, Jul–Aug. Mainly coastal on limestone or chalk. Flies day or night. **FP** Probably Wild Thyme. CMM, CMM

1369 Uresiphita polygonalis 33mm Migrant. Sep–Oct. Scarce migrant, from southern Europe and tropics. MF

1370 Sitochroa palealis 38mm Nb. Jun–Jul. In southern England in brecks of East Anglia, Thames valley and south coasts, on rough, open ground. **FP** Seedheads of Wild Carrot. JSB

1371 Sitochroa verticalis 32mm Local. Jun–Jul, Aug–Sep. Southern Britain on rough meadows. **FP** Creeping Thistle, Goosefoot, dock, Broom. NS

1372 Paracorsia repandalis 25mm Vagrant/Accidental. Rare migrant from southern Europe. CMM

1375 Ostrinia nubilalis European Corn Borer 32mm (♂), 38mm (♀) Local. Jun–Jul. First established in Britain in 1930s. Now found in Thames valley and along south coast, reinforced by migration from Continent. Sexually dimorphic. **FP** Stems of Mugwort. In Europe can be pest on Maize. NS, CMM

1376 Eurrhypara hortulata Small Magpie 35mm Common. Jun–Jul. Throughout Britain, less common in north. **FP** Usually on rolled or spun leaves of Common Nettle. CMM, CMM

1377 Perinephela lancealis 32mm Local. Jun–Jul. In damp woodland and marsh in southern Britain. Sexually dimorphic; male has distinctly long, narrow forewings. **FP** Leaves, flowers and seedheads of Hemp Agrimony. CMM

1378 Phlyctaenia coronata 24mm Common. Jun–Jul. In England and Wales from Lancashire southwards. Easily disturbed from Elder in daytime. **FP** In web under leaf of Elder. JSB

1380 Phlyctaenia perlucidalis 24mm Local. Jun–Jul. First recorded 1951 in Woodwalton Fen, occasionally recorded since in south-east England, including the one shown from Dorset. **FP** Possibly thistles. CMM

1381 Anania funebris White-spotted Sable Moth 22mm Na. Jun–Jul. Unmistakable day-flying moth scattered throughout Britain, often on limestone. **FP** In web under leaves of Goldenrod. PGC

1382 Anania verbascalis 24mm Nb. Jun–Jul. In south-east England, mainly in coastal counties. In open wooded heaths, coastal shingle. **FP** Wood Sage. NS

1362

1362

1363

1364

1365

PYRALES: PYRALIDAE (cont.)

1383 *Psammotis pulveralis* 26mm Migrant. Jun–Jul. Scarce visitor to southern England, including Dorset, from marshy areas of Europe. **FP** Under leaves of Water Mint, Gypsywort. CMM

1384 *Phlyctaenia stachydalis* 22mm pRDBK. Jun–Aug. In southern England and Wales. Similar to more common *P. coronata* but shorter, blunter wings. **FP** Spun leaf of Woundwort. JSB

1385 *Ebulea crocealis* 25mm Common. Jul–Aug. Common in southern England, local esewhere in rough damp meadows. **FP** Common Fleabane, Ploughman's Spikenard. JSB

1386 *Opsibotys fuscalis* 28mm Common. Jun. Throughout in meadows, marsh, open woods, moors. **FP** Flowers and seeds of Yellow Rattle, Common Cow Wheat. DJP

1387 *Nascia cilialis* 25mm Na. Jun–Jul. Inhabits fens of East Anglia, and also in Hampshire. **FP** Sedges, including Greater Pond Sedge. NS

1388 *Udea lutealis* 25mm Common. Jul–Aug. Throughout Britain on rough ground. **FP** Various herbaceous plants, including Bramble, Knapweed, thistle, plantain. JSB

1389 *Udea fulvalis* 28mm Migrant. Jul–Aug. Scarce migrant but possibly resident in Dorset. Similar to *U. prunalis* below, but browner. **FP** Catmint. CMM

1390 *Udea prunalis* 25mm Common. Jun–Jul. Throughout, usually associated with blackthorn. Greyer than *U. fulvalis*. **FP** Leaves of various plants, including Deadnettle, Woundwort, Dog's Mercury, Honeysuckle. NS

1392 *Udea olivalis* 25mm Common. Jun–Jul. Throughout Britain in woods, hedgerows, gardens. **FP** Leaves of various plants, including Dog's Mercury, Hop, dock. NS

1395 *Udea ferrugalis* **Rusty-dot Pearl** 22mm Migrant. Any month. Throughout Britain. **FP** Polyphagous. JSB

1397 *Mecyna asinalis* **Madder Pearl** 35mm Nb. May–Oct. South and west coasts of England and Wales. **FP** Leaves of Wild Madder. CMM

1398 *Nomophila noctuella* **Rush Veneer** 30mm Migrant. Any month. Can be abundant, throughout. Variable, but always long, narrow wings. **FP** Clover, Knotgrass, etc. CMM, CMM

1399 *Dolicharthria punctalis* 23mm Nb. Jul–Aug. On cliffs and beaches by the sea from Sussex to Cornwall. Very long legs, rests with head up. **FP** Dead or decaying leaves of Bird's-foot Trefoil, clover, plantain, Eel-grass. CMM

1400 *Antigastra catalaunalis* 22mm Vagrant/Accidental. Scarce, from tropics and southern Europe. Similar long legs and resting position to *Dolicharthria punctalis*. CMM

1402 *Diasemia reticularis* 18mm Migrant. May–Sep. Striking but scarce migrant from Europe and the tropics, possibly former resident. **FP** Possibly Ox-tongue. CMM

1403 *Diasemiopsis ramburialis* 20mm Migrant. Jun–Oct. Striking but scarce migrant from Europe and the tropics. Similar to *D. reticularis* above. **FP** Unknown. CMM

1404 *Hymenia recurvalis* 22mm Migrant. Scarce autumn migrant from tropics. **FP** Pest on Maize, Beet. CMM

1405 *Pleuroptya ruralis* **Mother of Pearl** 35mm Common. Jul–Aug. Throughout most of Britain, this micro is larger than many macros. Wings have pearly sheen. **FP** Rolled leaves of Common Nettle. CMM, JSB

1408 *Palpita vitrealis* 33mm Migrant. Scarce migrant from southern Europe. Wings shining translucent white, brown leading edge, several tiny black spots. **FP** Olive, Jasmine. CMM

1413 *Hypsopygia costalis* **Gold Triangle** 21mm Common. Jul–Aug. In southern Britain in gardens, farms, woods. Rests with wings spread or closed. **FP** Dry vegetable matter in hay, thatch, dead leaves. CMM

PYRALES: PYRALIDAE (cont.)

1414 Synaphe punctalis 24mm Nb. Jun–Aug. Inhabits coastal counties of southern England. Female is smaller and paler than male. **FP** In mosses on ground. SR

1415 Orthopygia glaucinalis 25mm Common. Jul–Aug. Widespread in Britain, south of Lancashire. **FP** Decaying vegetable refuse, thatch, haystacks, birds' nests, dead leaves. JSB

1417 Pyralis farinalis Meal Moth 25mm Common. Jun–Aug. Widespread but usually only found inside stables, grain stores, mills, farm buildings, etc. **FP** Stored grain. CMM

1421 Aglossa pinguinalis Large Tabby 32mm Local. Jun–Jul. Widespread in barns, outhouses, sheep pens. Runs rather than flies if disturbed. **FP** Hay refuse in barns, sheep dung. SR

1424 Endotricha flammealis 21mm Local. Jul–Aug. In southern Britain, easily disturbed by day from bracken, gorse, etc. **FP** Greater Bird's-foot Trefoil, then decaying leaves. CMM, CMM

1425 Galleria mellonella Wax Moth 30mm Common. Jun–Oct. Lives in beehives throughout Britain. **FP** Feeds on honeycomb, hence the name. JSB

1426 Achroia grisella Lesser Wax Moth 20mm Common. Jul–Oct. Lives in beehives throughout Britain. Can be so abundant in hives as to destroy the bee colony. **FP** Feeds on old wax in beehives. NS

1428 Aphomia sociella Bee Moth 35mm (♂), 33mm (♀) Common. Jun–Aug. In nests of bees and wasps throughout Britain. Sexually dimorphic. **FP** Feeds on honeycombs. CMM, JSB, JSB

1414 ♂ · 1415 · 1417 · 1421 · 1424 · 1425 · 1426 · 1424 pale aberration · 1428 ♀ · 1428 ♂ · 1428 ♂

1429 *Melissoblaptes zelleri* 35mm pRDB3. Jun–Aug. Very local in coastal sandhills in Kent and East Anglia. **FP** Moss in sandhills. JPo

1432 *Anerastia lotella* 18mm Common. Jul. On coastal sandhills around Britain and the brecks of East Anglia. **FP** Roots of Marram, Sheep's Fescue. SR, JSB

1433 *Cryptoblabes bistriga* 17mm Local. Jun–Jul. In oak woods in England and Wales. **FP** Folded leaf of oak, occasionally Alder. JSB

1435 *Conobathra tumidana* 22mm Migrant. Jul–Sep. Possibly resident in south. Raised red scales are distinctive. **FP** Spun oak leaves. NS

1436 *Conobathra repandana* 24mm Common. Jul–Aug. In oak woods in England from Durham southwards. **FP** Spun oak leaves. NS

1437 *Acrobasis consociella* 20mm Common. Jul–Aug. In oak woods throughout Britain. **FP** Gregarious on spun oak leaves. NS

1438 *Trachycera suavella* 25mm Local. Jul–Aug. In Blackthorn thickets in southern England. **FP** In silken gallery on leaves of Blackthorn. NS

1439 *Trachycera advenella* 20mm Common. Jul–Aug. Throughout Britain in old Hawthorn hedges. **FP** Flowers, buds, leaves of Hawthorn, also Rowan. PGC, JSB

1440 *Trachycera marmorea* 18mm Local. Jun–Aug. In southern England and Wales in stunted Blackthorn bushes. **FP** On Blackthorn, in web like small piece of sheep's wool. NS, JSB

1429 ♀ — 1432 — 1432
1433 — 1435 — 1436
1437 — 1438 — 1440
1439 — 1439 — 1440

PYRALES: PYRALIDAE (cont.)

1441 *Oncocera semirubella* 30mm Nb. Jun–Jul. On chalk and limestone downs and sea cliffs in southern England. Stunning. Two forms, one has white streak along leading edge. Easily disturbed in sun, flies at night. **FP** Common Bird's-foot Trefoil, White Clover. CMM, NS

1442 *Pempelia palumbella* 26mm Common. Jul–Aug. On heaths throughout. Dark tuft of scales near head is distinctive. **FP** In web on heathers, Milkwort, Thyme. NS, CMM

1443 *Pempelia genistella* 25mm Na. July. On heaths of southern England, especially near coast. **FP** In silk web on Gorse. CMM, CMM, PGC

1444 *Pempelia obductella* 25mm pRDB2. Jul–Aug. Very rare on chalk downs in Kent. **FP** In spinning on Marjoram. JPo

1445 *Pempelia formosa* 24mm Local. Jun–Aug. In Elm hedges in south-eastern England. **FP** In web on upper surface of leaves of Elm. CMM

1447a *Sciota adelphella* 25mm Migrant. Jun–Jul. Rare migrant and occasional colonist in south-east England. **FP** Willow, poplar. NS

1449 *Elegia similella* 18mm Nb. Jun–Jul. Very local in mature oak woods in southern England. **FP** In silk web on leaves of oak. JPo

1451 *Pyla fusca* 25mm Common. Jun–Jul. Throughout on heaths and moorland, particularly favouring burnt areas for camouflage. **FP** In web on heather, possibly Bilberry. NS

1451a *Etiella zinckenella* 30mm Vagrant/Accidental. Jul–Oct. Scarce migrant from southern Europe. **FP** Legumes. CMM

1452 *Phycita roborella* 28mm Common. Jul–Aug. In oak woods in southern Britain. **FP** Spun oak leaves. CMM, JSB

1453 *Pima boisduvaliella* 23mm pRDB3. Jun–Aug. Coastal sand dunes and shingle banks in south-east England. Flies at dusk. **FP** Pods of Sea Pea, Common Bird's-foot Trefoil, Spiny Restharrow. NS

1454 *Dioryctria abietella* 30mm Common. Jul–Aug. Widespread. Similar to *D. simplicella* but generally slightly larger and less grey. **FP** Scots Pine. NS

1454a *Dioryctria schuetzeella* 24mm Naturalised, alien host. Jul. In south-east England. First discovered in Kent, 1980. **FP** Spun needles of Norway Spruce. NS

1454b *Dioryctria sylvestrella* 35mm Naturalised. Jul–Aug. First recorded 2001 in Britain in Dorset, but had been previously misidentified as large *D. abietella*. **FP** Scots Pine. CMM, JSB

1455 *Dioryctria simplicella* 28mm Common. Jul–Sep. Throughout Britain in pine woods. Smaller and plainer grey than *D. abietella*. **FP** Scots Pine. NS, NS

1443

1443

1443

1445

1447a

1449

1451

1452

1452

1451a

1453

1454

1454a

1454b

1454b

1455

melanic

1455

PYRALES: PYRALIDAE (cont.)

1456 *Epischnia bankesiella* 25mm Na. Jul. Found only on limestone cliffs of Purbeck and Portland in Dorset and in south Wales. **FP** Leaves of Golden Samphire. BS
1457 *Hypochalcia ahenella* 26mm Local. Jun–Aug. In southern Britain on dry, sparsely vegetated downs. **FP** Possibly Rock Rose, Field Wormwood. CMM
1458 *Myelois circumvoluta* **Thistle Ermine** 35mm Common. Jul. In southern half of Britain on rough ground, in gardens, parks. **FP** Seedheads and stems of various thistles. CMM, JSB
1461 *Assara terebrella* 24mm Local. Jun–Aug. In south of England in mature spruce woods. **FP** In cones of Norway Spruce. CMM
1462 *Pempeliella dilutella* 22mm Common. Jul–Aug. On chalk and limestone coasts around Britain, inland on chalk downs. Associated with yellow ants. **FP** Wild Thyme. SR
1463 *Pempeliella ornatella* 25mm pRDB3. Jun–Aug. Local on coastal chalk downs of southern England. **FP** Wild Thyme. CMM
1465 *Nephopterix angustella* 22mm Nb. Jun–Jul, Sep–Oct. Widespread but local in southern England. **FP** Inside Spindle berries. NS
1467 *Ancylosis oblitella* 22mm Nb. May, Jul–Aug. First colonised Thames estuary in 1950s, now in south-east England to Midlands on salt marshes and rough ground. **FP** Goosefoot. CMM

1470 *Euzophera pinguis* 28mm Local. Jul–Aug. In Britain from Yorkshire southwards. **FP** Under live bark of ash. CMM
1474 *Ephestia parasitella unicolorella* 20mm Local. Jun–Sep. Southern England, often amongst Ivy. **FP** Probably dry vegetable matter, including Ivy. CMM, CMM
1475 *Ephestia kuehniella* **Mediterranean Flour Moth** 24mm Synanthropic. Apr–Oct. Throughout, in warm buildings such as flour mills, bakeries, granaries. **FP** Stored cereals, including flour, pasta, biscuits. SR
1479 *Plodia interpunctella* **Indian Meal Moth** 17mm Synanthropic. Jun–Sep. Throughout, in food warehouses. **FP** Stored grain, dried fruits, nuts, etc. SR
1481 *Homoeosoma sinuella* 22mm Local. Jun–Aug. In open dry habitats such as downs, dunes, quarries, sea cliffs in southern Britain. **FP** Roots of plantain. CMM, JSB
1483 *Phycitodes binaevella* 24mm Local. Jul. Scattered throughout England on light soils. **FP** Seedheads of Spear Thistle. CMM, NS
1485 *Phycitodes maritima* 20mm Local. May–Aug. Mainly coastal in southern Britain. Very similar to *P. saxicola*; needs genitalia examination for certainty. **FP** Flowers of Yarrow, Common Ragwort. JSB
1486 *Apomyelois bistriatella subcognata* 25mm Nb. Jun–Jul. In southern Britain in areas of burnt Gorse. **FP** In fungus *Daldinia concentrica* on burnt Gorse or dead birch. CMM, NS

1456 | 1457 | aberration | 1458
1461 | 1465 | 1462 | 1463
1458

1467

1470

1474

unicolorella 1474

1475

1479

1481

1483

1483

1481

1485

1486

1486

PLUME MOTHS: PTEROPHORIDAE

In this unusual-looking group of moths, the wings are held out from the body, usually forming a characteristic 'T' shape. The wings are generally split into fingers, or plumes.

In some, this is obvious, such as White Plume Moth *Pterophorus pentadactyla* (from the Greek for 'combined wing in five fingers'), which is common and often found in gardens where the larvae feed on bindweed. In other species the plumes are rolled up like a furled umbrella and show little detail, such as *Emmelina monodactyla* (from the Greek for 'single finger'), which is also common and feeds on bindweed in gardens. Most will come to light and several species can be easily disturbed by day.

1487 Agdistis meridionalis 25mm pRDB3. Jul–Oct. On coastal cliffs of south-west Britain, from Dorset to Wales. Similar to *A. bennetii* below, but smaller, not found on marshes. **FP** Rock Sea-lavender. BS

1488 Agdistis bennetii 30mm Local. Jul–Aug. On coastal salt marshes of south-east England, from Dorset to Durham. Can be abundant at dusk. Both *Agdistis* species, though Plumes, do not have wings split into 'fingers'. **FP** Common Sea-lavender. CMM

1490 Oxyptilus parvidactylus 20mm Local. Downs of Kent and Surrey, Breckland of East Anglia. **FP** Mouse-ear Hawkweed. JPo

1491 Crombrugghia distans 20mm Nb. Scattered throughout England on sandy heaths, dunes, downs. **FP** Mouse-ear Hawkweed. JPo

1494 Capperia britanniodactyla 20mm Nb. Jun–Jul. Widespread in warm, dry, stony, south-facing habitats. **FP** Wood Sage. Larva chews stem, causing plant to wilt, then feeds on wilted leaves. CMM

1495 Marasmarcha lunaedactyla 20mm Common. Jul. Well distributed on coasts of Britain from Yorkshire southwards. Pale crescent at cleft in forewing is distinctive. **FP** Restharrow. CMM

1496 Cnaemidophorus rhododactyla 25mm pRDB2. Jul–Aug. Inhabits south-east England. **FP** Leaves and flowers of Dog Rose. CMM

1497 Amblyptilia acanthadactyla 20mm Common. Jul, Sep–May. Throughout in various habitats, including gardens, hedges, coasts. Often comes indoors to hibernate. Similar to *A. punctidactyla* below, but brown rather than grey. **FP** Flowers and seeds of various herbaceous plants, including heather, Restharrow, Crane's-bill, Goosefoot. CMM

1498 Amblyptilia punctidactyla 20mm Common. Jul, Sep–May. Similar distribution, habitat and appearance to *A. acanthadactyla* but grey. Both have two dark tufts protruding from trailing edge. **FP** Flowers and seeds of various herbaceous plants, including Woundwort, Columbine, Primrose, Stork's-bill. JSB

1501 Platyptilia gonodactyla 25mm Common. May–Jun, Sep. Widespread in open grassy habitats. **FP** Stems and flowers of Colt's-foot, Butterbur. NS

1502 Platyptilia isodactylus 25mm Local. Jun, Aug–Sep. Inhabits fens and marshes in southern half of Britain. **FP** Marsh Ragwort. JSB

1487

1488

PLUME MOTHS: PTEROPHORIDAE (cont.)

1503 *Platyptilia ochrodactyla* 25mm Nb. Jul. Widespread in England and Wales. Found amongst stands of Tansy by torchlight at dusk. Example shown is worn, should be browner, with distinct bands of brown and white on hind leg. **FP** Inside stems of Tansy. CMM

1504 *Platyptilia pallidactyla* 25mm Local. Jun–Jul. Throughout Britain in dry, sandy, rough ground. Similar to above but hind leg not banded. **FP** Yarrow. CMM

1505 *Stenoptilia pneumonanthes* Gentian Plume 22mm RDB2. Probably extinct. Formerly on damp heaths of south-east Dorset. **FP** Inside seedheads of Marsh Gentian. JPo

1507 *Stenoptilia zophodactylus* 22mm Local. Jul–Sep. Inhabits dry sandy areas, cliffs, dunes, heaths in southern Britain. Legs are white. **FP** Flowers and seeds of Gentian, Common Centuary, Yellow Wort. JSB, CMM

1508 *Stenoptilia bipunctidactyla* 22mm Common. May–Oct. Throughout Britain. Can be similar to other *Stenoptilia*, needs dissection to be certain. **FP** Flowers and leaves of scabious. JBH

1509 *Stenoptilia pterodactyla* 25mm Common. Jun–Aug. Throughout Britain. Similar to *S. bipunctidactyla*, but browner, wingtips edged white. **FP** Stems and flowers of Germander Speedwell. CMM

1510 *Merrifieldia leucodactyla* 21mm Common. Jun–Aug. Widespread in Britain, especially the south, on chalk cliffs, limestone downs, etc. Easily disturbed by day. **FP** Wild Thyme. SR, CMM

1512 *Merrifieldia baliodactylus* 25mm Local. Jul–Aug. Mainly southern England on dry chalk and limestone downs. Similar to *M. leucodactyla*, but dark mark in centre of forewing edge. **FP** Wild Marjoram. SR

1513 *Pterophorus pentadactyla* White Plume Moth 30mm Common. Jun–Jul, Sep. Large, common, distinctive, frequent in gardens and on rough ground, easily disturbed by day. **FP** Bindweed. CMM

1514 *Pterophorus galactodactyla* 25mm Local. Jun–Jul. Mainly on brecks of East Anglia. **FP** Greater Burdock leaves. SP

1515 *Pterophorus spilodactylus* 25mm pRDB2. Jul–Sep. On Isle of Wight and southern chalk downs. **FP** White Horehound. BY

1503 1504 1505 1507

1507

1508

1509

1510

1510

1512

1513

1515

1514

PLUME MOTHS: PTEROPHORIDAE (cont.)

1516 *Pselnophorus heterodactyla* 20mm pRDB1. Scattered records from Suffolk, Gloucestershire, Cumbria, Scotland. **FP** Wall Lettuce, Marsh Hawk's-beard. JPo

1517 *Adaina microdactyla* 15mm Common. May–Aug. The smallest Plume, slightly tinged pale yellow. **FP** Inside stems of Hemp Agrimony, forming a gall. CMM

1519 *Euleioptilus carphodactyla* 20mm Nb. Jun, Aug–Sep. On chalk and limestone coasts of central southern England. **FP** Flower heads of Ploughman's Spikenard. CMM

1523 *Oidaematophorus lithodactyla* 29mm Common. Jul–Aug. On rough ground, mainly in southern Britain. **FP** Leaves of Common Fleabane, Ploughman's Spikenard. CMM

1524 *Emmelina monodactyla* 25mm Common. Any month. Throughout Britain, in fields, hedges, gardens, parks. Pairs of spurs on hind legs are of unequal lengths. **FP** Bindweed leaves and flowers. CMM, CMM

1524a *Emmelina argoteles* 25mm First discovered June 2005 in Wicken Fen, Cambridgeshire. Genitalia examination required to separate this from *E. monodactyla*. Status uncertain. **FP** Hedge Bindweed. JBH

BUTTERFLIES

This colourful group of insects are day-flyers, with clubbed antennae, and visit flowers to suck nectar through their hollow proboscis, as the Brimstone shown below is doing. All except skippers rest with their wings raised up over their backs.

Males of several species can also be found sucking minerals from damp ground, urine, etc. They can also be attracted to human sweat (*see* p.11). This is believed to enhance their coloration, helping to attract females. 'Butterfly' is the vernacular term given to members of the five lepidopteran families that follow.

This Brimstone is using its long, hollow proboscis to sip nectar. PE

SKIPPERS: HESPERIIDAE

Skippers are small and rather moth-like. They are not given to long flights, just 'skipping' over the vegetation of their rough grassland habitat. They live in discrete colonies.

1525 Chequered Skipper *Carterocephalus palaemon* 30mm RDB4. May–Jun. Found only in north-west Scotland around Fort William. Visits spring flowers such as bluebell and bugle. **FP** Purple Moor-grass. PE, PE

1526 Small Skipper *Thymelicus sylvestris* 28mm Common. Jun–Aug. Common in Wales and England from Northumberland southwards wherever there is rough, tall, flowery grassland. Similar to Essex Skipper but tips of antennae are orange, not black. **FP** Yorkshire-fog, Creeping Soft-grass. PE

1527 Essex Skipper *Thymelicus lineola* 28mm Common. Jun–Aug. Found in south and east England from the Severn to the Wash. Similar to Small Skipper. **FP** Cock's-foot, Creeping Soft-grass, Tor-grass. PE

1528 Lulworth Skipper *Thymelicus acteon* 25mm Na. Jun–Sep. Restricted to south-facing chalk and limestone downs and cliffs around Lulworth, Dorset, but abundant. Favours tall grass with flowers and thistles. **FP** Tor-grass. PE

1529 Silver-spotted Skipper *Hesperia comma* 30mm RDB3. Jul–Sep. Inhabits warm, chalk downland with short turf in south-east England. **FP** Sheep's-fescue. PE, PE

1531 Large Skipper *Ochlodes venata* 35mm Common. May–Aug. Common from southern Scotland southwards, wherever there is rough grass. **FP** Various grasses, including Cock's-foot, Purple Moor-grass. PE

1532 Dingy Skipper *Erynnis tages* 30mm Common. Apr–Jun, Aug. Local throughout Britain, especially on sunny south-facing downs. Also heaths, dunes, sea-cliffs, open woods. **FP** Common and Greater Bird's-foot Trefoil, Horseshoe Vetch. PE

1534 Grizzled Skipper *Pyrgus malvae* 25mm Common. Mar–Jul, Aug. Scattered throughout southern Britain in open woods, dunes, heaths, chalk downs. Favours short vegetation in warm spots. **FP** Various plants, including Wild Strawberry, Agrimony, Creeping Cinquefoil, Bramble. PE, PE

1528

1529

1529

1531

1532

1534

1534

SWALLOWTAILS: PAPILIONIDAE

There is one resident Swallowtail, which is unmistakable and found only in the fens of Norfolk, and one very rare migrant.

1539 Swallowtail *Papilio machaon* 90mm RDB2. May–Jul. Only in Norfolk Broads. **FP** Milk-parsley. PE, PE
1540 Scarce Swallowtail *Iphiclides podalirius* 80mm Vagrant/Accidental. Very rare migrant from southern Europe. Occurs also in Asia, China. **FP** Blackthorn, Bullace, Cherry. CMM

1539

1539

1540

YELLOWS AND WHITES: PIERIDAE

These are large, fairly plain, slow flyers, and are mainly solitary. The family includes the Large and Small (Cabbage) Whites, the yellow Brimstone and migrant Clouded Yellows.

1541 Wood White *Leptidea sinapis* 40mm Nb. May–Jun, Jul–Aug. Scattered colonies in southern Britain in open, coppiced woodland. Always rests with wings closed. **FP** Legumes, including Meadow Vetchling, Tuberous Pea, Bitter and Tufted Vetch. PE
1541a Réal's Wood White *Leptidea reali* 40mm Ireland only. May–Jun, Jul–Aug. Visually the same as above, but slightly different genitalia and DNA. **FP** Legumes, including Meadow Vetchling, Tuberous Pea, Bitter and Tufted Vetch. JBH
1543 Pale Clouded Yellow *Colias hyale* 50mm Migrant. Very similar to Clouded Yellow, but caterpillar different. From southern Europe and Africa. **FP** Legumes, including clovers. PE
1544 Berger's Clouded Yellow *Colias alfacariensis* 50mm Migrant. Very similar to Clouded Yellow, but caterpillar different. From southern Europe and Africa. **FP** Legumes, including clovers. PE
1545 Clouded Yellow *Colias croceus* 50mm Migrant. Regular migrant from southern Europe and North Africa. Can breed in good summers. Larvae can survive over winter in Bournemouth, Dorset. **FP** Legumes, including clovers, Lucerne. PE
1546 Brimstone *Gonepteryx rhamni* 60mm Common. Aug–Nov, Mar–Jun. Spring flight is after hibernation. Well distributed through England and Wales in wooded and scrubby areas. Rests with wings closed. **FP** Purging and Alder Buckthorn. PE
1548 Black-veined White *Aporia crataegi* 70mm Extinct. Jun–Aug. Formerly in south-east England. Not seen since 1925. **FP** Blackthorn, Hawthorn. PE, CMM

♀ egg laying   1541

1541a

1543

1545

♂s collecting minerals   1544

1546

1548

1548

YELLOWS AND WHITES: PIERIDAE (cont.)

1549 Large White *Pieris brassicae* 65mm Common. Apr–Sep. Common throughout Britain. The largest White, female has two black spots on forewing. **FP** Brassicas, including Cabbage, Nasturtium, crucifers including Garlic Mustard. PE, PE

1550 Small White *Pieris rapae* 50mm Common. Apr–Oct. Common throughout Britain. Smaller than Large White, with indistinct black wingtip. **FP** Cabbage and other Brassicas, Nasturtium, Garlic Mustard and other crucifers. PE

1551 Green-veined White *Pieris napi* 45mm Common. Apr–Sep. Throughout Britain in damp meadows, damp woods, moorland. Distinctive underside. **FP** Crucifers, including Garlic and Hedge Mustard, Cuckooflower, Charlock. PE, PE

1552 Bath White *Pontia daplidice* 50mm Vagrant/ Accidental. Jun–Sep. Very scarce migrant, favouring hot, open sites. **FP** Crucifers, Mignonette. PE

1553 Orange-tip *Anthocharis cardamines* 45mm (♂), 50mm (♀) Common. Apr–Jul. Throughout most of Britain in damp woods and meadows, hedgerows, etc. Only male has orange tips; under-side distinctive. **FP** Lady's Smock, Garlic Mustard. PE, PE, PE

COPPERS, HAIRSTREAKS AND BLUES: LYCAENIDAE

Members of this family are small, mostly with bright, metallic colours and often spotted underwings, and usually found in small colonies.

1555 Green Hairstreak *Callophrys rubi* 33mm Common. Apr–Jul. Throughout, but more common in south. Inhabits moors, heaths, woods, hedges, downs, especially warm sheltered hillsides. Male is territorial. **FP** Gorse, Bilberry, Broom, buckthorn, Rock-rose, Bird's-foot Trefoil, etc. PE, PE

1556 Brown Hairstreak *Thecla betulae* 38mm Nb. Jul–Sep. Scattered colonies in south and west Britain in woodland edges, hedges, scrubby areas. Males congregate high in a 'master tree'. Only female has golden blotches on upper forewings. **FP** Blackthorn. PE, PE

1557 Purple Hairstreak *Neozephyrus quercus* 36mm Common. Jun–Sep. Flies in canopy of mature oaks throughout Britain. **FP** Oaks. PE, PE

1558 White Letter Hairstreak *Satyrium w-album* 36mm Nb. Jul–Aug. In England and Wales wherever elms still occur, including young trees. **FP** Elms. PE

1555

1556

1555

1556 ♀

1557

1558

1557

COPPERS, HAIRSTREAKS AND BLUES: LYCAENIDAE (cont.)

1559 Black Hairstreak *Stryrium pruni* 37mm RDB4. Jun–Jul. South and east Midlands only, in sheltered mature Blackthorn thickets. Orange band on underside has black spots. **FP** Blackthorn. PE

1561 Small Copper *Lycaena phlaeas* 34mm Common. Apr–Oct. Throughout Britain on warm flowery hillsides, heaths, in open woods, on embankments. **FP** Common and Sheep's Sorrel. KDR

1562 Large Copper *Lycaena dispar* 45mm (♂), 50mm (♀) Extinct. Jul–Aug. Formerly in East Anglia, not seen since 1864. **FP** Water Dock. PE, PE

1567 Long-tailed Blue *Lampides boeticus* 33mm (♂), 40mm (♀) Migrant. Jul–Oct. Very rare migrant, seen Hampshire 2006. **FP** Everlasting and other Peas, Broom. PE, PE, PE

1567a Geranium Bronze *Cacyreus marshalli* 40mm Vagrant/Accidental. First seen in Lewes, Sussex in 1997, probably imported and breeding on potted geraniums. **FP** Geranium, Pelargonium. PE, PE
1569 Small Blue *Cupido minimus* 24mm Local. May–Jun, Aug. Colonies, often small, scattered throughout Britain in calcareous grassland. Britain's smallest butterfly. **FP** Kidney Vetch. PE, PE
1570 Short-tailed Blue *Everes argiades* 25mm Vagrant/Accidental. Jul–Aug. Very rare migrant. **FP** Lucerne, Common Bird's-foot Trefoil, clover. PE

COPPERS, HAIRSTREAKS AND BLUES: LYCAENIDAE (cont.)

1571 Silver-studded Blue *Plebejus argus* 25mm Nb. Jul–Aug. Mainly found on heathlands of southern England, also East Anglia and north Wales. **FP** Gorse, heather, Common Bird's-foot Trefoil, Common Rock-rose, Horseshoe Vetch. PE, PE, PE

1572 Brown Argus *Aricia agestis* 28mm Local. May–Jun, Jul–Sep. On chalk and limestone downs in southern England and coastal Wales. **FP** Common Rock-rose. PE

1573 Northern Brown Argus *Aricia artaxerxes* 28mm Nb. Jun–Aug. Small colonies on limestone in northern England and Scotland. Similar to above but with white mark on forewing. **FP** Common Rock-rose. PE, PE

1574 Common Blue *Polyommatus icarus* 35mm Common. May–Jun, Aug–Sep. Throughout Britain, almost anywhere. **FP** Various legumes, including Bird's-foot Trefoil, Restharrow, Black Medick, clover. PE, PE, PE

1575 Chalk-hill Blue *Lysandra coridon* 38mm Local. Jul–Sep. Inhabits warm chalk and limestone downs with short turf in southern England. **FP** Horseshoe Vetch, in association with ants. PE, PE, PE

1576 Adonis Blue *Lysandra bellargus* 38mm Nb. May–Jun, Aug–Sep. Inhabits warm chalk and limestone downs with short turf in southern England. Similar to Common Blue but white wing margins have black lines. **FP** Horseshoe Vetch, in association with ants. PE, PE, PE

1574

1574

1574

1575

1575

1576

1575

1576

1576

COPPERS, HAIRSTREAKS AND BLUES: LYCAENIDAE (cont.)

1578 Mazarine Blue *Cyaniris semiargus* 35mm Extinct. Jun–Jul. Extinct since around 1900. Common in Europe. **FP** Red Clover. SS
1580 Holly Blue *Celastrina argiolus* 35mm Common. Mar–Jun, Jul–Sep. In England and Wales wherever Holly and Ivy occur, including urban areas. **FP** Buds of Holly, Ivy. PE, PE
1581 Large Blue *Maculinea arion* 50mm Extinct. Jun–Jul. Extinct in 1979, but re-introduced from Sweden. Requires Wild Thyme in association with red ants' nests. **FP** Flowers of Wild Thyme, then ant grubs within their nest. PE, PE

DUKE OF BURGUNDY: LYCAENIDAE, RIODININAE

There is only one British member of this sub-family of the Lycaenidae, though it looks similar to a Fritillary. The sub-family is known as the Metalmarks, due to the markings on tropical members.

1582 Duke of Burgundy Fritillary *Hamearis lucina* 30mm Nb. May–Jun. Small colonies on west-facing limestone and chalk, as well as open woods, in England, mainly southern. The smallest Fritillary. **FP** Cowslip, Primrose. PE, PE

BUTTERFLIES: ADMIRALS, PEACOCK, COMMA, ETC.; FRITILLARIES: NYMPHALIDAE

These are mainly large, gaudy, strong flyers, with dark underwings. Fritillaries are medium to large, unmistakable but not easy to separate to species level, with orange and black upperwings and often silver-spotted underwings. They are usually found in discrete woodland colonies.

1584 White Admiral *Limenitis camilla* 60mm Common. Jun–Aug. In mature deciduous woods in southern England. Often seen on Bramble flowers. **FP** Honeysuckle in shady situations. PE, PE

ADMIRALS, PEACOCK, COMMA, ETC.; FRITILLARIES: NYMPHALIDAE (cont.)

1585 Purple Emperor *Apatura iris* 70mm (♂), 85mm (♀) Nb. Jun–Aug. Inhabits large woods in southern England. Males congregate high up in a 'master tree', usually oak. **FP** Sallows, Grey Willow, Crack Willow. PE, PE, PE

1590 Red Admiral *Vanessa atalanta* 65mm Migrant. Mar–Oct. Annual mass-migrant from southern Europe and North Africa. Breeds in summer. Migrates south back across the English Channel in autumn. **FP** Common Nettle. PE, PE

1591 Painted Lady *Vanessa cardui* 60mm Migrant. Apr–Oct. Annual mass-migrant from southern Europe and North Africa. Breeds in summer. **FP** Thistles. PE

1593 Small Tortoiseshell *Aglais urticae* 50mm Common. Mar–May, Jul, Sep–Nov. Ubiquitous. Autumn generation hibernates to emerge and mate in spring. **FP** Common and Small Nettle. PE

1594 Large Tortoiseshell *Nymphalis polychloros* 65mm RDB1. Possibly extinct resident, migrant. Larger but duller than Small Tortoiseshell. **FP** Elm, Birch, Aspen and other poplars. CMM, PE

1596 Camberwell Beauty *Nymphalis antiopa* 80mm Migrant. Unmistakable. Scarce migrant, mostly seen on east coast. From Scandinavia and central Europe. **FP** Elm, poplar. RDJ

1597 Peacock *Inachis io* 70mm Common. Jul–Nov, Feb, May. Spring flight is after hibernation. Common throughout Britain. **FP** Common Nettle. PE

1591

1593

1594

1594

1596

1597

1597

ADMIRALS, PEACOCK, COMMA, ETC.; FRITILLARIES: NYMPHALIDAE (cont.)

1598 Comma *Polygonia c-album* 60mm Common. Sep–Nov, Mar–May, Jul. Spring flight is after hibernation. Common in England and Wales. Named after the white 'comma' mark on underside. **FP** Common Nettle, Hop. PE, PE

1599 European Map *Araschnia levana* 40mm Vagrant/Accidental. Rare migrant. European species. **FP** Common Nettle. PE, PE, PE

1600 Small Pearl-bordered Fritillary *Boloria selene* 42mm Local. May–Jul, Aug. On open moors, damp grassland and coasts of western Britain. Underside much more richly marked than Pearl-bordered Fritillary. Underside of hind wing is good guide to identification for all Fritillaries. **FP** Common Dog and Marsh Violet. PE, PE

1601 Pearl Bordered Fritillary *Boloria euphrosyne* 45mm Nb. Apr–Jun, Aug. Scattered colonies in south and west England, Wales and Scotland in open woodland. Flight period starts earlier than Small Pearl-bordered Fritillary. **FP** Violets. PE, PE

1603 Queen of Spain Fritillary *Issoria lathonia* 50mm Vagrant/Accidental. Migrant and occasional resident in Suffolk. **FP** Field and Wild Pansy. PE, PE

1598

1598

2nd generation 1599

1599

1st generation

1599

1600

1600

1601

1601

1603

1603

ADMIRALS, PEACOCK, COMMA, ETC.; FRITILLARIES: NYMPHALIDAE (cont.)

1606 High Brown Fritillary *Argynnis adippe* 65mm RDB2. Jun–Aug. Now confined to a few sites on Dartmoor in Devon, Lake District and Wales. Needs sheltered sunny spots in open areas with bracken. Similar to Dark Green Fritillary but has row of rust-coloured spots with pale centres on underside of hind wing. **FP** Violets. PE, PE

1607 Dark Green Fritillary *Argynnis aglaja* 65mm Local. Jun–Sep. Scattered throughout Britain on open flowery downs, dunes, cliffs, moors and woods. **FP** Violets. PE

1608 Silver-washed Fritillary *Argynnis paphia* 75mm Local. Jun–Sep. Britain's largest Fritillary. Found in woodland in southern Britain. **FP** Common Dog-violet. PE, PE

1610 Marsh Fritillary *Eurodryas aurinia* 45mm Nb.

May–Jul. Colonies mainly in south-west Britain, usually in marshy woods and damp flowery meadows. Has row of black dots near outer edge on both sides of hind wing but not on forewing. **FP** Devil's-bit Scabious. PE, PE

1612 Glanville Fritillary *Melitaea cinxia* 45mm RDB3. May–Jun. Named after Lady Glanville who discovered it 300 years ago, this Fritillary is at the extreme north of its range, though common in Europe. It is found only on undercliffs of southern Isle of Wight, and in the Channel Islands. **FP** Ribwort Plantain. PE, PE

1613 Heath Fritillary *Mellicta athalia* 42mm RDB2. May–Aug. Tiny colonies only in Devon, Cornwall, Kent and Essex. Needs warm open coppiced woodlands or heathland valleys. **FP** Common Cow Wheat, Ribwort Plantain, Germander Speedwell. PE, PE

1606

1606

1607

1608

1608

1610

1610

1612

1612

1613

1613

BROWNS: NYMPHALIDAE, SATYRINAE (FORMERLY SATYRIDAE)

Browns are largish butterflies, in shades of brown except for the Marbled White, with a black eyespot near the forewing tip, visible on both sides. They are generally found flying gently in tall grasslands. They are now generally included as a sub-family, the Satyrinae, of the Nymphalidae rather than as a separate family.

1614 Speckled Wood *Pararge aegeria* 48mm Common. Mar–Oct. Common in England up to Yorkshire, Wales and northern Scotland. Prefers shady woods. **FP** Grasses, including Yorkshire Fog, False Brome, Cock's-foot. PE, PE
1615 Wall *Lasiommata megera* 45mm Common. Apr–Jun, Jul–Sep. Common in most of Wales and England up to the Pennines. Likes hot, dry, open ground on dunes, coasts, downs, railway cuttings. **FP** Grasses, including Yorkshire Fog, Tor-grass, Wavy Hair-grass, Cock's-foot. PE, PE
1617 Mountain Ringlet *Erebia epiphron* 37mm Na. Jun–Jul. Inhabits open mountainsides around 500–800m, only in Scottish Highlands and Lake District. **FP** Mat-grass. PE, PE
1618 Scotch Argus *Erebia aethiops* 35mm (♂), 40mm (♀) Local. Jul–Aug. In rough boggy pasture in Scotland and Lake District. **FP** Purple and Blue Moor-grass. PE, PE, PE
1619 Arran Brown *Erebia ligea* Possibly form of Scotch Argus from Western Isles of Scotland. NOT ILLUSTRATED
1620 Marbled White *Melanargia galathea* 55mm Local. Jun–Aug. Likes hot, dry, flower-rich meadows, verges, embankments, coasts, downs in Britain from Yorkshire southwards. **FP** Sheep's Fescue, Red Fescue, Tor-grass. PE, PE

1621 Grayling *Hipparchia semele* 58mm Local. Jun–Sep. Occurs all around the coast of Britain on hot, dry cliffs, dunes, southern heaths. Always rests with wings closed, usually only hind wing showing. **FP** Grasses, including Bristle Bent, Sheep's-fescue, Tufted Hair-grass. PE
1625 Gatekeeper/Hedge Brown *Pyronia tithonus* 45mm Common. Jun–Aug. Common from Yorkshire southwards. Frequents open woods, lanes with hedgerows and gates, heaths, downs. Black eye-spot has two white pupils. **FP** Grasses, including Cock's-foot, Timothy, Couch, fescues. PE, PE
1626 Meadow Brown *Maniola jurtina* 55mm Common. May–Sep. Throughout Britain, the most common British butterfly. Found on chalk downland, road verges, coastal dunes, in open woods and urban areas. **FP** Grasses, including fescues, meadow-grass, bents, Rye-grass. PE, PE
1627 Small Heath *Coenonympha pamphilus* 35mm Common. May–Jun, Jul–Oct. Throughout Britain on light, dry grasslands, downs, heaths, cliffs. Rests with wings closed. **FP** Fescues, bents, meadow-grass. PE
1628 Large Heath *Coenonympha tullia* 41mm Local. Jun–Aug. Found in Ireland, Wales, northern England and Scotland on blanket bog, peat mosses, wet moors. **FP** Hare's-tail and Common Cottongrass. PE

1614   1614   1617
1615   1615   1617

BROWNS: NYMPHALIDAE, SATYRINAE (FORMERLY SATYRIDAE) (cont.)

1629 Ringlet *Aphantopus hyperantus* 50mm Common. Jun–Aug. Likes damp woods, shady hedgerows, river banks throughout most of Britain. **FP** Coarse grasses, including Cock's-foot, Tor-grass, Tufted Hair-grass, False Brome. PE (all 4 photos)

1630 Monarch *Danaus plexippus* 110mm Vagrant/Accidental. Regular trans-Atlantic migrant from North America. Hundreds may be seen in a good year. Foodplant does not grow in Britain. **FP** Milkweed. PE, PE

MACRO MOTHS

British moths range from one of the smallest in the world, *Enteucha acetosae*, with a wingspan of only 3–4mm, to the 'flying mouse' size of spectacular hawk-moths, such as Privet, Convolvulus and Death's-head with wingspans of as much as 120mm.

Moths are artificially split into two groups, on no particular scientific basis, known as Micros and Macros. Generally speaking the Micros are more primitive and smaller then Macros, but some primitive, though large, moths have a sort of honorary Macro status. These are the five swifts, five leopards, Goat, Festoon and Triangle, ten foresters and burnets and 15 clearwings that resemble flies and hornets. Conversely, there are Macros smaller than some Micros, such as some of the snouts, minors, wainscots, waves, etc.

For the purposes of this book, I have placed these honorary Macros, although having low log numbers, in with the other Macros as is customary.

Three of the 24 Small Elephant Hawk-moths that came to an mv light one mid-June night on the Dorset coast. CMM

SWIFTS: HEPIALIDAE

A primitive group (which is why, taxonomically, they are placed among the Micros) of five British species. There are approximately 500 species worldwide.

Swifts have long wings held almost upright against the body at rest, and very short antennae. They are sexually dimorphic, with females generally larger and plainer than males, though the female Ghost Swift could not be said to be plain at all. They fly at dusk, and will come to light. Female Swifts lay eggs by scattering them in flight above suitable vegetation. Larvae live underground in plant roots, usually for 2 years. They are white, having no need for camouflage underground.

14 Ghost Moth *Hepialus humuli* 48mm (♂), 58mm (♀) Common. Jun–Aug. Sexually dimorphic: male is white like ghost, with display flight at dusk, known as 'lekking'; female larger with orange markings. Throughout Britain. **FP** Underground in grass roots. RPJ, DGG

15 Orange Swift *Hepialus sylvina* 32mm (♂), 40mm (♀) Common. Jul–Aug. Male orange marked, larger female more drab. In grasslands throughout. **FP** Underground for 2 years in herbaceous roots, including Bugloss, dock, Bracken, Dandelion. DF, DF

16 Gold Swift *Hepialus hecta* 30mm (♂), 34mm (♀) Local. Jun–Jul. Gold markings on male are obvious,

female drab. Eggs scattered in flight over Bracken. Throughout. **FP** In Bracken and grass roots, for 2 years. NS, DF

17 Common Swift *Hepialus lupulinus* 30mm (♂), 35mm (♀) Common. May–Jul. Often abundant at dusk. Male smaller and brighter. Throughout, but local in Scotland. **FP** Grass and herbaceous roots. DF, NS

18 Map-winged Swift *Hepialus fusconebulosa* 40mm (♂), 55mm (♀) Local. May–Jul. Variable size, variable markings, but always with chequered fringe unlike other swifts. Widespread but local on moors, heaths, open woods. **FP** Usually in Bracken roots. CMM

LEOPARD AND GOAT MOTHS: COSSIDAE

There are only three British members of this family, though there are around 700 species worldwide. Adults fly at night and are attracted to light but do not feed. Eggs are laid on the foodplant. Larvae are white and bore inside living wood and stems of host plants, often for several years, where they also pupate.

160 Reed Leopard *Phragmataecia castaneae* 32mm RDB2. Jun–Jul. Very local in Cambridge, Norfolk Broads and east Dorset. Body much longer than wings. **FP** In Common Reed stems, up to 3 years. CMM

161 Leopard Moth *Zeuzera pyrina* 50mm Common. Jun–Aug. Unmistakable. Found Yorkshire southwards.

Female much larger than male. **FP** In branches of woody shrubs and trees for 3 years. DJP

162 Goat Moth *Cossus cossus* 70mm Nb. Jun–Jul. Large and chunky. Occasionally comes to light. Widespread but local. **FP** In trunks of living trees for 4 years, often in colonies in damp locations. Larvae smell of goat. CMM, CMM

15 ♀

15 ♂

16 ♀

16 ♂

17 ♀

17 ♂

♂ gallicus 18

160 ♂

161

162

162

FORESTER AND BURNET MOTHS: ZYGAENIDAE

There are ten British species of these day-flying moths, three foresters and seven burnets. They are attracted to downland flowers on sunny days and do not fly at night. The three foresters (not named because of living in forests but possibly because of their metallic green wings and bodies) all look similar, with forward-pointing antennae, which are not clubbed, and have similar flight periods. However, the larvae, which overwinter, do have specific, separate foodplants. The thin cocoons are hidden low down amongst the foodplants.

The burnets are notoriously difficult to identify as there can be significant variations in markings within a single population and these can overlap with markings of different species. They all have some combination of red and black forewing markings, red hind wings and furry black bodies, warning predators that they are toxic. Occasionally there are aberrations where the red spots are replaced with yellow. Antennae are clubbed and forward-pointing, rather like those of butterflies. The larvae form papery cocoons often found high on grass stems, and can overwinter twice. Locality is an important identification tool, as several species are very scarce and have restricted distribution.

163 Forester *Adscita statices* 28mm (♂) Local. Jun–Jul. Flies in sun, larger than Cistus Forester. **FP** On Common Sorrel. PB

164 Cistus Forester *Adscita geryon* 25mm (♂) Nb. Jun–Jul. Flies in sun, in chalk and limestone areas, mainly in south. **FP** On Rock Rose. NS, SH

165 Scarce Forester *Jordanita globulariae* 22mm (♀) Na. Jun–Jul. Flies in sun, on calcareous grassland. **FP** On knapweeds. DGG

166 Scotch Burnet *Zygaena exulans* 26mm RDB3. Jun–Jul. Flies in sun on Scottish mountains in Cairngorms at about 800m, very local. Five small red spots. **FP** Crowberry. RL

167 Slender Scotch Burnet *Zygaena loti* 28mm RDB3. Jun–Jul. Inner Hebrides islands of Mull and Ulva only. Flies in sun. Outer pair of spots merged. **FP** Common Bird's-foot Trefoil. SH

168 New Forest Burnet *Zygaena viciae* 25mm RDB1. Jul. Flies in sun. Now extinct in New Forest and found only on one site on west coast of Argyll. **FP** Common Bird's-foot Trefoil, Meadow Vetchling. SR

169 Six-spot Burnet *Zygaena filipendulae* 34mm Common. Jun–Aug. Day-flying, visits knapweed, thistle flowers, etc. Throughout Britain. **FP** Bird's-foot Trefoil. MSP, PB

170 Five-spot Burnet *Zygaena trifolii* 30mm Local. Jul–Aug. Similar to Narrow-bordered, slight larval differences including shorter hairs. Southern UK. Flies in sun, nectaring. **FP** Greater Bird's-foot Trefoil. CS
f. decreta 30mm Local. Jul–Aug. Damp grassland and heaths in south and west England. **FP** Greater Bird's-foot Trefoil.
f. palustrella 30mm Local. May–Jun. Dry chalk and limestone downs in southern England. **FP** Common Bird's-foot Trefoil.

171 Narrow-bordered Five-spot Burnet *Zygaena lonicerae* 32mm Common. Jun–Jul. Similar to above but common in England and Wales, *citrina* form rare. Rear from larvae to be certain of identity. Inhabits rough grassland. Long setae on larvae are diagnostic. **FP** On Meadow Vetchling, trefoils. DF, DF

172 Transparent Burnet *Zygaena purpuralis* 34mm Na. Jun–Jul. Hebridean islands, Mull of Kintyre and west Argyll, mainly on coastal cliffs. **FP** Wild Thyme. SH

163 ♂

164 ♂

♀

164 ♂

165 ♀

166

167

168

169

169

170

citrina

171

171

172

FESTOON AND TRIANGLE: LIMACODIDAE

There are only two British representatives of this family, from approximately 1,000 species worldwide. Both are small (Triangle is smaller than many Micros) and they rest with the abdomen raised. Females are larger and paler than males. Adults do not feed but do come to light. Larvae are slug-shaped (*see* Caterpillars section, p.269) – the family name comes from the Latin for slug.

173 Festoon *Apoda limacodes* 20mm (♂), 26mm (♀) Nb. Jun–Jul. Woods and heaths, central southern England. **FP** Oaks, Beech. CMM, CMM
174 Triangle *Heterogenea asella* 15mm (♂) RDB3.

Jun–Jul. As small as some Micros. Distinctive triangular forewing, tent-like resting pose. Scarce, in ancient oak woods of central southern England. **FP** Mainly oak, sometimes beech. CMM

♀ 173

♂ 173

♂ 174

CLEARWING MOTHS: SESIIDAE

There are 15 species of clearwing moth on the British list, from about 1,000 worldwide. They resemble and mimic flies and hornets, with transparent wings and bodies distinctively-marked with red or yellow bands, though their heads and eyes are much smaller. They fly actively in sunshine, but are rarely seen. They do not come to light.

Adults are difficult to find except shortly after emerging, when they can sometimes be found resting on the host tree trunk in early morning. Males can be lured to artificial pheromones that mimic the scent of the female. (Pheromones can be obtained from entomological suppliers, *see* Equipment Suppliers, p.341.) Larvae are white, and live and pupate inside stems, branches, trunks or roots of trees and shrubs, often for 2 years. Empty pupae sometimes remain protruding from trunks after emergence and are easily spotted.

370 Hornet Moth *Sesia apiformis* 40mm Nb. Jun–Jul. The size of a Hornet, but yellow rather than red-brown markings, and no wasp-waist. Has yellow head and shoulder markings. Presence often confirmed by exit holes and pupal cases. Southern Britain only. **FP** Feeds on live wood low down inside trunk of Black, Lombardy and other Poplars, for up to 3 years. KDR, KDR

371 Lunar Hornet Moth *Sesia bembeciformis* 36mm Common. Jul–Aug. Smaller than Hornet Moth, with black head and shoulders, yellow collar. Rarely seen except early morning after emergence. Throughout Britain. **FP** Inside sallows, willows, sometimes poplar, for 2 years. DF

372 Dusky Clearwing *Paranthrene tabaniformis* 27mm May–Jul. Probably extinct. Comes to pheromones. **FP** Poplar. CMM

CLEARWING MOTHS: SESIIDAE (cont.)

373 Currant Clearwing *Synanthedon tipuliformis* 18mm Nb. Jun–Jul. Comes readily and commonly to pheromones in sunshine. Throughout. **FP** Currant bushes, inside stems. CMM

374 Yellow-legged Clearwing *Synanthedon vespiformis* 22mm Nb. May–Aug. Day flying, male (with black tail fan) comes to pheromones. Woodland in southern Britain. **FP** Under bark of recently felled stumps of oak, chestnut, elm, etc. DF

375 White-barred Clearwing *Synanthedon spheciformis* 30mm Nb. May–Jul. Abdomen has only one creamy band; antennae white near tip. Central and south-east England. Comes to pheromones. **FP** Alder and birch, in trunk or roots. JG

376 Welsh Clearwing *Synanthedon scoliaeformis* 30mm

RDB3. Jun–Jul. On damp, acid, hills and moors, Wales and Scotland. **FP** Mature Downy Birch, beneath bark for 2 years. DGG

377 Sallow Clearwing *Synanthedon flaviventris* 19mm Nb. Jun–Jul. Two-year life cycle, adults hatch only in even years. Comes to pheromones. In open woods and damp heaths in southern England. **FP** Inside sallows, willows, forming gall in twigs and shoots about 10mm thick. MSP

378 Orange-tailed Clearwing *Synanthedon andrenaeformis* 20mm Nb. May–Jul. Smaller than Welsh Clearwing, more yellowish tail fan, and two bars on abdomen. Central southern England, on chalk and limestone. **FP** Wayfaring-tree, inside stems about 20mm thick for 2 years. DF

373 374 375 376 377 378

379 Red-belted Clearwing *Synanthedon myopaeformis* 20mm Nb. Jun–Aug. Red band on abdomen, and black wings. In mature orchards from Yorkshire southwards. **FP** Apple, Pear, Hawthorn. DF

380 Red-tipped Clearwing *Synanthedon formicaeformis* 20mm Nb. May–Aug. Red band on abdomen, and red tips to wings. Widespread but local in damp, marshy areas. **FP** In trunks and stems of Osiers and willow. DF

381 Large Red-belted Clearwing *Synanthedon culiciformis* 27mm Nb. May–Jun. Red band on abdomen plus red marks at base of forewing. Widespread in open woodland. **FP** Under bark of birch and Alder, especially on cut stumps. DF

382 Six-belted Clearwing *Bembecia ichneumoniformis* 23mm Nb. Jun–Aug. Southern Britain, on chalk downs, rough pastures. **FP** Bird's-foot Trefoils and vetches, in roots. DF

383 Thrift Clearwing *Synansphecia muscaeformis* 18mm Nb. Jun–Jul. Inhabits west coasts of Britain. Unlikely to find other Clearwings in same habitat. The smallest Clearwing. **FP** On Thrift on rocky coasts. CMM

384 Fiery Clearwing *Pyropteron chrysidiformis* 25mm RDB1. Jun–Jul. Very scarce in coastal Kent only. Unmistakable orange-red wings. **FP** In roots of Curled Dock or Common Sorrel. DE, KT

EGGAR MOTHS: LASIOCAMPIDAE

Another family with around 1,000 species worldwide, with 12 species on the British list. Eggars are chunky, medium to large moths, generally in shades of brown, with females usually larger than males. Most have a white spot and/or a central band on the forewing.

Males have feathered antennae for detecting female pheromones (scent). Males of the two largest species, Oak Eggar and Fox Moth, fly by day in sunshine as well as at night, seeking females. All come to light, but not to sugar as they cannot feed. Larvae are large and colourful, usually covered with hairs, which can irritate, helping protect themselves from hungry birds. Tough cocoons for pupation are usually above ground, attached to vegetation.

1631 December Moth *Poecilocampa populi* 35mm (♂), 45mm (♀) Common. Oct–Jan. Unmistakable, especially given the flight period. Throughout Britain, in woods, scrub, hedges. **FP** Deciduous trees, including birch, oak, Hawthorn, elm. CMM, CMM

1632 Pale Eggar *Trichiura crataegi* 30mm (♂) Common. Aug–Sep. Unmistakable, especially given the flight period. Throughout in woods, parks, hedges, heaths. **FP** Birch, Blackthorn, Hawthorn, oak, heather, Bilberry. PAD, DF

1633 Small Eggar *Eriogaster lanestris* 35mm (♂) Nb. Feb–Mar. Decreasing. Southern UK to Yorkshire. Pupates for 2 or 3 years. **FP** Hedgerows of Blackthorn, Hawthorn, in communal web. CMM, CMM

1634 Lackey *Malacosoma neustria* 32mm (♂), 44mm (♀) Common. Jul–Aug. Common throughout southern Britain up to Yorkshire in open woodland. **FP** Broadleaved trees and shrubs. DF, CMM

1635 Ground Lackey *Malacosoma castrensis* 32mm (♂), 44mm (♀) Na. Jul–Aug. Females very similar to above,

males differ. Only found in south-east England salt marshes and shingle. **FP** Salt-marsh plants, including Sea Plantain, Sea Lavender, Sea Wormwood, initially in communal web. CMM, CMM

1636 Grass Eggar *Lasiocampa trifolii trifolii* 45mm Na. Aug–Sep. Local but common on coastal dunes, southern and western UK. Also on acid heaths in Dorset. Comes to light. **FP** Marram Grass, Tree Lupin, Bramble, Creeping Willow and others. CMM

1636 Pale Grass Eggar *Lasiocampa trifolii trifolii, flava* 45mm RDB. Aug–Sep. Very pale form of above only at Dungeness, Kent. **FP** Marram Grass, Tree Lupin, Bramble, Creeping Willow and others. CB

1637 Oak Eggar *Lasiocampa quercus* 60mm (♂), 80mm (♀) Common. Jul–Aug. Males fly in afternoon sun, females at dusk. Very similar form *callunae* **Northern Eggar** flies slightly earlier in year. Throughout on heaths, moors, downs and in woods. **FP** Heather, Bilberry, Bramble, Hawthorn, sallows, etc. PGC, DF, NS

1631 ♀   1631 ♂   1633 ♂
1632 ♂   1632 ♂   1633 ♂

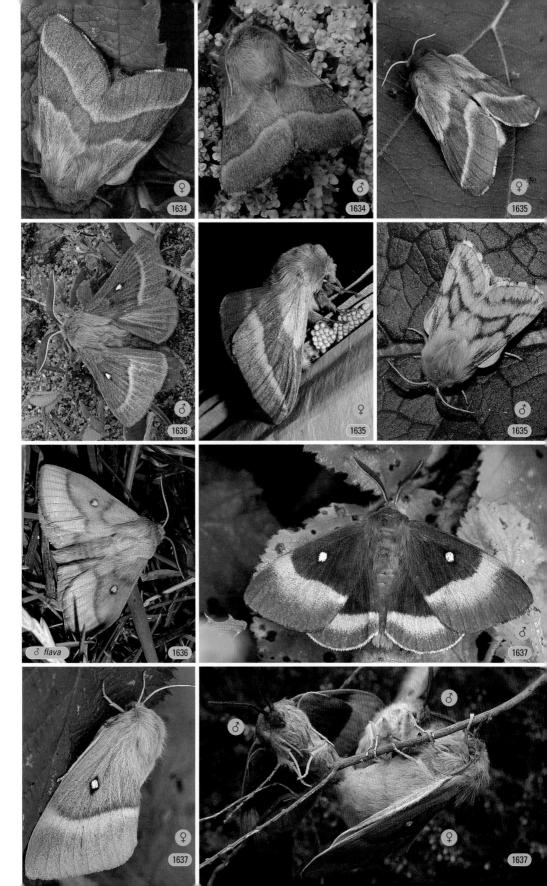

1634 ♀

1634 ♂

1635 ♀

1636 ♂

1635 ♀

1635 ♂

♂ flava 1636

1637 ♂

1637 ♀

♂ ♂

♀ 1637

EGGAR MOTHS: LASIOCAMPIDAE (cont.)

1638 Fox Moth *Macrothylacia rubi* 55mm (♂), 65mm (♀) Common. May–Jun. Usually only females at light, males fly in day. No white forewing spot. **FP** Heather, Bilberry, Creeping Willow, Bramble, etc. CMM

1639 Pine Tree Lappet *Dendrolimus pini* 60mm Vagrant/Accidental. Jun–Aug. Very rare migrant. **FP** Pines. NS, NS

1640 Drinker *Euthrix potatoria* 55mm (♂), 70mm (♀) Common. Jul–Aug. Throughout the UK. Distinguished by diagonal dark line to tip of forewing with two white spots. **FP** Coarse grasses and reeds. DF, DF

1641 Small Lappet *Phyllodesma ilicifolia* 45mm Presumed extinct. Apr–May. Formerly in Yorkshire. **FP** Bilberry. CS

1642 Lappet *Gastropacha quercifolia* 70mm Common. Jun–Aug. Widespread in southern UK. Unmistakable. **FP** Blackthorn, Hawthorn, Buckthorn, Apple on small, isolated bushes. CMM

1639

♀ ♂ 1638

1639

♀ 1640

♂ 1640

1641

1642

EMPEROR MOTHS: SATURNIIDAE

Emperor moths are members of the silk-moth family. There is one resident Emperor, and one occasional accidental introduction from the Continent. The world's largest moth, the Atlas from the forests of South-east Asia, is a member of this family.

The adult is unmistakable, with eye-spots on all wings. The female is larger than the male and ground-colours are different. Males fly strongly in daylight and are attracted to freshly hatched females in early May. Both sexes may come to light, but not to sugar as they do not feed. Markings of the colourful caterpillars change depending on the instar (development stage). They overwinter as a pupa in a tough silk cocoon.

1643 Emperor *Saturnia pavonia* 65mm (♂), 80mm (♀) Common. Apr–May. Widespread throughout the UK. Unmistakable. Males fly strongly in sunshine to find freshly emerged females, attracted by their pheromones. **FP** Woody plants, including heather, Bramble, Black-thorn, Hawthorn, sallows. CMM, RL, RL

1643a Great Peacock Moth *Saturnia pyri* 120mm Vagrant/Accidental. Similar to female Emperor but very much larger. From southern Europe, probably never a genuine migrant. DGG

♀ 1643

♂ 1643

♀ ♂ 1643

1643a

KENTISH GLORY: ENDROMIDAE

There is only one British species, and this is found only in Scotland in young birch woods. The species was formerly found locally in England but is now extinct, although it is still present throughout most of Europe. Like the Emperor, males fly by day and both sexes come to light.

1644 Kentish Glory
Endromis versicolora 60mm (♂), 70mm (♀) Na. Apr–May. Widespread in Europe but now only found in highlands of Scotland in the UK. **FP** Youngish birch in open woods and moor. DGG, CMM, CMM

HOOK-TIPS: DREPANIDAE

Seven species of this family occur in Britain, out of 400 species worldwide. One is a migrant, and all but one, the Chinese Character, have hooked tips to the forewing (the Beautiful Hook-tip looks similar but is not related). They fly at night and come to light but do not feed.

Larvae feed on tree leaves, and have the hind pair of claspers modified to a distinctive raised point like a tail (see Caterpillars section, p.269). They overwinter as cocooned pupae amongst fallen leaves.

1645 Scalloped Hook-tip *Falcaria lacertinaria* 30mm (♂), 40mm (♀) Common. Apr–Jun, Jul–Aug. Unmistakable; female paler. Rests with tent-like wings. Widespread throughout the UK. **FP** Birch. PGC
1646 Oak Hook-tip *Watsonalla binaria* 30mm Common. May–Jun, Jul–Sep. Widespread in the UK to south Scotland, in oak woods, hedgerows, parkland, etc. Female larger than male. **FP** Oaks. DGG
1647 Barred Hook-tip *Watsonalla cultraria* 32mm Local. May–Jun, Jul–Sep. Well distributed in south England, especially in Beech woods on chalk. Local further north. Similar to Oak Hook-tip but only one faint dot on forewing. **FP** Beech. DGG
1648 Pebble Hook-tip *Drepana falcataria* 35mm Common. May–Jun, Jul–Aug. Common throughout Britain. Scottish form much paler. Pebble-like spot on forewing. **FP** Woods, heaths, gardens, scrub, mostly on birch, sometimes alder. CMM
1649 Dusky Hook-tip *Drepana curvatula* 38mm Rare migrant. Aug. Seen rarely in south-east England. Similar to Pebble Hook-tip, but without the 'pebble'. Hind wing same brown as forewing. **FP** Birch, Alder, oak in Europe. RPJ
1650 Scarce Hook-tip *Sabra harpagula* 40mm RDB3. Jun–Jul. Large brown and gold central blotch on forewing, outer edge also has sharp projecting angle. **FP** Small-leaved Lime, only in Gloucestershire and Monmouthshire. CMM
1651 Chinese Character *Cilix glaucata* 22mm Common. Apr–Jun, Jul–Sep. Unmistakable colour and pose. Looks like a bird-dropping. Common throughout. **FP** Blackthorn, Hawthorn, Crab-apple, Bramble, etc. CMM

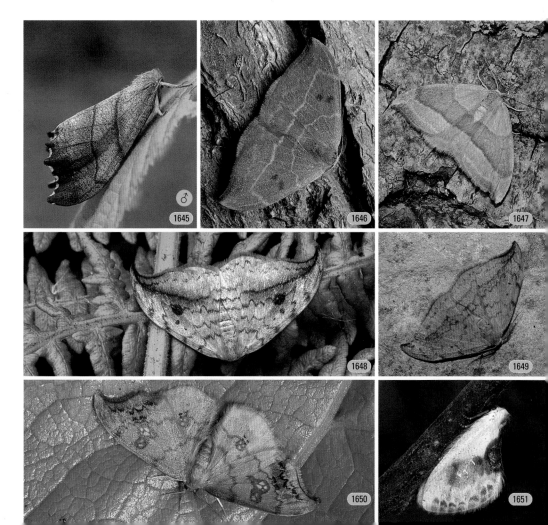

THYATIRIDAE

There are nine British members of this family, which resemble Noctuids but usually rest with wings close to the body and rather upright. Several adults have prominent tufts on the thorax, especially the Frosted Green, and all will come to light and sometimes to sugar or flowers.

    The single-brooded larvae feed on leaves of Brambles or various trees. Species of the Thyatiridae overwinter as pupae amongst leaves, except for Oak Lutestring, which passes the winter as an egg.

1652 Peach Blossom *Thyatira batis* Common. 35mm May–Jul. Throughout the UK. Cannot be confused with anything else. **FP** Bramble, almost anywhere. CMM
1653 Buff Arches *Habrosyne pyritoides* 40mm Common. Jun–Aug. Unmistakable. Common in south, scarce in Scotland. **FP** Bramble in open woodland. CMM
1654 Figure of Eighty *Tethea ocularis octogesimea* 38mm Common. May–Jul. Throughout England and Wales to Yorkshire. White '80' marking is diagnostic. Figure of Eight similar mark but flies in autumn; Poplar Lutestring has less well-defined mark. **FP** Woods, commons, parks, etc., on Aspen and other poplars. CMM
1655 Poplar Lutestring *Tethea or* 40mm Local. May–Aug. Slightly similar to above, but more wavy lines (lutestrings) on forewings. Local in southern UK, scarce in north. **FP** Broadleaved woods with Aspen. DGG
1656 Satin Lutestring *Tetheella fluctuosa* 38mm Local. Jun–Aug. Has dark crescent in centre of forewing plus sub-apical streak. Mostly in south-east England, also

Gloucestershire, Wales, Lake District and Inverness. **FP** On Birch or Alder in mature woods and heaths. RW
1657 Common Lutestring *Ochropacha duplaris* 32mm Common. Jun–Aug. Similar to above, but pair of dots in forewing centre, and smaller overall. Widespread in light woods but not usually on chalk/limestone soils. **FP** Mostly on birch, sometimes Alder, hazel, oak. DF
1658 Oak Lutestring *Cymatophorima diluta hartwiegi* 35mm Local. Aug–Sep. Mature oak woodland in southern UK, scarce in north. Slightly similar to Poplar Lutestring, but flies later in year and is without central mark. **FP** Oak. CMM
1659 Yellow Horned *Achlya flavicornis* 40mm Common. Mar–Apr. Common throughout England and Wales. Comes to light and sallow blossom in spring. **FP** Woods, heaths and moors on birch. CMM
1660 Frosted Green *Polyploca ridens* 35mm Local. Apr–May. Common in mature oak woods in south UK. **FP** Oaks. CMM

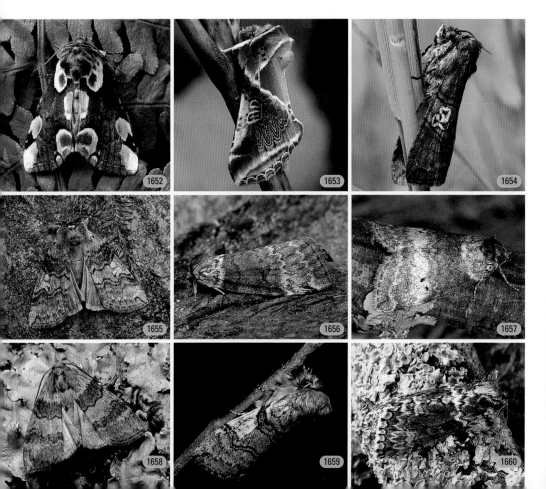

1652 1653 1654
1655 1656 1657
1658 1659 1660

GEOMETERS: GEOMETRIDAE

This is the second largest Macro-moth family, after the Noctuids, containing around 300 species, which are unevenly split into six sub-families. Archiearinae contains the two orange underwings, below. Alsophilinae has only one member, the March Moth, also below. The Geometrinae has ten species, which are mostly green, known as the emeralds. Sterrhinae contains the 39 mochas and waves, Larentiinae has 110 carpets and 50 pugs whilst the remaining 90 are in the Ennominae.

Most of these moths have large wings, relative to body size, that are rather broad and butterfly-like. The wings are usually flat when at rest, often showing part of the hind wing as well. They generally have fairly weak flight, fly at night or at dusk and come to light, except the Archiearinae, which are the exact opposite. They fly strongly in spring sunshine and not at night.

A few species that fly in winter have flightless females such as March Moth, Winter Moth and Mottled Umber. This conserves energy on cold or even freezing nights. They rest on tree trunks and wait for males to find them.

The larvae are the common denominator of the Geometers. Although they all look different, most of them do not have the first three pairs of prolegs. They move by arching the body and then straightening out and are generally known as 'loopers' because of this. They generally feed exposed on the foodplant but are often beautifully camouflaged to resemble a twig, and can be very difficult to see.

GEOMETERS: GEOMETRIDAE, ARCHIEARINAE AND ALSOPHILINAE

1661 Orange Underwing *Archiearis parthenias* 33mm Local. Mar–Apr. Flies in sunshine around tops of birch trees in spring before leaves develop. Widespread but local throughout the UK. **FP** Birch. DGG
1662 Light Orange Underwing *Archiearis notha* 33mm Nb. Mar–Apr. As above but in mature Aspen woods.

Southern England. **FP** Aspen. CMM, CMM
1663 March Moth *Alsophila aescularia* 33mm Common. Feb–Apr. Male flies in early spring, female is wingless. Wings overlap at rest. Throughout the UK, most wooded land. **FP** Sundry broadleaved trees and shrubs. CMM

1661

1662

1663

1662

GEOMETERS: GEOMETRIDAE, GEOMETRINAE

1664 Rest Harrow *Aplasta ononaria* 25mm RDB3. Jun–Jul. Two known colonies in Kent only. **FP** Restharrows. CMM

1665 Grass Emerald *Pseudoterpna pruinata atropunctaria* 35mm Common. Jun–Aug. Blue-green pigment quickly fades to almost white. Widespread from south Scotland southwards. **FP** Gorse, Broom, Petty Whin. NS

1665a Jersey Emerald *Pseudoterpna coronillaria* 35mm Migrant. Jun–Jul. Similar to above, but greyer. Resident on Jersey. **FP** Gorse, Broom. CMM

1666 Large Emerald *Geometra papilionaria* 55mm Common. Jun–Aug. Woods and heaths throughout the UK. Unmistakable large Emerald with brown and white legs. **FP** Usually birch, also Alder, hazel, Beech. CMM

1667 Blotched Emerald *Comibaena bajularia* 30mm Local. Jun–Jul. Can be common locally in southern UK in oak woodland. **FP** Oak. CMM, CMM

1668 Essex Emerald *Antonechloris smaragdaria maritima* 35mm Presumed extinct. Jun–Jul. Formerly on coastal salt marsh in Essex and Kent. **FP** Sea Wormwood. CMM

1669 Common Emerald *Hemithea aestivaria* 30mm Common. Jun–Jul. Found in woods, hedgerows, parks, gardens, etc. **FP** Various trees and shrubs, including Hawthorn, Blackthorn, birch, oak, sallows. CMM

1670 Small Grass Emerald *Chlorissa viridata* 22mm Na. Jun–Jul. Flies by day and at dusk. Very local on damp heathland in central southern UK, also Cumbria. Differs from the more common Little Emerald in having near straight, not curved, white line on hind wing. **FP** Heathers, Creeping Willow, Gorse. CMM

1672 Sussex Emerald *Thalera fimbrialis* 35mm RDB1. Jul–Aug. Only found on shingle beach at Dungeness, Kent. Similar to Common Emerald but hind wing has two points, not just one. **FP** Wild Carrot. CMM

1673 Small Emerald *Hemistola chrysoprasaria* 35mm Local. Jun–Aug. Downs, hedges and wood edges on chalk. Often fades to almost white. **FP** Traveller's Joy. CMM

1674 Little Emerald *Jodis lactearia* 22mm Common. May–Jun. Open woods, heaths, hedges, etc. Similar to Small Grass Emerald but curved hind-wing line. **FP** Trees and shrubs, including birch, hazel, Hawthorn, oak, Sweet Chestnut, Bilberry, etc. DF

GEOMETERS: GEOMETRIDAE, STERRHINAE

1675 Dingy Mocha *Cyclophora pendularia* 26mm RDB3. May–Jun, Jul–Aug. Found only in east Dorset and west Hampshire, mainly on damp heaths with isolated, scrubby willows. Similar to Birch Mocha but much greyer and more mottled. **FP** Small-leaved Willow and sallows. CMM

1676 Mocha *Cyclophora annularia* 24mm Nb. May–Jun, Jul–Aug. Very local in southern England in mature maple woods. Unmistakable moth with yellow and chocolate markings. **FP** Field Maple. PGC

1677 Birch Mocha *Cyclophora albipunctata* 24mm Local. May–Jun, Jul–Aug. Throughout Britain, but more common in south. Generally looks pinkish overall. **FP** Birch in woods and heaths. CMM, NS

1678 Blair's Mocha *Cyclophora puppillaria* 28mm Migrant. Aug–Oct. Scarce. Plain red-brown with faint discal spots. **FP** Evergreen Oak in Europe. CMM

1678a Jersey Mocha *Cyclophora ruficiliaria* 26mm Migrant. Resident in Jersey, first seen Dorset mainland 2003. Discal spots have absolutely no outline. **FP** Oak. KT

1675

1676

1677

aberration 1677

1678

1678a

1679 False Mocha *Cyclophora porata* 26mm Local. May–Jun, Aug–Sep.
Scattered in southern Britain. Freckled with orange but also discal spots.
FP Open woods and heathland on oak. CMM
1680 Maiden's Blush *Cyclophora punctaria* 28mm Local. May–Jun, Aug. Freckled
with orange but no discal spots. Throughout Britain, can be common in south.
FP On oaks, prefers old woods. CMM
1681 Clay Triple-lines *Cyclophora linearia* 30mm Local. May–Jul, Aug–Oct. First
brood orange-brown, second brood smaller (25mm), pinker with distinct dark-
edged discal spot on hind wing. **FP** On Beech, can be numerous in mature
woods. NS, DF
1682 Blood-vein *Timandra comai* 33mm Common. May–Jul, Jul–Sep.
Widespread in most of the UK, scarce in Scotland. Damp woods, hedges,
gardens, etc. **FP** Dock, orache, sorrel, Knotgrass, etc. CMM
1683 Lewes Wave *Scopula immorata* 25mm Extinct. Jun–Jul. Formerly in Sussex,
not seen since 1961. Warm, dry pastures in Europe. CMM
1684 Sub-angled Wave *Scopula nigropunctata* 30mm RDB2. Jul–Aug. Breeds in
Kent, also occurs as migrant. Hind wings have a point, all four wings have
distinct black dot. CMM

GEOMETERS: GEOMETRIDAE, STERRHINAE (cont.)

1685 Streaked Wave *Scopula virgulata* 25mm Vagrant/ Accidental. Only record from Kent in 1870. DGG
1686 Middle Lace Border *Scopula decorata* 20mm Vagrant/Accidental. Unconfirmed migrant. DGG
1687 Lace Border *Scopula ornata* 22mm Na. May–Jun, Jul–Sep. Southern England on chalk and limestone grassland. Scarce. **FP** Thyme, Wild Marjoram. CMM
1688 Tawny Wave *Scopula rubiginata* 19mm RDB3. Jun–Jul, Aug–Sep. On Breckland areas of Norfolk and Suffolk only. **FP** Unknown. CMM, NS
1689 Mullein Wave *Scopula marginepunctata* 26mm Local. Jun–Jul, Aug–Sep. Mainly coastal in England and Wales but also Thames valley, scarce in Scotland. **FP** Mugwort, Yarrow, Marjoram, Wood Sage, etc. DF
1690 Small Blood-vein *Scopula imitaria* 30mm Common. Jul–Aug. Widespread to Midlands, scarcer north. Roughly similar to Blood Vein but without pink. **FP** Privet. CMM
1691 Rosy Wave *Scopula emutaria* 24mm Nb. Jun–Jul. Coastal in southern UK. Can be abundant on salt-marsh edges at dusk. Has faint pink tinge. **FP** Possibly Sea Lavender. CMM
1692 Lesser Cream Wave *Scopula immutata* 26mm

Local. Jun–Aug. On Breckland heaths and also damp grassland and marsh. More rounded wings than Cream Wave, with distinct black dot on each wing. Widespread. **FP** Meadowsweet, Common Valerian. NS
1693 Cream Wave *Scopula floslactata* 30mm Local. May–Jun. Widespread throughout Britain, in woodland. Wings more pointed than species above, black dots faint or absent. **FP** Bedstraws, Woodruff, vetches. CMM
1694 Smoky Wave *Scopula ternata* 26mm Local. Jun–Jul. Mostly northern UK but also Exmoor. **FP** Heather, Bilberry. RPJ
1696 Bright Wave *Idaea ochrata cantiata* 22mm RDB1. Jun–Aug. Very local on coasts, sandhills and golf courses of Suffolk, Essex and Kent. **FP** Grasses and herbs. CMM
1697 Ochraceous Wave *Idaea serpentata* 20mm Vagrant/Accidental. Jul. Dubious records only from 100 years ago. Possible colony on Jersey. CMM
1698 Purple-bordered Gold *Idaea muricata* 18mm Nb. Jun–Jul. Stunning little moth, easily disturbed by day, also flies at dawn and comes to light. Scattered through England and Wales on damp heathland. **FP** Marsh Cinquefoil. CMM, CMM

1689

1690

1691

1692

1693

1694

1696

1697

1698

1698

GEOMETERS: GEOMETRIDAE, STERRHINAE (cont.)

1699 Least Carpet *Idaea rusticata atrosignaria* 20mm Local. Jun–Aug. South-east England from Essex round to Dorset. **FP** Ivy, Traveller's Joy. CMM

1701 Dotted-border Wave *Idaea sylvestraria* 20mm Nb. Jun–Aug. Dotted border and black dot in centre of fairly plain wings. Local, mainly on heaths in south. **FP** Unknown in wild. CMM

1702 Small Fan-footed Wave *Idaea biselata* 20mm Common. Jun–Aug. Common throughout the UK, in woods, gardens, hedges, etc. **FP** Unknown in wild. DF

1704 Silky Wave *Idaea dilutaria* 18mm RDB2. Jun–Jul. Only three colonies known, Avon Gorge near Bristol, Gower peninsula in Glamorgan, and Caernarvonshire. Looks silky, no fringe dots, only very faint central dots. **FP** Common Rock-rose. DF

1705 Dwarf Cream Wave *Idaea fuscovenosa* 20mm Local. Jun–Jul. Like a creamy version of Dotted Border Wave but with fainter dots. **FP** Unknown in wild. DF

1706 Isle of Wight Wave *Idaea humiliata* 20mm Presumed extinct. Jul. Formerly resident on sea cliffs on Isle of Wight. Red-brown forewing streak. **FP** Restharrows, speedwells. CMM

1707 Small Dusty Wave *Idaea seriata* 20mm Common.

Jun–Jul, Aug–Sep. Throughout the UK. In gardens, hedges, etc., easily disturbed by day. **FP** Ivy and withered leaves. CMM

1708 Single-dotted Wave *Idaea dimidiata* 20mm Common. Jun–Aug. Damp woods, hedges, gardens, etc. Dark patch at centre of forewing trailing edge is diagnostic. **FP** Cow-parsley, Burnet-saxifrage, Hedge Bedstraw. DF

1709 Satin Wave *Idaea subsericeata* 22mm Common. Jun–Jul, Aug–Sep. Woods, hedges, gardens, heaths, mostly in southern UK. Paler, larger and commoner than Silky Wave. **FP** Unknown in wild. DF

1710 Weaver's Wave *Idaea contiguaria britanniae* 22mm Na. Jun–Jul. Heathery hillsides only in north-west Wales. **FP** Heather, Crowberry and Navelwort. NS

1711 Treble Brown Spot *Idaea trigeminata* 22mm Local. May–Jul, Aug–Sep. Woods, hedges, gardens, mostly in southern UK. Dark outer band on forewing, black dot on each wing. **FP** Ivy. DF

1712 Small Scallop *Idaea emarginata* 25mm Local. Jun–Aug. Locally widespread in southern UK. Male and female differ, but both have scalloped wing margins. Damp woods and fens. **FP** Bedstraws. DF, PAD

1705

1706

1707

1708

1709

1710

1711

1712 ♀

1712 ♂

GEOMETERS: GEOMETRIDAE, STERRHINAE (cont.)

1713 Riband Wave *Idaea aversata* 30mm Common. Jun–Aug, Sep–Oct. Two forms, both common. Similar to Plain Wave but outer band is indented at margin. **FP** Bedstraws, Primrose, Dandelion, Chickweed. CMM (below), DF

1714 Portland Ribbon Wave *Idaea degeneraria* 25mm RDB3. Jun–Jul. Resident on Isle of Portland, Dorset, but otherwise migrant. Shaded between first and second cross lines. **FP** Unknown in wild. CMM

1715 Plain Wave *Idaea straminata* 30mm Local. Jun–Aug. Scarce and local throughout the UK in open woods and scrubby heaths. Outer band not indented at forewing margin like in Riband Wave. **FP** Unknown in wild. CMM

1716 Vestal *Rhodometra sacraria* 25mm Migrant. Summer. Usually creamy with pink-brown stripe. Could be confused with Straw Belle, which has freckled wings. Can breed in summer in the UK, producing extreme pink forms. **FP** Knotgrass. CMM, CMM, CMM

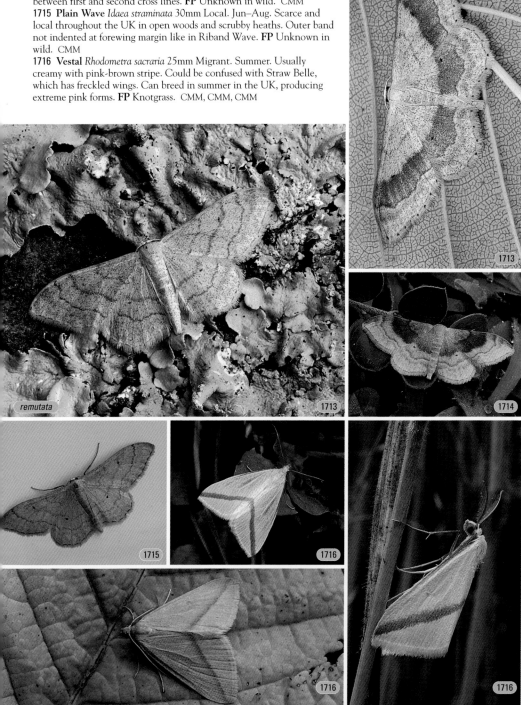

remutata   1713

1713

1714

1715

1716

1716

1716

CARPETS: GEOMETRIDAE, LARENTIINAE

1718 Oblique Striped *Phibalapteryx virgata* 22mm Nb. May–Jun, Aug. Found in scattered, varied, locations: Brecklands, chalk downs and coastal sand dunes from Wales and Yorkshire southwards. **FP** Lady's Bedstraw. SR

1719 Oblique Carpet *Orthonama vittata* 26mm Local. May–Jun, Aug–Sep. Local but widespread in marshes, bogs, damp woods, water meadows. More brown than the grey of Oblique Striped. **FP** Marsh, Heath and other Bedstraws. CMM

1720 Gem *Orthonama obstipata* 20mm (♂), 28mm (♀) Migrant. Summer. Regular migrant from southern Europe and North Africa. Can breed in good summers but does not overwinter. **FP** Herbaceous plants. CMM, CMM

1721 Balsam Carpet *Xanthorhoe biriviata* 28mm Local (alien foodplant). May–Jun, Jul–Sep. Very local in central southern England along rivers and water meadows where balsams are established. Dark mark on outer edge is different from other carpets. **FP** Orange Balsam, Small Balsam. DGG

1722 Flame Carpet *Xanthorhoe designata* 25mm Common. May–Jun, Jul–Aug. Common throughout the UK, in woods, gardens, hedges, heathland, etc. **FP** Unknown in wild. CMM

1723 Red Carpet *Xanthorhoe decoloraria* 30mm Common. Jun–Aug. Northern UK only, on mountain moorland and rocky hillsides. Similar to Flame Carpet but central band is broader and without the two projections. **FP** Lady's Mantle. DF

CARPETS: GEOMETRIDAE, LARENTIINAE (cont.)

1724 Red Twin-spot Carpet *Xanthorhoe spadicearia*
26mm Common. May–Jun, Jul–Aug. Throughout the
UK. **FP** Bedstraws, etc. DF
1725 Dark-barred Twin-spot Carpet *Xanthorhoe
ferrugata* 25mm Common. May–Jun, Jul–Aug.
Widespread in most of Britain, scarce in Scotland.
Central band is black and has inner edge notched at
leading edge. **FP** Herbaceous plants. DF
1726 Large Twin-spot Carpet *Xanthorhoe quadrifasiata*
26mm Local. Jun–Aug. Damp old woods, scrubby
heathland in central England. **FP** Bedstraws, Primrose,
violets. CMM
1727 Silver-ground Carpet *Xanthorhoe montanata* 34mm
Common. May–Jul. Damp woods, hedges, gardens,
heaths, etc. throughout the UK. **FP** Bedstraws,
Primrose, etc. CMM, SR
1728 Garden Carpet *Xanthorhoe fluctuata fluctuata*
27mm Common. Apr–Oct. Ubiquitous. **FP** Brassicas,
including Garlic Mustard. CMM
1730 Spanish Carpet *Scotopteryx peribolata* 30mm
Migrant. Aug–Sep. Resident only in Channel Isles.
FP Gorse, Broom. AC

1731 Chalk Carpet *Scotopteryx bipunctaria cretata* 34mm
Nb. Jul–Aug. Light grey day- and night-flying moth.
Widespread on limestone and chalk downs, quarries.
FP Trefoils, clovers, vetches. CMM
1732 Shaded Broad-bar *Scotopteryx chenopodiata* 36mm
Common. Jun–Aug. Found anywhere throughout the
UK. **FP** Clovers, vetches. CMM
1733 Lead Belle *Scotopteryx mucronata* 30mm Local.
May–Jun. Very similar markings, habitat and foodplants
to July Belle, but slightly earlier flight period. On acid
heaths and moors. Central dark spot is tear-shaped.
Local populations, less widespread than species below.
FP Gorse, Broom, Dyer's Greenweed, Petty Whin. RL
1734 July Belle *Scotopteryx luridata plumbaria* 30mm
Common. Jun–Aug. Better distributed than Lead Belle.
On acid heaths and moors as well as shingle beaches
and downs. **FP** Gorse, Broom, Dyer's Greenweed, Petty
Whin. DGG
1735 Ruddy Carpet *Catarhoe rubidata* Nb. Jun–Jul.
26mm Local in southern UK on chalk downs, sea cliffs.
Pink look is unmistakable. **FP** Hedge and Lady's
Bedstraw. CMM

CARPETS: GEOMETRIDAE, LARENTIINAE (cont.)

1736 Royal Mantle *Catarhoe cuculata* 25mm Local. Jun–Jul. Local throughout, on chalk downs, brecks, limestone quarries and sea cliffs. **FP** Hedge and Lady's Bedstraw. CMM

1737 Small Argent and Sable *Epirrhoe tristata* 24mm Common. May–Jul. Northern UK on high moors and limestone grassland, as well as Devon area. **FP** Heath Bedstraw. DGG, CMM

1738 Common Carpet *Epirrhoe alternata* 25mm Common. May–Jun, Jul–Sep. Common anywhere throughout the UK. Similar to Wood Carpet but outer white band on forewing has wavy grey line running through it. **FP** Bedstraws and Cleavers. CMM

1739 Wood Carpet *Epirrhoe rivata* 28mm Local. Jun–Aug. Widespread in southern UK on downs, sea cliffs, old hedges, etc. **FP** Hedge and Lady's Bedstraw. CMM

1740 Galium Carpet *Epirrhoe galiata* 30mm Local. May–Aug. Slate blue-grey appearance, with concave leading edge to forewing. Coastal cliffs and dunes, inland chalk grassland as well as open moors. **FP** Bedstraws. CMM

1736

1737

1738

1737

1739

1740

1741 Many-lined *Costaconvexa polygrammata* 24mm Extinct, Migrant. Not seen in Cambridgeshire since 1879. Occasional migrant. **FP** Bedstraws. DF
1742 Yellow Shell *Camptogramma bilineata* 27mm Common. Jun–Aug. Unmistakable, though yellow can vary to brown. Found throughout the UK. **FP** Bedstraws, cleavers, dock, sorrel, Wormwood, etc. DF
1743 Yellow-ringed Carpet *Entephria flavicinctata* 35mm Nb. May, Aug. Golden orange markings diagnostic. Northern UK on limestone mountains and cliffs. **FP** Saxifrages and Stonecrop. SH
1744 Grey Mountain Moth *Entephria caesiata* 34mm Common. Jun–Aug. Northern UK on rocky mountains and moorland. **FP** Heathers and Bilberry. DF
1745 Mallow *Larentia clavaria* 40mm Common. Sep–Nov. Widespread in south, on waste ground, marshes, gardens, road verges, etc. **FP** Mallows and Hollyhock. KT
1746 Shoulder Stripe *Anticlea badiata* 33mm Common. Feb–Apr. Woods, hedges, gardens, etc. **FP** Wild Rose. DF
1747 Streamer *Anticlea derivata* 33mm Common. Apr–May. Woods, hedges, gardens, etc. 'Streamer' in centre of forewing is diagnostic. **FP** Wild Rose. CMM
1748 Beautiful Carpet *Mesoleuca albicillata* 36mm Common. May–Aug. Unmistakable. Sparsely distributed throughout Britain in woodland. **FP** Bramble, Raspberry. DF
1749 Dark Spinach *Pelurga comitata* 38mm Common. Jul–Aug. Scattered throughout Britain. Note the dark dot in centre of forewing. **FP** Goosefoot, Orache. PAD, CMM

1741

1742

1743

1744

1745

1746

1747

1748

1749

1749

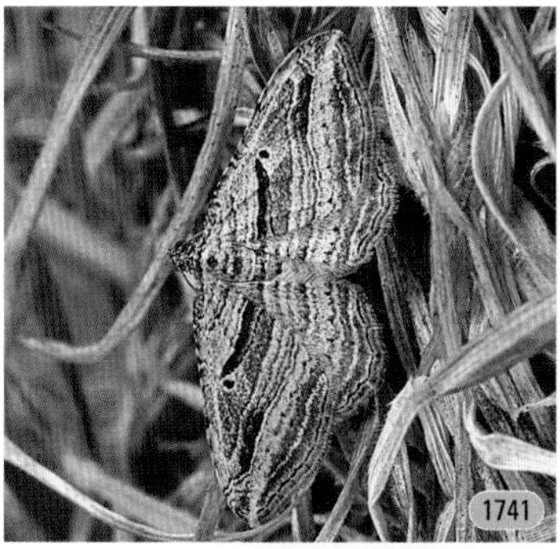

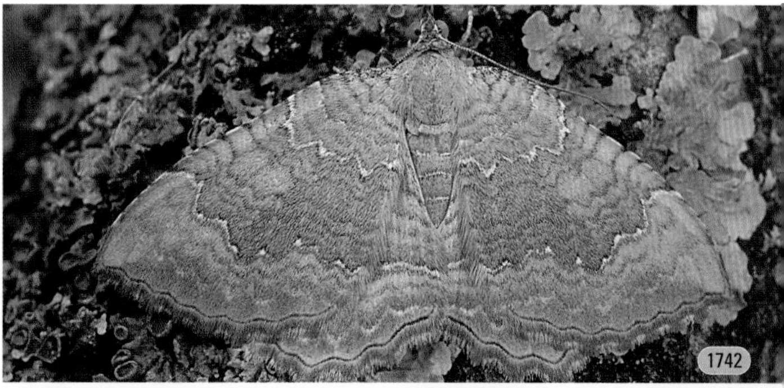

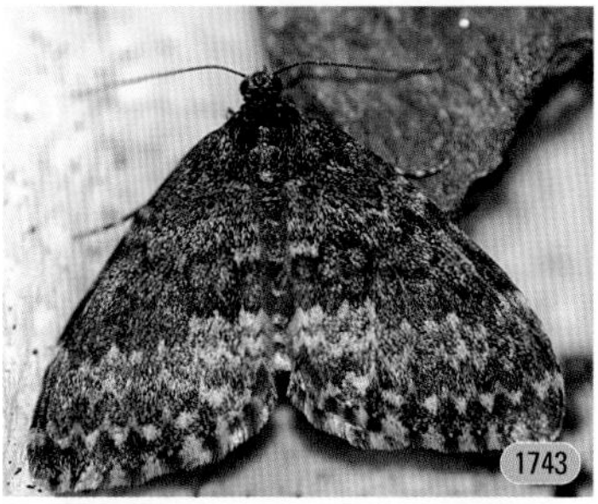

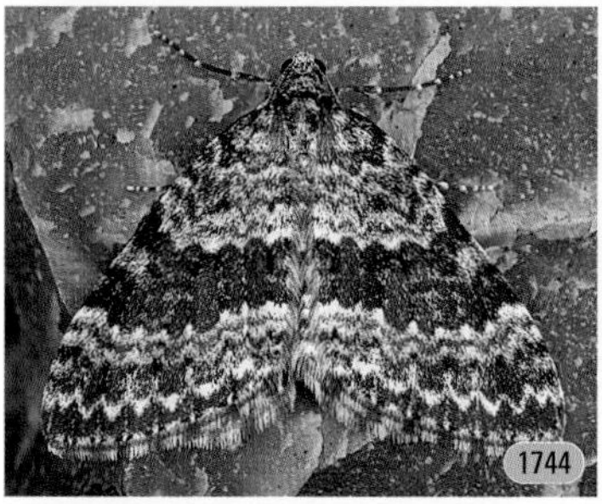

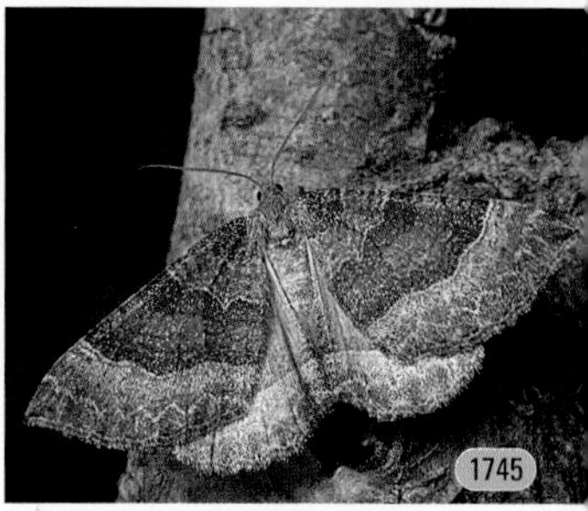

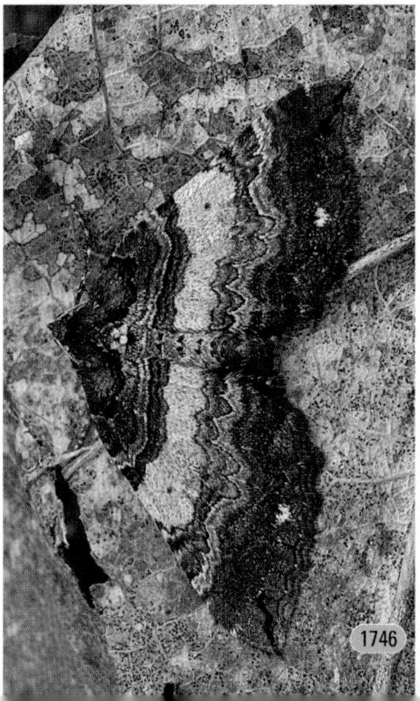

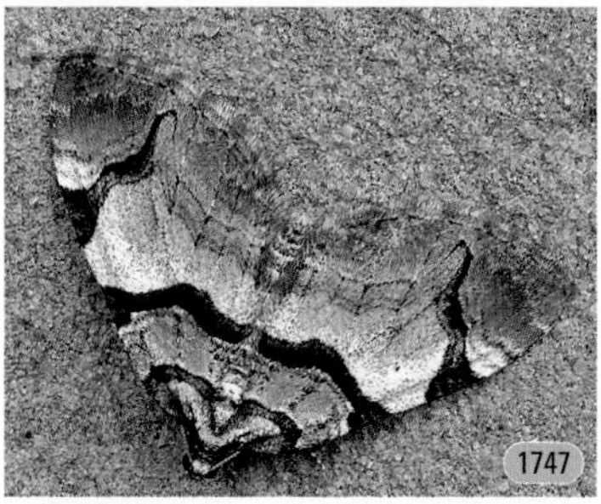

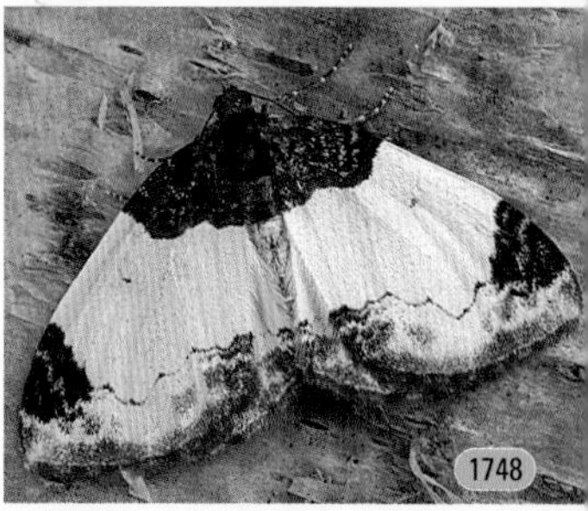

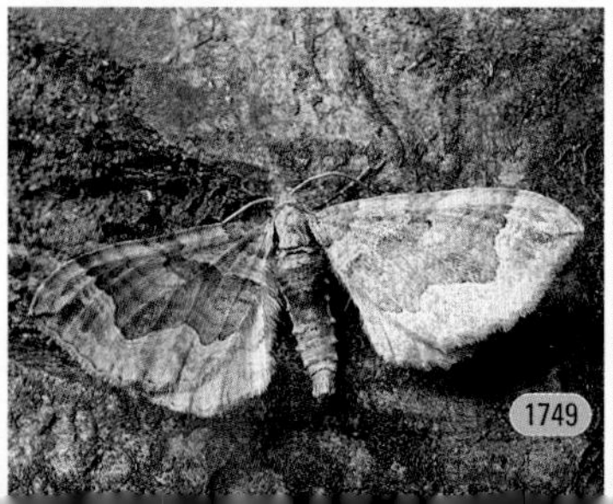

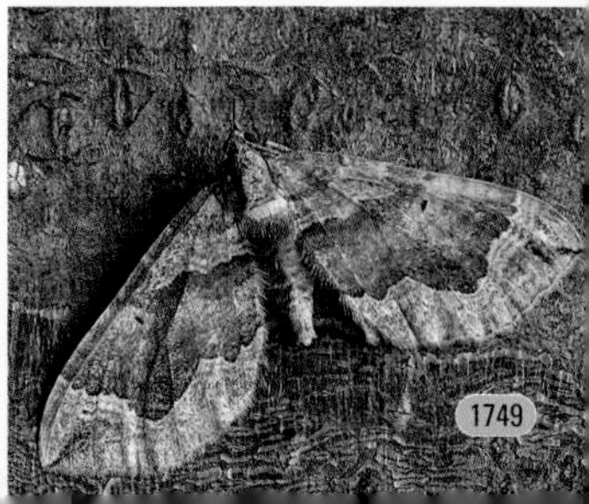

CARPETS: GEOMETRIDAE, LARENTIINAE (cont.)

1750 Water Carpet *Lampropteryx suffumata* 36mm
Common. Apr–May. Thinly distributed throughout the
UK. Very similar to Devon Carpet, but larger, with
inner edge of main forewing band double-notched at
costa. **FP** Bedstraws, cleavers. NS

1751 Devon Carpet *Lampropteryx otregiata* 30mm Nb.
May–Jun, Aug–Sep. Smaller and scarcer than above,
but similar habitats of damp woods, fens, moors, etc.
FP Marsh and Fen Bedstraw. CMM

1752 Purple Bar *Cosmorhoe ocellata* 25mm Common.
May–Jul, Aug–Sep. Common anywhere throughout the
UK. **FP** Hedge and Heath Bedstraw. CMM

1753 Striped Twin-spot Carpet *Nebula salicata latentaria*
30mm Common. May–Jul. Common in northern
England and Scotland on moors, woods, sand dunes.
FP Bedstraws. NS

1754 Phoenix *Eulithis prunata* 40mm Common.
Jul–Aug. In low numbers throughout the UK. Abdomen
in male curled up at rest. In woods and gardens. **FP**
Black and Red Currant, Gooseberry. CMM

1755 Chevron *Eulithis testata* 36mm (♂), 26mm (♀)
Common. Jul–Sep. V-shaped chevron in central band and
whitish frosting are characteristic. Throughout the UK on
scrubby heaths, moors, woods, marshes, etc. **FP** Sallows,
Creeping Willow, Aspen, Hazel, heather. CMM, DGG

1756 Northern Spinach *Eulithis populata* 32mm
Common. Jul–Aug. Northern and western UK on

upland moors and heaths. Inner central cross-band has
no chevron, outer cross-band has two projections at rear
edge. **FP** Bilberry. DGG

1757 Spinach *Eulithis mellinata* 34mm Common.
Jun–Aug. Outer edge of central band has single
projection. Lowland moth of gardens and allotments as
well as woodland. **FP** Black and Red Currant. NS

1758 Barred Straw *Eulithis pyraliata* 36mm Common.
May–Aug. Throughout the UK in gardens, hedges,
wood edges, etc. Wings held out away from body.
FP Cleavers, bedstraws. DF

1759 Small Phoenix *Ecliptopera silaceata* 30mm
Common. Apr–Jun, Jul–Aug. Rests with abdomen
curled upwards. Dark central band usually with pale-
marked veins across. **FP** Willowherbs and Enchanter's
Nightshade. DGG

1760 Red-green Carpet *Chloroclysta siterata* 30mm
Common. Sep–Nov, Mar–May. Spring flight period for
female only after hibernation. Throughout the UK.
Variable colour. Narrower resting pose and smaller than
Autumn Green Carpet. **FP** Broadleaved trees, oak,
Apple, Cherry, etc. DGG, CMM

1761 Autumn Green Carpet *Chloroclysta miata* 40mm
Local. Sep–Nov, Mar–May. Female hibernates.
Widespread but scarcer in south. Larger, broader-winged
and paler than above. Broadleaved woods, scrub.
FP Sallows, Rowan, etc. SR

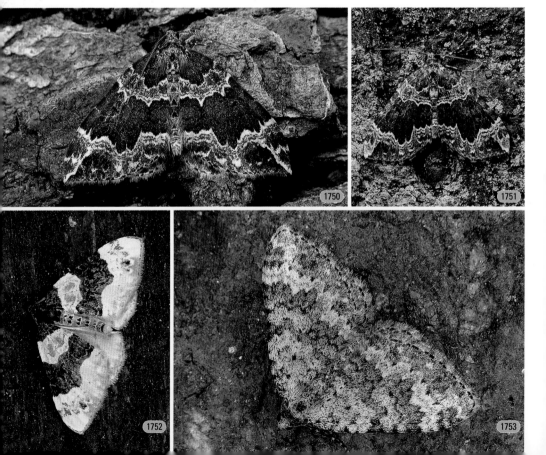

CARPETS: GEOMETRIDAE, LARENTIINAE (cont.)

1762 Dark Marbled Carpet *Chloroclysta citrata* 32mm
Common. Jul–Sep. Local in south, common elsewhere.
Variable markings, very similar to Common Marbled
Carpet. Usually has longer, more pointed projection on
rear of central band. **FP** Sallows, birch, Bilberry. DF,
DGG, RPJ
1763 Arran Carpet *Chloroclysta concinnata* Na. Jul–Aug.
From Arran and Hebrides only. Local form of Common
Marbled Carpet. **FP** Heather, Bilberry. NOT ILLUSTRATED
1764 Common Marbled Carpet *Chloroclysta truncata*
32mm Common. May–Jun, Aug–Oct. Found anywhere
throughout the UK in gardens, woods, grassland, moors,
etc. Very variable. **FP** Various trees and shrubs. CMM,
DF, CMM, DGG

1765 Barred Yellow *Cidaria fulvata* 27mm Common.
Jun–Aug. Unmistakable. Widespread throughout
Britain. **FP** Dog Rose, Burnet Rose. CMM
1766 Blue-bordered Carpet *Plemyria rubiginata rubiginata*
28mm Common. Jun–Aug. Widespread in damp woods
and marsh. **FP** Alder, Blackthorn, etc. DF, NS
1767 Pine Carpet *Thera firmata* 30mm Common.
Jul–Nov. Similar to Grey Pine Carpet but redder, with
deep V notch in front edge of central band. **FP** Scots
Pine. CMM
1768 Grey Pine Carpet *Thera obeliscata* 30mm
Common. May–Jul, Sep–Nov. Can be abundant
throughout the UK in pine woods. **FP** Scots Pine,
Norway Spruce, Douglas Fir. CMM (left), DGG, NS

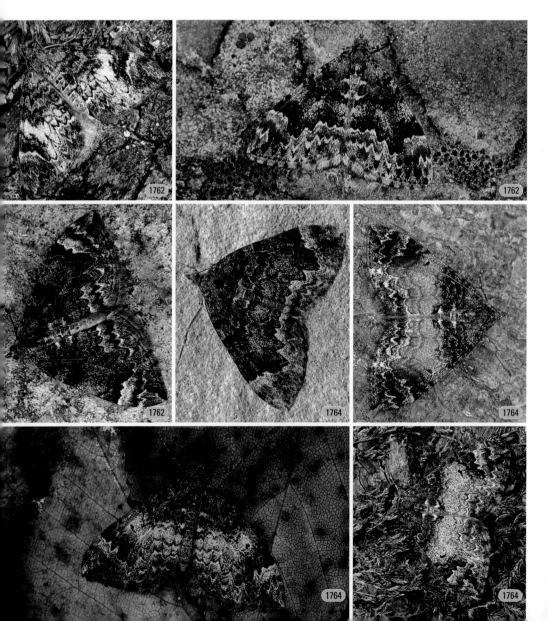

1766

1765

1766

1767

1768

Pine Carpet

1767

Grey Pine Carpet

1768

1768

CARPETS: GEOMETRIDAE, LARENTIINAE (cont.)

1769 Spruce Carpet *Thera britannica* 30mm Common. May–Jul, Sep–Nov. Throughout the UK. **FP** Conifers. CMM
1770 Chestnut-coloured Carpet *Thera cognata* 25mm Nb. Jul–Aug. Scotland and northern UK. **FP** Juniper. DJP
1771 Juniper Carpet *Thera juniperata* 28mm Common. Sep–Nov. Throughout the UK on chalk downs and in gardens with junipers. Noticeable dark dash near tip of wings. **FP** Junipers, including cultivated ones in gardens. DF
1771a Cypress Carpet *Thera cupressata* 28mm Local. Jun–Jul, Oct–Nov. Recent colonist first recorded in Sussex 1984, now breeding in southern counties. **FP** Monterey and Leyland Cypress in parks and gardens. CMM
1772 Netted Carpet *Eustroma reticulata* 28mm RDB2. Jul–Aug. Very local in Lake District and north Wales in wet woods by streams and lakes. **FP** Touch-me-not Balsam (but not Indian Balsam). RPJ
1773 Broken-barred Carpet *Electrophaes corylata* 28mm Common. May–Jun. Common throughout the UK. In woodland, parks, bushy areas. Centre bar usually has a break. **FP** Trees and shrubs, including oak, Hawthorn, birch. DGG, CMM

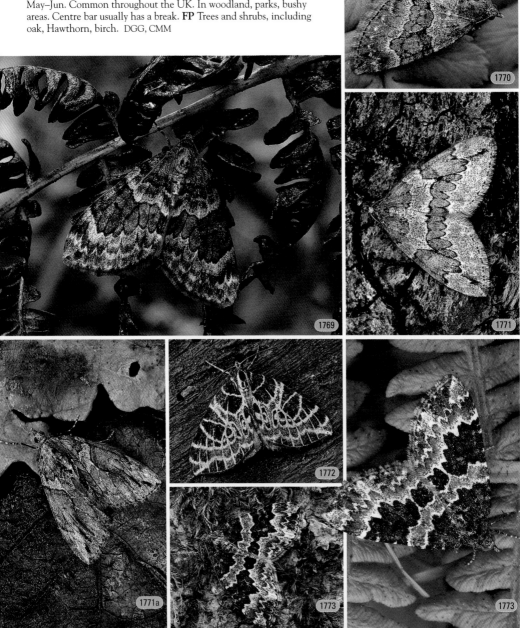

1774 Beech-green Carpet *Colostygia olivata* 30mm
Local. Jul–Aug. Woodland, moors and coastal cliffs,
often on chalk or limestone, throughout the UK.
FP Bedstraws. DF

1775 Mottled Grey *Colostygia multistrigaria* 30mm
Common. Mar–Apr. Throughout the UK on downs,
heaths, moors, woodland. **FP** Bedstraws. CMM

1776 Green Carpet *Colostygia pectinataria* 25mm
Common. May–Jul, Aug–Sep. Brilliant green when fresh
but quickly fades to dingy off-white. Found in any
habitat throughout the UK. **FP** Bedstraws. CMM, NS

1777 July Highflyer *Hydriomena furcata* 32mm
Common. Jul–Aug. Common throughout the UK. Very
variable, but black mark at point of wing is diagnostic.
FP Sallows, Creeping Willow, Bilberry, heather, hazel.
NS, CMM, NS, RPJ

1778 May Highflyer *Hydriomena impluviata* 30mm
Common. May–Jul. Earlier flight period than above
species. Black streaks near point of wing. Throughout
the UK in damp alder woods. **FP** Alder. DGG, NS

1774
1776
1775
aberration
1776
1777
1777
1777
1777
1777
1778
1778

CARPETS: GEOMETRIDAE, LARENTIINAE (cont.)

1779 Ruddy Highflyer *Hydriomena ruberata* 30mm Local. May–Jun. Generally a northern species. On moors, heaths, bogs. **FP** Eared and Grey Willow. RL, RL, DF

1780 Slender-striped Rufous *Coenocalpe lapidata* 28mm RDB3. Sep–Oct. On rough pasture and open moorland in central and north Scotland. **FP** Unknown in wild. CMM

1781 Small Waved Umber *Horisme vitalbata* 32mm Common. May–Jun, Aug. Southern UK on chalk soils, in bushy areas and hedgerows. **FP** Traveller's Joy. CMM

1782 Fern *Horisme tersata* 40mm Common. Jun–Aug. Southern UK on chalk soils, in bushy areas and hedgerows. **FP** Traveller's Joy. DF

1784 Pretty Chalk Carpet *Melanthia procellata* 40mm Common. Jun–Aug. Southern UK on chalk soils, in bushy areas and hedgerows. **FP** Traveller's Joy. CMM, SH

1785 Barberry Carpet *Pareulype berberata* 28mm RDB1. May–Jun, Aug. Very scarce, sometimes in tiny colonies on a single bush, in central southern UK. **FP** Barberry. CS

1786 White-banded Carpet *Spargania luctuata* 30mm Na. May–Jun, Jul–Aug. Colonies established in Kent,

Sussex, Norfolk and Suffolk since 1950 in large woods. **FP** Rosebay Willowherb. BU

1787 Argent and Sable *Rheumaptera hastata* 36mm Nb. May–Jun. Flies in sun in birch woods in England and Wales. Scottish race is smaller, living on boggy moorland. **FP** Birch leaves. Bog Myrtle in Scotland. DGG

1788 Scarce Tissue *Rheumaptera cervinalis* 45mm Local. Apr–Jun. Scattered in southern UK, in hedges, gardens, parks. **FP** Barberry, including cultivated species. RW

1789 Scallop Shell *Rheumaptera undulata* 35mm Common. Jun–Jul. Widespread throughout the UK, more common in the south. Unmistakable. Mostly in damp woods. **FP** Sallows, Aspen, Bilberry. CMM

1790 Tissue *Triphosa dubitata* 45mm Local. Aug–Oct, Apr–May. Spring flight is after group hibernation in caves. In woodland, scrub, hedges, acid heaths. Hindwing margin is more scalloped than Scarce Tissue. **FP** Buckthorn, Alder Buckthorn. CMM

1791 Brown Scallop *Philereme vetulata* 30mm Local. Jun–Jul. Chalk downs, woods and fens, mostly in southern England but not south-west. **FP** Buckthorn. RL

1779 ♂ · 1779 ♀ · 1779 · 1780 ♂ · 1781

1782

1784

1785

1784

1786

1789

1787

1788

1790

1791

CARPETS: GEOMETRIDAE, LARENTIINAE (cont.)

1792 Dark Umber *Philereme transversata britannica* 40mm Local. Jul. Mostly in southern UK on chalk and limestone downland, woods and fens. **FP** Buckthorn. CMM

1793 Cloaked Carpet *Euphyia biangulata* 30mm Nb. Jul. Identified by double projection from rear of central band. Local in southern England and south Wales in damp woods and old hedges. **FP** Stitchwort.　SH

1794 Sharp-angled Carpet *Euphyia unangulata* 26mm Local. Jun–Aug. Only single projection from rear of central band. In woods and old hedges in southern UK. **FP** Unknown in wild, probably Chickweed.　DF

1795 November Moth *Epirrita dilutata* 36mm Common. Oct–Nov. This and following two *Epirrita* species are all very similar and very variable, needing dissection to be sure of identity. In woods, gardens, hedges and scrub. Central dot, if present, may touch front of central band. **FP** On most broadleaved trees and shrubs.　CMM, CMM, CMM

1796 Pale November Moth *Epirrita christyi* 36mm Common. Sep–Nov. Central dot, if present, clear of central band. Widespread in mature woods. **FP** Deciduous trees, including oak, Hawthorn, elm, Beech, hazel.　RL

1797 Autumnal Moth *Epirrita autumnata* 36mm Common. Oct–Nov. Silvery look and dark V mark in central band help distinguish this species. Central dot well clear of band. Widespread in open mixed woods, heaths and moors. **FP** Birch, Alder, heather.　RL, CMM

1798 Small Autumnal Moth *Epirrita filigrammaria* 30mm Common. Aug. This species flies in August in northern upland moorland, unlike the three species above, and is smaller. **FP** Heather, Bilberry, sallows.　IK

1799 Winter Moth *Operophtera brumata* 27mm (♂), 7mm (♀) Common. Oct–Jan. Common throughout the UK anywhere near trees and shrubs. Male flies weakly even on cold nights, female is wingless. **FP** Broadleaved trees, some pines, heathers, Bog Myrtle.　NS, NS, CMM

CARPETS: GEOMETRIDAE, LARENTIINAE (cont.)

1800 Northern Winter Moth *Operophtera fagata* 32mm Common. Oct–Dec. Most common in central England, scarcer elsewhere. Male larger than Winter Moth, paler with silky look, hind wings project beyond forewings. Female flightless. **FP** Birch, Alder, Beech in woods, heathland, scrub and gardens. CMM

1801 Barred Carpet *Perizoma taeniata* 26mm Na. Jun–Aug. Uncommon, in damp woodland in north Devon, north Wales, north England and Scotland. **FP** Moss seed capsules. JPo, MJH

1802 Rivulet *Perizoma affinitata* 26mm Common. May–Jul. In open woods, chalk downs, road verges throughout most of the UK. Single indent in front of central white band. **FP** In seeds of Red Campion. DF

1803 Small Rivulet *Perizoma alchemillata* 20mm Common. Jun–Jul. Smaller than Rivulet, central white band has double indentation. Common in woods, marshes, downs, etc. **FP** Flowers and seeds of Hemp Nettle. DF

1804 Barred Rivulet *Perizoma bifaciata* 20mm Local. Jul–Aug. Local in southern UK, scarce in north-east England and Scotland. Chalk downs, rough pasture. Can pupate for up to 5 years. **FP** Red Bartsia seeds, Eyebright. IK

1805 Heath Rivulet *Perizoma minorata ericetata* 18mm Nb. Jul–Aug. Flies in sunshine. Found on limestone hills, moorland and upland pasture in Scotland, northern England and the Burren in Ireland. **FP** Eyebright seeds. RL

1806 Pretty Pinion *Perizoma blandiata* 20mm Nb. Jun–Jul. Moorland and limestone hills in Scotland, 'machair' in Hebrides and the Burren in Ireland. **FP** Eyebright seeds and flowers. CMM

1807 Grass Rivulet *Perizoma albulata* 21mm Local. May–Jul. Chalk grassland, coastal dunes. Local throughout the UK. **FP** Seeds of Yellow Rattle. CMM

1808 Sandy Carpet *Perizoma flavofasciata* 26mm Common. Jun–Jul. Throughout the UK in open woodland, mature hedges, downs and dunes. **FP** Seeds of Red Campion, also White and Bladder Campion. CMM

1809 Twin-spot Carpet *Perizoma didymata* 26mm Common. Jun–Aug. Males fly in afternoon sun. Found throughout Britain in woods, moors, dunes, hedgerows. **FP** Willowherbs, Bilberry, heather, Red Campion, etc. CMM

1810 Marsh Carpet *Perizoma sagittata* 33mm Na. Jun–Jul. Very local in marshes and fens of east England, Norfolk, Suffolk, Cambridge, etc. **FP** Seeds of Common Meadow Rue. RL

PUGS: GEOMETRIDAE, EUPITHECIA

There are over 50 members of this Geometer sub-family on the British list.

Pugs are small moths, which generally rest with their wings extending approximately at right angles to the body. The tip of the tail is often turned up. Deciding that the moth is a Pug is relatively easy (though the Small Dusty Wave does also look like a Pug), but identification is often tricky. Many of them seem to be similar 'little brown jobs', especially when the moth is not fresh. Identification notes, flight period, distribution, scarcity and habitat will all help, along with the photographs. They come to light.

Larvae are often colourful, mostly feeding on flowers and seeds of host plants. They generally overwinter in the ground as pupae, though some do so as eggs on the foodplant.

1811 Slender Pug *Eupithecia tenuiata* 16mm Common. Jun–Jul. In damp woods, lakesides, ditches, etc. Dark blotches along forewing and distinct black dot. **FP** Catkins of Goat, Eared and Grey Willow. DF

1812 Maple Pug *Eupithecia inturbata* 17mm Local. Jul–Aug. Found in mature Field Maple woods on limestone. **FP** Flowers of Field Maple. DF

1813 Haworth's Pug *Eupithecia haworthiata* 16mm Local. Jun–Jul. From Yorkshire southwards, in woods, hedges, etc., on chalk or limestone. Light red-brown band at base of abdomen. **FP** Traveller's Joy flowers. NS

1814 Lead-coloured Pug *Eupithecia plumbeolata* 18mm Nb. May–Jun. Open woods and sandhills. **FP** Flowers of Common Cow Wheat, Yellow Rattle. CMM

1815 Cloaked Pug *Eupithecia abietaria* 25mm Local (alien foodplant). Jun–Jul. Large, distinctive and scarce in mature plantations of Norway Spruce. **FP** In cones of Norway Spruce and other spruces, firs, Larch. DF

1816 Toadflax Pug *Eupithecia linariata* 20mm Common. Jul–Aug. Smaller, darker and 'neater', with later flight period than Foxglove Pug. On chalk and limestone downs, verges, etc. **FP** Common Toadflax, Snapdragon in gardens. RW

1817 Foxglove Pug *Eupithecia pulchellata* 24mm Common. May–Jun. Throughout the UK wherever foodplant grows. **FP** Foxglove flowers. RW

1811

1812

1816

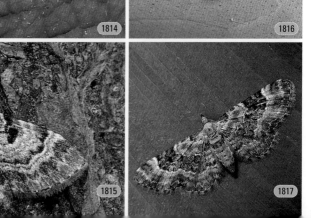

1813

1814

1815

1817

1818 Marbled Pug *Eupithecia irriguata* 20mm Nb. Apr–May. Distinctive. Mature oak woods in southern England, especially New Forest. **FP** Pedunculate Oak. CMM, CMM
1819 Mottled Pug *Eupithecia exiguata* 24mm Common. May–Jun. Mainly England and Wales. **FP** Hawthorn, Blackthorn, Dogwood, Barberry. CMM
1820 Pinion-spotted Pug *Eupithecia insigniata* 22mm Nb. Apr–May. Southern England. Distinctive but scarce. **FP** Hawthorn. PAD
1821 Valerian Pug *Eupithecia valerianata* 18mm Nb. Jun–Jul. Widespread but local throughout the UK in damp woods, fens and marsh. Usually paler than the example shown, but elongated forewing spot, outer white zig-zag and white mark at trailing corner of wings aid identification. **FP** Flowers and seeds of Common Valerian. DGG
1822 Marsh Pug *Eupithecia pygmaeata* 16mm Local. May–Jun. Widely scattered localities throughout, in fens, grassland, sandhills. Small dark Pug without central spot but with white mark in trailing corner. **FP** Field Mouse-ear. NS
1823 Netted Pug *Eupithecia venosata* 25mm Local. May–Jun. Unmistakable Pug, inhabiting chalk and limestone downs and cliffs, widespread. **FP** Seed-pods of Bladder and Sea Campion. CMM
1824 Fletcher's (Pauper) Pug *Eupithecia egenaria* 22mm RDB3. May–Jun. Large grey Pug with elongated forewing spot. Very scarce, found only in Wye Valley and Norfolk/Suffolk. **FP** Flowers of Small- and Large-leaved Lime. NS
1825 Lime-speck Pug *Eupithecia centaureata* 22mm Common. Apr–Oct. Found almost anywhere throughout the UK. Unmistakable. Wings held well clear of body. **FP** Flowers of assorted herbaceous plants. CMM
1826 Triple-spotted Pug *Eupithecia trisignaria* 20mm Local. Jun–Jul. Widespread. Name derives from group of central forewing dot and two dark marks at front edge. **FP** Wild Angelica and Hogweed seeds and flowers. DF

PUGS: GEOMETRIDAE, EUPITHECIA (cont.)

1827 Freyer's Pug *Eupithecia intricata* 24mm Common (alien foodplant). May–Jun. Parks and gardens in southern England and Wales. Similar subspecies found in Scotland and the Burren, Ireland. Large, with central forewing mark and dark belt on abdomen. **FP** Exotic junipers and cypress. NS

1828 Satyr Pug *Eupithecia satyrata* 20mm Common. May–Jun. Moorland form common on uplands, lowland form local and scarce on heaths, downs, etc. Chequered black and white veins are distinctive, with very straight leading edge to forewing. **FP** Flowers of heather, Cross-leaved Heath, Meadowsweet, Devil's-bit Scabious, etc. DF

1830 Wormwood Pug *Eupithecia absinthiata* 23mm Common. Jun–Jul. Dark marks on forewing edge, large elongated central spot and black band on abdomen. Widespread, including in urban gardens, open woods, grassland, coastal marsh, etc. **FP** Composite flowers, including wormwoods, Yarrow, Sea Aster, Michaelmas Daisy, Mugwort. DF

1831 Ling Pug *Eupithecia absinthiata* 21mm f. *goossensiata* Local. Jun–Jul. Similar to above, but smaller. Considered to be a local form of Wormwood Pug found on heaths and moorland. **FP** Heather flowers. DF

1832 Currant Pug *Eupithecia assimilata* 22mm Common. May–Jun, Aug. Widespread in gardens, hedgerows and open woods. Plain brown wing with dark leading edge marks, central black dot and bright white mark in trailing corner. **FP** Wild Hop, Black and Red Currant. DF

1833 Bleached Pug *Eupithecia expallidata* 26mm Nb. Jun–Aug. Large, pale Pug, with dark marks on forewing edge, large central spot, dark ring on abdomen. Scattered mostly in southern UK in woodland rides. **FP** Goldenrod flowers. RW

1834 Common Pug *Eupithecia vulgata* 20mm Common. May–Jun, Aug. Widespread and common throughout the UK. Scottish form more strongly marked. Also a melanic form. **FP** Sallows, Hawthorn, Bramble, Ragwort, Yarrow, etc. CMM

1835 White-spotted Pug *Eupithecia tripunctaria* 21mm Local. May–Sep. Local throughout, on verges, river banks, hedges, woods, fens, etc. Similar to 1832 but three or more white marks along outer edge of hind wing, white mark on thorax and weak dark central spot. **FP** In July on Elder flowers, later in Wild Angelica and Parsnip seeds. CMM

1836 Campanula Pug *Eupithecia denotata* 23mm Na. Jul. Local in south-east England on chalk and limestone downs. Plainish brown with central spot and curved forewing edge. **FP** Nettle-leaved and Giant Bellflower seedheads. DF

1836 Jasione Pug *Eupithecia denotata jasioneata* Na. Jul. Subspecies of Campanula Pug, named after its food plant *Jasione montana*. Local in south-west England and Wales on non-calcereous sea cliffs. Slightly smaller and greyer than above species. **FP** Sheep's-bit seeds. NOT ILLUSTRATED

1837 Grey Pug *Eupithecia subfuscata* 22mm Common. May–Jun. Found almost anywhere throughout the UK. Brown-grey with central spot and wavy cross lines. **FP** Flowers and leaves of wide variety of herbaceous and woody plants. CMM

1838 Tawny-speckled Pug *Eupithecia icterata* 25mm Common. Jul–Aug. Large, unmistakable in south, northern form without tawny central patch and is more sandy coloured with wavy cross lines but similar brown hind wing. Widespread. **FP** Yarrow, Sneezewort. CMM

1839 Bordered Pug *Eupithecia succenturiata* 24mm Common. Jul–Aug. Found on rough, open land, verges, gardens, mainly in the south. **FP** Mugwort. NS

1840 Shaded Pug *Eupithecia subumbrata* 22mm Local. Jun–Jul. Whitish, forewing edge very straight, tiny central spot. Mainly south and east England but also Gower in south Wales. **FP** Seeds of goosefoot, Orache. NS

1841 Yarrow Pug *Eupithecia millefoliata* 24mm Nb. Jun–Jul. Scarce, mostly in coastal south-east England. Well patterned with wavy cross lines and central spot. **FP** Yarrow flowers and seeds. CMM

1842 Plain Pug *Eupithecia simpliciata* 22mm Local. Jun–Aug. Saltmarsh and tidal river banks in England. **FP** Seeds of Goosefoot, Orache. DF

1842a Goosefoot Pug *Eupithecia sinuosaria* Very rare migrant. **FP** Goosefoot, Orache. NOT ILLUSTRATED

1843 Thyme Pug *Eupithecia distinctaria constricta* 18mm Nb. Jun–Jul. Very local on sea cliffs and limestone hills, mainly on south and west coasts. Small, grey, with bold central and forewing edge marks. **FP** Wild Thyme. LG

1844 Ochreous Pug *Eupithecia indigata* 20mm Common. Apr–May. Similar to above, but different flight period and habitat, which is pine forest. **FP** Scots Pine. DGG

1845 Pimpinel Pug *Eupithecia pimpinellata* 25mm Local. Jun–Jul. Similar to Wormwood Pug but paler and greyer. Chalk and limestone downland in south and east England. **FP** Seeds of Burnet-saxifrage. DF

1846 Narrow-winged Pug *Eupithecia nanata* 21mm Common. Apr–Jun, Aug. Distinctive, on heaths and moors throughout Britain. **FP** Heather flowers. DF

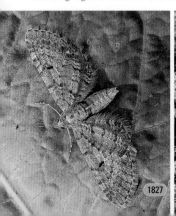
1827

1828

1830

PUGS: GEOMETRIDAE, EUPITHECIA (cont.)

1847 Scarce Pug *Eupithecia extensaria occidua* 24mm RDB3. Jun–Jul. Very striking. Slightly similar to Narrow-winged Pug. Very scarce on coastal salt-marshes in eastern England. **FP** Sea Wormwood. RL

1848 Angle-barred Pug *Eupithecia innotata* Common. May–Jun, Aug. This and the Ash and Tamarisk Pug are now all considered to be the same species, but living on different foodplants. Distinct acute angle in pale cross line outside central dot.
FP Sea Buckthorn, Hawthorn, Blackthorn, Elder in east England. NOT ILLUSTRATED

1849 Ash Pug *Eupithecia fraxinata* 24mm Common. May–Jun, Aug. Woods, hedges, parks, gardens. Looks similar to above. **FP** Ash. DF

1850 Tamarisk Pug *Eupithecia tamarisciata* Unconfirmed. May–Jun, Aug. East and south England. Coastal. Looks similar to above. **FP** Tamarisk. NOT ILLUSTRATED

1851 Golden-rod Pug *Eupithecia virgaureata* 21mm Local. May–Jun, Aug. Very similar to Grey Pug except for tuft of white scales on thorax. Mostly west England and Wales. In open woods, waste ground, verges.
FP Foodplant unknown for first generation, second generation on flowers of Golden Rod, Ragwort. DF

1852 Brindled Pug *Eupithecia abbreviata* 23mm Common. Mar–May. Can be abundant throughout the UK in oak woods. **FP** Oaks, Hawthorn. NS

1853 Oak-tree Pug *Eupithecia dodoneata* 20mm Common. Apr–Jun. Similar to Brindled Pug but smaller and with orange-brown streaks along leading and trailing edge of forewing. In woods and hedges in England and Wales. **FP** Hawthorn, Pedunculate Oak. CMM

1854 Juniper Pug *Eupithecia pusillata* 20mm Common. Jul–Sep. Variable, but white mark just beyond central black dot helps identification. Common throughout where foodplant is available. **FP** Junipers. IK, DF

1855 Cypress Pug *Eupithecia phoeniceata* Local 22mm (alien foodplant). Aug–Sep. Mostly in south but spreading. Unmistakable. **FP** Monterey and Leyland Cypress in parks and gardens. DF

1855a Channel Islands Pug *Eupithecia ultimaria* 17mm Local (alien foodplant). Jun–Aug. Found on south

coasts where foodplant is established. Small, grey-brown Pug with prominent central spot. **FP** Tamarisk. DF, PAD

1856 Larch Pug *Eupithecia lariciata* 22m Common. May–Jul. Similar to some other Pugs but has prominent white tuft on thorax. Often melanic. Widespread throughout Britain. **FP** Larch. DF

1857 Dwarf Pug *Eupithecia tantillaria* 20mm Common. May–Jun. Not particularly small, despite the name. Strongly marked on forewing edge with large central spot and dark band on abdomen. Throughout Britain. **FP** Norway Spruce, Douglas Fir, etc. CMM

1858 V-Pug *Chloroclystis v-ata* 18mm Common. May–Jun, Jul–Aug. Stunning bright green with strong V mark is unmistakable. Throughout, including urban gardens. **FP** Flowers of assorted plants, including Hemp Agrimony, Dog Rose, Elder, Bramble, etc. CMM

1859 Sloe Pug *Pasiphila chloerata* 18mm Common. May–Jul. Mainly southern distribution in mature Blackthorn hedges. Only discovered in 1971. Orange-brown band on abdomen is distinctive. **FP** Blackthorn flowers. NS

1860 Green Pug *Pasiphila rectangulata* 20mm Common. Jun–Jul. Widespread throughout, in parks, gardens, hedges, woodland. Lighter green than V-Pug and without the V. **FP** Flowers of Crab Apple, Apple, Pear, Cherry, Blackthorn, Hawthorn. CMM

1861 Bilberry Pug *Pasiphila debiliata* 20mm Nb. Jun–Jul. Very local in south and west England and Wales on heaths and moors where foodplant grows. Very light green with dotted cross lines. **FP** Bilberry. PGC

1862 Double-striped Pug *Gymnoscelis rufifasciata* 18mm Common. Mar–May, Jul–Aug. Throughout the UK, with occasional autumn generation in south. In woods, parks, gardens, hedges, moors. **FP** Many flowers, including Holly, Ivy, Gorse, Broom, Traveller's Joy, Ragwort, heather, etc. CMM

1863 Dentated Pug *Anticollix sparsata* 24mm Na. Jun–Jul. Large Pug with distinctive toothed, indented hind-wing margin. Southern UK in damp woods, scrub, fens, etc. **FP** Yellow Loosestrife growing in shade. CMM

1847

1849

melanic 1854

melanic 1855a

GEOMETERS: GEOMETRIDAE, LARENTIINAE

1864 Streak *Chesias legatella* 35mm Common. Sep–Nov. Throughout Britain, on heaths, commons, downs, moors. **FP** Broom. CMM

1865 Broom-tip *Chesias rufata* 32mm Nb. Apr–Jul. Heaths, commons, downs, moors throughout Britain, but scarce. **FP** Broom. NS

1866 Manchester Treble-bar *Carsia sororiata anglica* 24mm Nb. Jul–Sep. Damp heathland, moorland and mosses. Local in northern England and Scotland. Easily disturbed by day. **FP** Bilberry, Cowberry, Cranberry. BH

1867 Treble Bar *Aplocera plagiata* 40mm Common. May–Jun, Aug–Sep. Common throughout Britain in many habitats, including downs, moors, heaths, brecks, sand dunes, sea cliffs, especially hot, dry areas. First (basal) angle has rounded angle at forewing edge. **FP** St John's Wort. CMM

1868 Lesser Treble-bar *Aplocera efformata* 36mm Common. May–Jun, Aug–Sep. Common in south in many habitats, including downs, moors, heaths, brecks, sand dunes, sea cliffs, especially hot, dry areas. First (basal) bar has sharp acute angle at forewing edge. Slightly smaller than above species. **FP** St John's Wort. DGG

1870 Chimney Sweeper *Odezia atrata* 28mm Common. Jun–Jul. Unmistakable. Flies in sunshine. On chalk and limestone downs, unimproved grassland and damp meadows. Local in southern UK, common further north. **FP** Flowers of Pignut. DF, CMM

1871 Grey Carpet *Lithostege griseata* 30mm RDB3. May–Jul. Breck districts of Norfolk and Suffolk. Foodplant requires recently disturbed ground. **FP** Seeds of Flixweed. NS

1872 Blomer's Rivulet *Discoloxia blomeri* 23mm Nb. May–Jul. Local in damp woods with Wych Elm in central, but not south-east, England and Wales. **FP** Wych Elm. SH

1873 Welsh Wave *Venusia cambrica* 30mm Local. Jun–Aug. Black cross lines with a pair of black spikes are distinctive. On moorland and open woodland in Devon, Wales, Midlands and Scotland. **FP** Rowan. DGG

1874 Dingy Shell *Euchoeca nebulata* 22mm Local. May–Aug. Small plain sandy brown moth, which rests with wings upright. Local in England and Wales, scarce in Scotland. In damp woods, river banks, etc. **FP** Alder. NS, CMM

1875 Small White Wave *Asthena albulata* 18mm Common. May–Jul. Pure white with faint wavy lines. Throughout Britain, in broadleaved woods, especially ancient. **FP** Hazel, Hornbeam, birch, Wild Rose. NS

1876 Small Yellow Wave *Hydrelia flammeolaria* 20mm Common. May–Jul. Can be frequent in woodland in south, though scarce in north and Scotland. **FP** Field Maple, Sycamore, Alder. CMM

1877 Waved Carpet *Hydrelia sylvata* 23mm Nb. Jun–Aug. Similar to Welsh Wave, but cross lines not black and without black spikes. Rests with wings more widely spread than Welsh Wave. In woods, scrub, heaths, sandstone hills in south-west England, Wales, Sussex. **FP** Alder, birch, sallows, Sweet Chestnut. DGG

1878 Drab Looper *Minoa murinata* 20mm Nb. May–Jun, Aug. Small, dull brown day-flyer in ancient woods in central southern Britain. **FP** Wood Spurge. RW, DGG

1879 Seraphim *Lobophora halterata* 25mm Local. May–Jun. Local in woodland in southern Britain and central Scotland. Variable but with broad, dark cross-band near base of forewing. **FP** Aspen, Black Poplar. NS, NS

1864   1865   1866   1867

GEOMETERS: GEOMETRIDAE, LARENTIINAE (cont.)

1880 Barred Tooth-striped *Trichopteryx polycommata* 30mm Na. Mar–Apr. Can be found by torchlight, resting on foodplant. On chalk downs in central southern England as well as Brecklands and northern England to Scotland. **FP** Wild Privet. SH

1881 Early Tooth-striped *Trichopteryx carpinata* 30mm Common. Apr–May. Plain pale sandy or grey moth, sometimes pale green. Common throughout in woodland. **FP** Honeysuckle, birch, sallows, Alder. NS, CMM

1882 Small Seraphim *Pterapherapteryx sexalata* 20mm Local. May–Jun, Jul–Aug. Local in southern Britain, scarce in north. In damp woods and fens. **FP** Sallows. DJP

1883 Yellow-barred Brindle *Acasis viretata* 26mm Local. May–Jun, Jul–Aug. Green when fresh, but can fade to yellow. Local in southern Britain, scarce in north. Found in broadleaved woods, hedges, gardens. **FP** Holly, Ivy, Wild Privet, Dogwood, Guelder Rose, Hawthorn. CMM, CMM

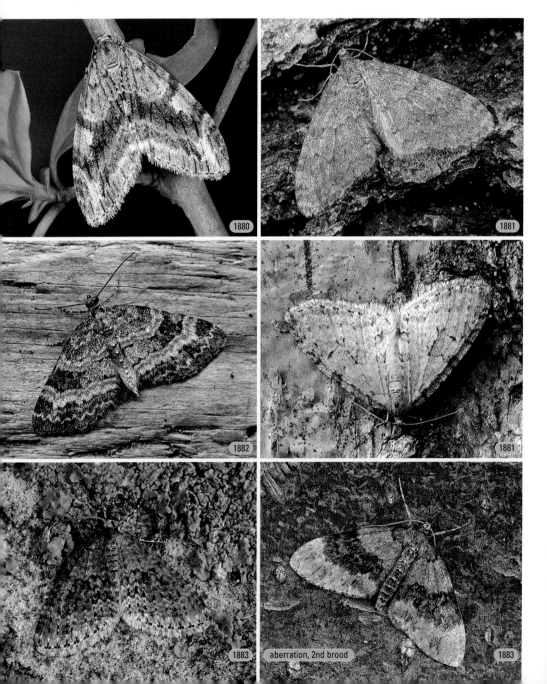

1880

1881

1882

1881

1883

aberration, 2nd brood 1883

GEOMETERS: GEOMETRIDAE, ENNOMINAE

1884 Magpie Moth *Abraxas grossulariata* 40mm
Common. Jun–Aug. Common throughout, including
abundant on heather in Outer Hebrides where it flies by
day. In woodland, gardens, parks, hedges. **FP** Heather in
north. Many small trees and shrubs elsewhere. DF
1885 Clouded Magpie *Abraxas sylvata* 40mm Local.
May–Jul. Local through southern Britain to Scottish
border counties, in woodland. **FP** Elms. CMM
1887 Clouded Border *Lomaspilis marginata* 27mm

Common. May–Jul, Aug. Variable but unmistakable. In
woods, commons, heaths, fens throughout. **FP** Aspen
and other poplars, sallows and other willows. NS, RW
1888 Scorched Carpet *Ligdia adustata* 25mm Local.
May–Jun, Aug. Mainly in southern UK in woods,
hedges, scrub, gardens. **FP** Spindle. CMM
1888a Dorset Cream Wave *Stegania trimaculata* 27mm
Vagrant/Accidental. Very rare migrant from Europe, first
seen in Dorset, 1978. **FP** Poplar. IK, RPJ

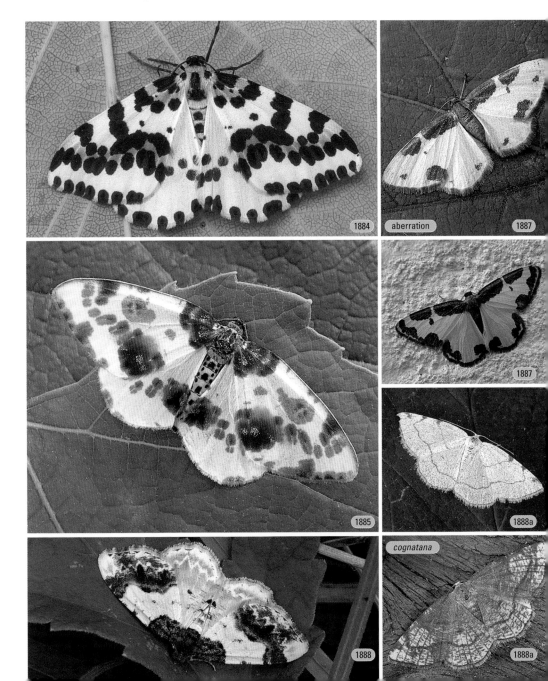

1884

aberration   1887

1887

1885

1888a

cognatana

1888

1888a

GEOMETERS: GEOMETRIDAE, ENNOMINAE (cont.)

1889 Peacock Moth *Macaria notata* 30mm Local. May–Jul, Jul–Aug. Local in open birch woods and heaths, mostly southern Britain, also central Scotland. Similar to Sharp-angled Peacock but more sandy coloured, larger central 'paw' mark, outer edge concavity dark-edged, not solid, and hind-wing edge lined rather than dotted. **FP** Birch. CMM

1890 Sharp-angled Peacock *Macaria alternata* 28mm Local. May–Jul, Aug. Frequent in south and south-west Britain, scarce elsewhere. Similar to Peacock Moth but slightly smaller, greyer, smaller 'paw print', solid dark outer concavity, dotted hind-wing border. **FP** Sallows and other willows, Blackthorn, Alder, Sea Buckthorn. CMM

1891 Dusky Peacock *Macaria signaria* 26mm Migrant. May–Jul. Scarce migrant from coniferous woods in Europe. **FP** Norway Spruce, Scots Pine, etc. CS

1893 Tawny-barred Angle *Macaria liturata* 33mm Common. May–Jun, Aug–Sep. Throughout Britain in pine woods. Unusual dark form retains yellow-orange bands. **FP** Scots Pine, Norway Spruce, etc. CMM, PAD

1894 Latticed Heath *Chiasmia clathrata* 26mm Common. May–Jun, Jul–Sep. Anywhere throughout the UK. Rests with wings up, like a butterfly. Very crisply marked, with dark veins. **FP** Lucerne, clover, trefoils. CMM, CMM

1895 Netted Mountain Moth *Macaria carbonaria* 21mm RDB3. Apr–Jun. Day-flying moth found only in central Scottish Highlands. **FP** Bearberry. DGG, SR

1896 Rannoch Looper *Itame brunneata* 24mm Na. Jun–Jul. Found in central Scotland in open pine and birch woodland. Similar to Dingy Shell but unlikely to be found in the same habitat. **FP** Bilberry. CMM

1897 V-Moth *Macaria wauaria* 30mm Local. Jul–Aug. Throughout, but scarce in gardens, orchards, allotments. **FP** Red and Black Currant, Gooseberry. CMM

1899 Frosted Yellow *Isturgia limbaria* 25mm Extinct. May–Jun, Jul–Aug. Extinct resident, not seen for a century. Formerly in south-east England and central Scotland. Orange upperwings with brown borders. **FP** Broom. NS

1901 Little Thorn *Cepphis advenaria* 28mm Nb. May–Jun. Usually rests with wings up as shown. Underside is same as upper. Scarce, in open woods, central southern England and Gloucestershire area. **FP** Bilberry, but also occurs where this is absent, so must have alternative foodplants. DGG

1902 Brown Silver-line *Petrophora chlorosata* 34mm Common. May–Jun. Common, sometimes abundant, in woods, heaths, commons, etc., wherever there is bracken. **FP** Bracken. CMM

1889   1890   1891   1893   *nigrofulvata* 1893

GEOMETERS: GEOMETRIDAE, ENNOMINAE (cont.)

1903 Barred Umber *Plagodis pulveraria* 35mm Local. May–Jun. In ancient broadleaved woodland, mainly in southern UK, scarce and scattered from Midlands north. **FP** Hazel, also birch, sallows, Hawthorn. CMM

1904 Scorched Wing *Plagodis dolabraria* 35mm Local. May–Jun. Unmistakable. Male's abdomen curls up at rest. Widespread but local, more common in south, in broadleaved woods, parks, scrub. **FP** Oaks, birch, sallows, Beech, Sweet Chestnut. CMM

1905 Horse Chestnut *Pachycnemia hippocastanaria* 30mm Nb. Apr–May, Aug. Can be abundant on southern lowland heaths and (at least in Dorset) in almost any month of the year. **FP** Heather, Cross-leaved Heath. CMM

1906 Brimstone Moth *Opisthograptis luteolata* 35mm Common. Apr–Oct. Unmistakable and common throughout in woods, hedges, gardens, scrub, heaths and downs. Three broods in south, one in north. **FP** Blackthorn, Hawthorn, Bullace, Rowan. CMM, CMM

1907 Bordered Beauty *Epione repandaria* 30mm Common. Jul–Sep. Widespread but local throughout the UK in damp woods, fens and marsh. **FP** Sallows, Grey Willow. CMM

1908 Dark Bordered Beauty *Epione vespertaria* 26mm RDB3. Jul–Aug. Extremely local in Aberdeenshire and Moray in Scotland, two colonies in Yorkshire and Northumberland in England. **FP** On low Aspens in Scotland, Creeping Willow in England. CMM, CMM

1909 Speckled Yellow *Pseudopanthera macularia* 28mm Common. May–Jun. Well distributed throughout, more frequent in southern UK. Flies in sun in open woodland. **FP** Wood Sage. CMM

1910 Lilac Beauty *Apeira syringaria* 38mm Local. Jun–Jul. Unmistakable, with lilac markings and curled (not flat) forewings. Widespread from northern England southwards. Woodland rides and clearings and wooded heaths. **FP** Honeysuckle, Wild Privet, ash. PGC

1911 Large Thorn *Ennomos autumnaria* 56mm Nb. Sep–Oct. Scarce, in south-east England only. Larger than other Thorns, wings held up. In woods. **FP** Various trees, including birch, oak, Sycamore, hazel, Hawthorn. NS

1912 August Thorn *Ennomos quercinaria* 38mm Local. Aug–Sep. Wings held nearly flat. Outer cross-line on forewing kinked near leading edge. In woods, gardens, parks and downs, mainly from Yorkshire southwards. **FP** Various trees, including birch, oak, Beech, Hawthorn. DF

1903 ♀   1904   1905   1906   1906

GEOMETERS: GEOMETRIDAE, ENNOMINAE (cont.)

1913 Canary-shouldered Thorn *Ennomos alniaria* 38mm
Common. Jul–Oct. Unmistakable yellow shoulders and
thorax. Common throughout Britain. **FP** Various trees,
including birch, sallows, Alder, lime. CMM
1914 Dusky Thorn *Ennomos fuscantaria* 44mm
Common. Jul–Oct. Common from Yorkshire southwards,
anywhere with ash trees. Dusky shading from outer cross-
line. **FP** Ash. AL, CMM
1915 September Thorn *Ennomos erosaria* 38mm
Common. Jul–Oct. Plainer and paler than August Thorn
and without central dot. Outer cross-line barely kinked.
Well distributed in woods, parks, gardens in southern
Britain, local in north. **FP** Oak, birch, lime, Beech. DF
1916 Clouded August Thorn *Ennomos quercaria* 38mm
Vagrant/Accidental. Two records, 19th century and
1992. From southern Europe. Similar to a very pale
September Thorn. DGG
1917 Early Thorn *Selenia dentaria* 43mm Common.
Feb–May, Aug–Sep. Wings upright and pressed together
is unique among Thorns. Common throughout in
woods, parks, gardens, hedges. **FP** Broadleaved woody
trees and shrubs. CMM
1918 Lunar Thorn *Selenia lunularia* 40mm Local.

May–Jun, Jul–Aug. Similar resting posture to Purple
Thorn with slightly curled wings forming a bowl shape.
Deep moon-shaped scallops on outer edge of hind wing
and no black dot on upper side of hind wing beyond silver
crescent. In open woods throughout but never common.
FP Oak, Ash, birch, Elm, Dog Rose, etc. CMM, SR
1919 Purple Thorn *Selenia tetralunaria* 44mm (spring)
37mm (summer) Common. Apr–May, Jul–Aug. Similar
posture to above, but has dark spot in centre of less-
scalloped hind wing, outer forewing cross-line bowed in.
Common in England and Wales, more local north of
Yorkshire. In woods, scrub, heaths, gardens. **FP** Hazel,
birch, oak, Hawthorn, etc. CMM, NS
1920 Scalloped Hazel *Odontopera bidentata* 44mm
Common. May–Jun. Similar to Scalloped Oak, but has
deeply-scalloped wing margins. Central dot is dark-
edged, not solid. Common throughout in woods, parks,
gardens, heath, etc. **FP** Woody plants and trees,
broadleaved and pines. CMM
1921 Scalloped Oak *Crocallis elinguaria* 38mm
Common. Jul–Aug. Common throughout, in woods,
hedges, parks, gardens, etc. **FP** Woody plants and trees,
broadleaved only. DF, DF

1916

1917 ♂

1918

spring brood 1919

1918

summer brood

1919

1921

aberration 1921

1920

GEOMETERS: GEOMETRIDAE, ENNOMINAE (cont.)

1922 Swallow-tailed Moth *Ourapteryx sambucaria*
54mm Common. Jun–Aug. Unmistakable,
common throughout, almost anywhere. **FP** Various
trees and shrubs, especially Ivy. CMM

1923 Feathered Thorn *Colotois pennaria* 43mm
Common. Sep–Dec. Common in autumn,
throughout, in woodland. Variable markings but
always with two cross-lines and slightly hooked
wingtip. Often with small silvery spot near
wingtip. Male has feathered antennae. **FP**
Broadleaved trees. CMM, NS, CMM, CMM

1924 Orange Moth *Angerona prunaria* 50mm Local.
Jun–Jul. Local, mainly in south-west and south-east.
Two forms are equally distributed. In woodland, old
hedges and wooded heaths. **FP** Woody plants and
shrubs, including heather, Traveller's Joy, Broom,
Blackthorn. TJN, NS

1925 Small Brindled Beauty *Apocheima hispidaria*
34mm Local. Feb–Mar. Found in old oak woods,
mainly from Dorset to Kent. Female is wingless.
Male has very hairy thorax. **FP** Oaks and some
other trees. CMM, NS

1926 Pale Brindled Beauty *Apocheima pilosaria*
42mm Common. Jan–Mar. Throughout Britain in
woods, parks, gardens. Female is wingless. Melanic
form *monachana* in London and Midlands. **FP**
Various trees and shrubs. CMM, NS

1922

♂ 1923

♀ 1923

♂ 1923

♂ 1923

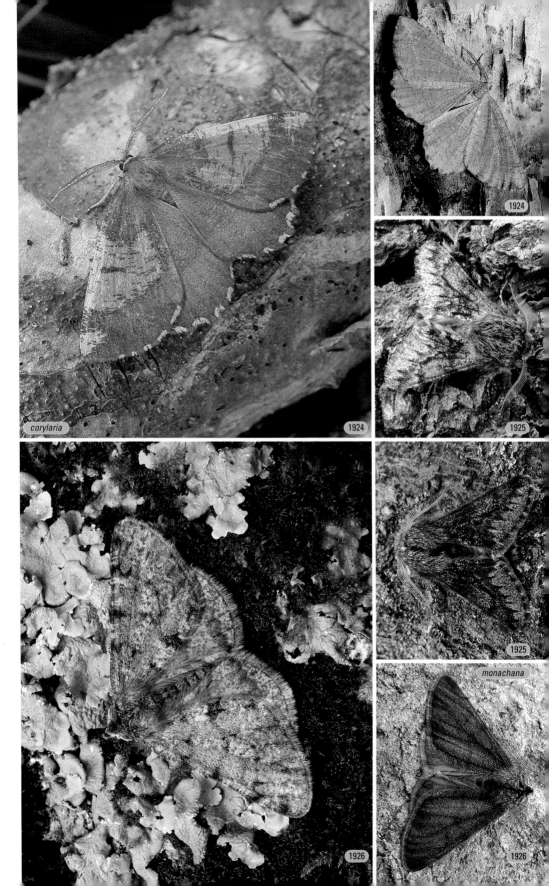

corylaria 1924

1924

1925

1925

monachana

1926

1926

GEOMETERS: GEOMETRIDAE, ENNOMINAE (cont.)

1927 Brindled Beauty *Lycia hirtaria* 45mm Common. Mar–May. Common in south and east England, local elsewhere. Female has wings. Melanic form found in London area. In woods, parks, gardens, including urban areas. **FP** Deciduous trees and shrubs. DGG, CMM

1928 Belted Beauty *Lycia zonaria* 28mm (♂), 9mm (♀) Na. Mar–Apr. Very local on coastal sand dunes in north Wales, north-west England, west Scotland and on machair in Hebrides. Both sexes found sitting on low herbage day or night. Both with brown-orange bars on abdomen. **FP** Bird's-foot Trefoil, plantain, clover, Creeping Willow, Burnet Rose. KT

1929 Rannoch Brindled Beauty *Lycia lapponaria scotica* 32mm (♂), 9mm (♀) Na. Mar–Apr. Somewhat similar to above, but different habitat. Both sexes have orange spots down back of abdomen. Moors and heaths of central Scottish Highlands. **FP** Bog Myrtle, heathers, Eared Willow. DGG, DGG

1930 Oak Beauty *Biston strataria* 50mm Common. Mar–Apr. Common in southern UK, scarce in Scotland. Prefers mature oak woodland. **FP** Oak, elm, hazel, Aspen, Alder. CMM, NS, RW

1931 Peppered Moth *Biston betularia* 50mm (♂), 60mm (♀) Common. May–Aug. Usual rural form is white peppered with black, but two other forms more common in urban areas. Throughout UK in woods, scrub, parks, gardens, urban areas. **FP** Assorted bushes, trees, plants. CMM, RW, CMM

1927

highland form

1927

♀

♂

1928

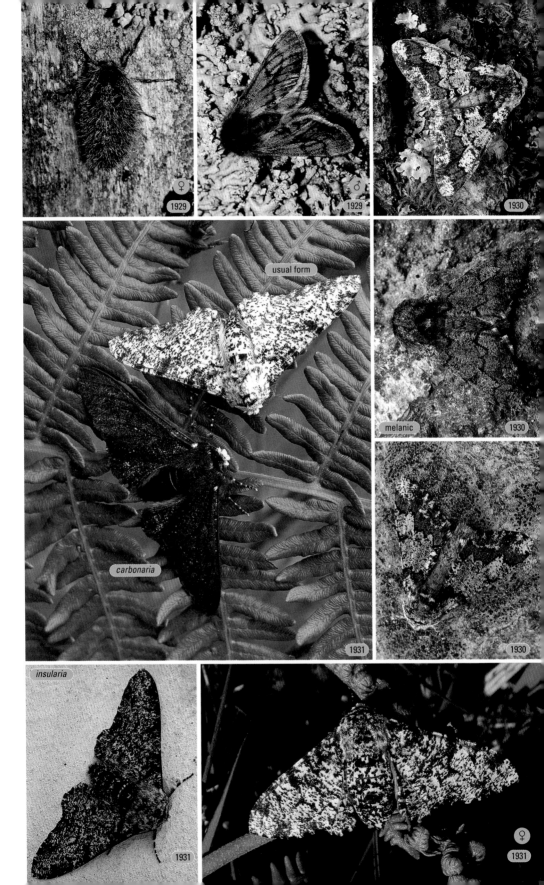

1929

1929

1930

usual form

melanic 1930

1931

1930

carbonaria

insularia

1931

1931

GEOMETERS: GEOMETRIDAE, ENNOMINAE (cont.)

1932 Spring Usher *Agriopis leucophaearia* 30mm
Common. Feb–Mar. Very variable forms. Smaller than
other similar moths. Can be abundant in mature oak
woods in England and Wales, only local in Scotland.
FP Oaks. NS, CMM, CMM

1933 Scarce Umber *Agriopis aurantiaria* 36mm
Common. Oct–Nov. Male is warm orange-yellow,
female wingless. No central spot between cross-lines.
Similar to Dotted Border, which flies in Spring.
Throughout, in open woods, scrub, parks, gardens.
FP Many trees and shrubs. NS, CMM

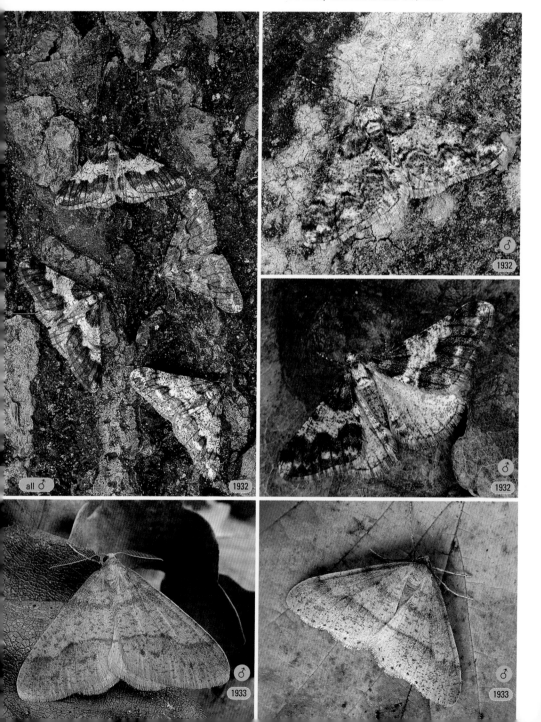

all ♂　　1932

♂　1932

♂　1932

♂　1933

♂　1933

1934 Dotted Border *Agriopis marginaria* 38mm
Common. Feb–Apr. Male is brown with conspicuous
black-dotted wing borders. Female flightless but with
vestigial wings. Throughout the UK in woods, scrub,
parks, gardens, heaths, moorland. **FP** Many trees and
shrubs. NS

1935 Mottled Umber *Erannis defoliaria* 45mm (♂), 12mm
(♀) Common. Oct–Jan. Male very variable, but with
dark, outer, many-angled cross-line and central black spot.
Female is flightless. Most frequent in woods but found
anywhere throughout Britain. **FP** Many trees and shrubs.
CMM, CMM, JV

1936 Waved Umber *Menophra abruptaria* 40mm
Common. Apr–Jun. Well spread in south and east
England, scarce elsewhere. Melanistic form usually in
London area. Inhabits woodland, scrub, urban parks and
gardens. **FP** Garden Privet, Lilac, Winter Jasmine in
gardens; rural foodplants not known. CMM, NS

1937 Willow Beauty *Peribatodes rhomboidaria* 40mm
Common. Jun–Aug, Aug–Oct. Deciduous and coniferous
woods, hedges, parks, gardens, including urban,
throughout Britain. Outer pair of cross-lines converge at
trailing edge, outer line has dot on each vein. Greyer
form in industrial areas, occasionally melanic examples.
FP Various trees, also Ivy, Traveller's Joy. CMM

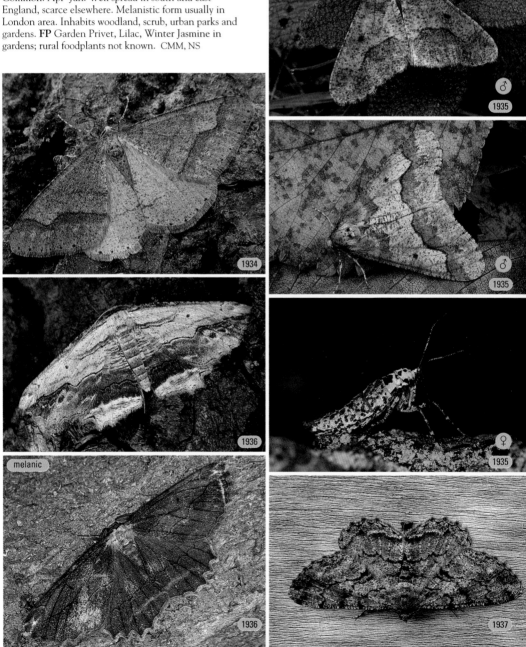

GEOMETERS: GEOMETRIDAE, ENNOMINAE (cont.)

1937a Feathered Beauty *Peribatodes secundaria* 40mm Local (alien foodplant). Jul–Aug. Very similar to Willow Beauty but without white apical spots on undersides of wings. Coniferous woodland, from 1981, in south-east England. **FP** Norway Spruce. NS

1937b Lydd Beauty *Peribatodes ilicaria* 40mm Vagrant/Accidental. Jul–Sep. First recorded 1990. Similar but richer markings than Willow and Feathered Beauty, with more-strongly curved cross-line on hind wing. **FP** Various trees and shrubs in Europe. NS

1937c Olive-tree Beauty *Peribatodes umbraria* 40mm Vagrant/Accidental. Oct. First recorded on Jersey, Channel Isles, in 2006. **FP** Olive, oaks. DGG

1938 Bordered Grey *Selidosema brunnearia* 40mm Na. Jul–Aug. On heaths of central southern England, chalk downs in Dorset (as well as heaths), sand dunes in Hampshire, mosses of Westmorland and Shropshire, Scotland and Hebrides. **FP** Mostly heather, also Bird's-foot Trefoil. CMM

1939 Ringed Carpet *Cleora cinctaria* 39mm Na. Apr–May. White oval mark ringed with black in centre of forewing is diagnostic. Central southern England on

lightly-wooded damp heaths. Also Scottish form on moorland. **FP** Birch, Bilberry, Bell and Cross-leaved Heathers. Bog Myrtle in Scotland. DF, SH

1940 Satin Beauty *Deileptenia ribeata* 42mm Common. Jun–Aug. Can be similar to Willow and Mottled Beauty, but hind-wing margins not scalloped. In woods and downs with conifers, especially Yew. **FP** Yew, Scots Pine, other conifers. MC, CMM

1941 Mottled Beauty *Alcis repandata* 45mm Common. Jun–Aug. Extremely variable, but dark outer cross-line on forewing and scalloped hind-wing edge are constant. Throughout Britain, almost anywhere. **FP** Many trees and plants. CMM, CMM, NS, CMM

1942 Dotted Carpet *Alcis jubata* 27mm Local. Jul–Aug. South-west England, west Wales, west Scotland in ancient oak woods. **FP** Beard Lichen. MSP

1943 Great Oak Beauty *Hypomecis roboraria* 60mm Nb. Jun–Jul. Found sparingly in large mature oak woods in central southern England. Much larger than Pale Oak Beauty, with significant dark patch where cross-lines converge on trailing edge. Underside has dark and then pale patch at apex. **FP** Pedunculate Oak. CMM, CMM

1937a 1937b 1937c 1938 ♀ 1939 1939

1940 ♂

1940

1941 ♂

1941 ♀

1941 ♀

1941 ♂

1942

1943 ♂

underside

1943 ♂

GEOMETERS: GEOMETRIDAE, ENNOMINAE (cont.)

1944 Pale Oak Beauty *Hypomecis punctinalis* 45mm Common. May–Jul. Smaller than Great Oak Beauty, without dark patch on trailing edge, and has pale spot in centre of hind wing. The two moths shown both came to the same trap in Dorset on the same evening, so illustrated the differences beautifully! Mainly south and east England. **FP** Mainly Pedunculate Oak, also birch, Hawthorn, sallows. CMM, CMM

1945 Brussels Lace *Cleorodes lichenaria* 30mm Local. Jun–Aug. Common from Dorset westwards, west Wales, west Scotland. **FP** On lichens. CMM, CMM

1946 Speckled Beauty *Fagivorina arenaria* 35mm Extinct. Jul–Aug. Formerly in Sussex and Hampshire, but not seen since 1898. **FP** Lichens on oak, Beech. CMM

1947 Engrailed *Ectropis bistortata* 40mm (2nd brood 32mm) Common. Mar–May, Jun–Oct. Throughout in woods, parks, gardens. Up to three generations. **FP** Various trees and shrubs, including Hawthorn, Spindle, birch, oak, sallows. CMM, CMM

1948 Small Engrailed *Ectropis crepuscularia* 40mm Local. May–Jun. Only one generation, but may not be a separate species to above. Very similar indeed, and similar habitats. **FP** Birch, sallows, Beech. DF

1949 Square Spot *Paradarisa consonaria* 40mm Local. Apr–Jun. Square, dark mark beyond centre of outer cross-line is diagnostic. In woodland. **FP** Oak, birch, Beech, Yew, Hornbeam, pines. DGG, CMM

1950 Brindled White-spot *Parectropis similaria* 37mm Local. May–Jun. Squarish white patch near outer edge of forewing is diagnostic. In ancient woods in southern Britain. **FP** Oaks, Hawthorn, hazel, birch. CMM

1951 Grey Birch *Aethalura punctulata* 30mm Common. May–Jun. Dull-looking, with four dark, forewing-edge marks. In birch woods and scrub. **FP** Birches, sometimes Alder. CMM

1952 Common Heath *Ematurga atomaria* 30mm (♂), 26mm (♀) Common. May–Jun, Aug. Similar to Latticed Heath, but markings less sharp, and wings held flat. On heaths and meadows throughout, flies by day. **FP** Heathers on heaths and moorland, clovers and trefoils on downland. DF, RW, CMM

1954 Bordered White *Bupalus piniaria* 36mm (♂), 32mm (♀) Common. May–Jun. Throughout Britain, though flight period may be later in north. In mature pine woodland. **FP** Scots Pine, other conifers. PGC, DGG

underside | 1944 | ♀ 1944

1945 | 1945 | 1946

melanic, 2nd brood 1947

1947

1948

1949

1949

1950

1951

♀ 1952

♂ 1952

♂ 1952

♂ 1954

♀ 1954

GEOMETERS: GEOMETRIDAE, ENNOMINAE (cont.)

1955 Common White Wave *Cabera pusaria* 30mm Common. May–Jun, Jul–Aug. In woods and scrub throughout. Bright white, with straight cross-lines. **FP** Birch, Alder, sallows. CMM

1956 Common Wave *Cabera exanthemata* 30mm Common. May–Jul, Jul–Sep. In damp woods throughout Britain. Light sandy colour with curved cross-lines. **FP** Sallows, Aspen and other poplars. CMM

1957 White-pinion Spotted *Lomographa bimaculata* 28mm Common. May–Jul. Widespread in woodland and scrub, mainly in southern Britain. **FP** Hawthorn, Blackthorn. CMM

1958 Clouded Silver *Lomographa temerata* 28mm Common. May–Jul. In woods and hedgerows throughout Britain, but scarce in Scotland. **FP** Hawthorn, Blackthorn, Plum, Wild Cherry, Apple, Aspen. DGG

1959 Sloe Carpet *Aleucis distinctata* 28mm Nb. Mar–Apr. Similar to Early Moth, which flies a month earlier, but slightly smaller and outer cross-line much more angulated. Local in Blackthorn hedges in south-east England. **FP** Blackthorn. RPJ

1960 Early Moth *Theria primaria* 30mm (♂), 7mm (♀) Common. Jan–Feb. Males found after dark sitting on bare twigs of foodplant with flightless females. Throughout, but local in Scotland, in woods, hedges, scrub. **FP** Hawthorn, Blackthorn. CMM, KT

1961 Light Emerald *Campaea margaritata* 40mm Common. May–Sep. Throughout Britain, in woods, parks, gardens, including urban. Distinctive near-straight cross-lines and red mark at wingtip. **FP** Oak, birch, Beech, Hawthorn, elm, etc. CMM

1962 Barred Red *Hylaea fasciaria* 38mm Common. Jun–Aug. Throughout Britain, in pine woods. Green form *prasinaria* is scarce. **FP** Scots Pine, Norway Spruce, etc. NS, CMM

1963 Scotch Annulet *Gnophos obfuscata* 38mm Nb. Jul–Aug. Much larger than Annulet, with concave forewing edge. Only in north and central Scotland on moors and mountains. **FP** Yellow Saxifrage, Stone Crop, heather. DGG

1964 Annulet *Charissa obscurata* 30mm Local. Jul–Aug. Very variable. Pale forms on limestone, dark forms on heaths. Usually dark-edged central spot on each wing. Local on rocky coasts and inland heaths throughout Britain. **FP** Sea Campion, Thrift, Common Rock-rose, Bird's-foot Trefoil, vetch, etc. CMM, BU

1965 Black Mountain Moth *Glacies coracina* 25mm (♂), 22mm (♀) Na. Jun–Jul. High moors and mountains above 600m. Flies in sunshine in central Highlands of Scotland. **FP** Crowberry. SH, RL

1966 Black-veined Moth *Siona lineata* 40mm RDB1. May–Jul. Found only in Kent in herb-rich chalk grassland. **FP** Knapweed, Common Bird's-foot Trefoil. MSP, SR, DGG

1955 1956 1957 1958 1959

♂ 1960

♀ 1960

♂ 1961

1962

prasinaria 1962

1963 ♂

on limestone 1964

1965 ♂

on heathland 1964

1965 ♀

1966

1966

1966

GEOMETERS: GEOMETRIDAE, ENNOMINAE (cont.)

1967 Straw Belle *Aspitates gilvaria* 30mm RDB3. Jun–Sep. Could be confused with Vestal, but has freckled wings. Kent and Surrey only, on chalk grassland. **FP** Common Bird's-foot Trefoil, Fairy Flax. DGG, MSP

1968 Yellow Belle *Semiaspilates ochrearia* 30mm Local. May–Jun, Aug–Sep. Southern coastal counties from Wales round to Lincolnshire, and Brecks of Suffolk/Norfolk. **FP** Sea Wormwood, Wild Carrot, Buck's-horn Plantain, Restharrow, Beaked Hawk's-beard, etc. CMM, PAD

1969 Grey Scalloped Bar *Dyscia fagaria* 40mm (♂), 30mm (♀) Local. May–Aug. On heaths of central southern England, moorland in north Wales, northern England and Scotland. **FP** Heather, Heath, Cross-leaved Heath. DGG, DF

1970 Grass Wave *Perconia strigillaria* 36mm Local. May–Jul. Can be frequent on heaths of central southern England. Scarce in Devon and Cornwall and scattered sites in remainder of Britain. **FP** Heather, Bell-heather, Broom, Gorse flowers, Petty Whin. PGC, CMM

HAWK MOTHS: SPHINGIDAE

The English name reflects the size and powerful flight of these moths. There are 17 hawk-moths on the British list, though over 1,000 worldwide, mainly tropical. Nine species are resident and eight are migrants. Some of these strong flyers migrate to Britain from as far as North Africa and the Canary Islands.

Several of the largest and brightest, such as Privet and Elephant Hawk-moth, are also common and widespread and wonderful ambassadors for moth-watching. In addition to being big and bright they are often docile and can be persuaded to rest on a child's hand, always popular in schools.

The two Bee Hawk-moths and the Hummingbird Hawk-moth fly in daylight and visit flowers for nectar. The Hummingbird Hawk is a migrant that in some years can be common and breed. It is often seen hovering in front of Buddleia bushes and other sources of nectar in gardens or at hanging flower baskets in town centres.

The remainder of the species fly at night and may also visit flowers as well as coming to light. Convolvulus Hawks have a particular fondness for tobacco flowers. The caterpillars are solitary and usually have stripes or spots and a spike like a tail at their rear end. Hawk-moths generally overwinter as pupae in the ground below the foodplant.

1972 Convolvulus Hawk-moth *Agrius convolvuli*
110mm Migrant. Aug–Nov. Very large, regular migrant from southern Europe, Africa. Often seen in gardens nectaring on tobacco plants at dusk. **FP** Bindweed. CMM, DGG

1973 Death's-head Hawk-moth *Acherontia atropos*
120mm Migrant. Aug–Nov. Very large migrant from southern Europe, Africa, Middle East. Can squeak if handled. Named after the skull-like marking on thorax. **FP** Potato family. CMM, TD

HAWK MOTHS: SPHINGIDAE (cont.)

1976 Privet Hawk-moth *Sphinx ligustri* 110mm Common. Jun–Jul. Frequent, mainly in southern UK in woods, hedges, scrub, downs, gardens. **FP** Privet, Lilac, ash, Guelder-rose. CMM, CMM

1978 Pine Hawk-moth *Hyloicus pinastri* 80mm Local. May–Aug. Mainly in south and east England in conifer woods and wooded heathland. **FP** Scots Pine and others. DF

1979 Lime Hawk-moth *Mimas tiliae* 60mm (♂), 70mm (♀) Common. May–Jul. Mainly found from Yorkshire southwards in lowland woods, parks, urban gardens.

FP Limes, also elm, birch, Alder. NS

1980 Eyed Hawk-moth *Smerinthus ocellata* 80mm Common. May–Jul. Widely distributed in England and Wales in woods, parks, gardens, beside rivers. Exposes eye-spots on hind wings when disturbed. **FP** Willows, including sallows, Apples. CMM

1981 Poplar Hawk-moth *Laothoe populi* 80mm (♂), 90mm (♀) Common. May–Jul. Common throughout Britain. Hind wing projects well beyond front of forewing at rest. Buff form is scarce. **FP** Aspen and other poplars, sallows and other willows. RW, CMM, CMM, CMM

1976

1976

1978

♀, asymmetrical wing markings 1979

1980

♀ 1981

♂ 1981

buff form

♀ 1981

♂ 1981

HAWK MOTHS: SPHINGIDAE (cont.)

1982 Narrow-bordered Bee Hawk *Hemaris tityus* 44mm Nb. May–Jun. Throughout Britain but always scarce and local. Flies by day, visiting flowers in woods, heaths, downland. Hind wing has narrow dark border. **FP** Devil's-bit Scabious, Small and Field Scabious. DF, CMM
1983 Broad-bordered Bee Hawk *Hemaris fuciformis* 42mm Nb. May–Jul. Found locally from Yorkshire southwards. Flies by day, visiting flowers of Honeysuckle, Rhododendron, etc., in woodland rides. Hind wing has broad dark border. **FP** Wild Honeysuckle. Young larvae eat distinctive rows of holes either side of central vein of leaves. DF, KDR
1984 Hummingbird Hawk-moth *Macroglossum*

stellatarum 50mm Migrant. Apr–Nov. Regular migrant that can breed here in hot summers. Adult can hibernate over winter. Regular visitor to garden Buddleia flowers, etc., hovering to feed, looking and sounding like a humming-bird. **FP** Lady's and Hedge Bedstraw. DGG, CMM, CMM, CMM
1984a Willowherb Hawk-moth *Proserpinus proserpina* 50mm Vagrant/Accidental. May–Jul. Only two UK sightings, in 1985 and 1995. From southern Europe, North Africa. **FP** Willowherbs. CS
1985 Oleander Hawk-moth *Daphnis nerii* 110mm Migrant. Aug–Oct. Rare, from southern Europe, North Africa. **FP** Oleander, Lesser Periwinkle. KT, KT

1982

1983

1982

1983

1984

1984

1984

1984

1984a

♂ 1985

♀ 1985

♂ 1985

HAWK MOTHS: SPHINGIDAE (cont.)

1986 Spurge Hawk-moth *Hyles euphorbiae* 70mm
Migrant. May–Oct. Rare, from central and southern
Europe. **FP** Spurges. NS, CMM
1987 Bedstraw Hawk-moth *Hyles galii* 70mm Migrant.
May–Aug. Scarce but regular visitor from southern and
eastern Europe. **FP** Bedstraws, Rosebay Willowherb,
madders. DGG
1990 Striped Hawk-moth *Hyles livornica* 80mm
Migrant. Apr–Oct. Breeding migrant, usually in south.
Thorax has four white stripes. **FP** Rosebay Willowherb,
Hedge Bedstraw. CMM, CMM

1991 Elephant Hawk-moth *Deilephila elpenor* 65mm
Common. May–Aug. Throughout Britain, almost
anywhere. **FP** Willowherbs, bedstraws. KDR, GF
1992 Small Elephant Hawk-moth *Deilephila porcellus*
44mm Local. May–Jul. Widely distributed but local.
Can be abundant on limestone grassland in south, also
on heaths, chalk downs, beaches. **FP** Bedstraws. DF,
CMM, PGC
1993 Silver-striped Hawk-moth *Hippotion celerio* 75mm
Migrant. May–Oct. Scarce visitor from North Africa.
FP Grape Vine, Virginia Creeper. CMM

1986   1986
1987   1990   1990

1991

1991

1992

1992

1992

1993

PROMINENTS AND KITTENS: NOTODONTIDAE

There are 27 species of these moths on the British list, of which 21 are resident, though there are around 2,500 worldwide. The wings of prominents are usually held tight to the body and have clusters of hairs on the trailing edges of the hind wings, which show as projecting tufts when seen from the side, hence the name. The Pebble Prominent has one tuft, though some species have three.

The moths cannot feed so will not come to flowers or sugar, but the males, and occasionally females, will come to light. Larvae feed on trees and shrubs and are often strikingly marked. They raise both head and tail-end together if disturbed. The kittens have anal claspers modified into a pair of tails, and the Puss Moth can extend red filaments from these when threatened. The Lobster Moth larva supposedly resembles its namesake (*see* illustrations in the Caterpillars section, p.300). Pupation is usually underground over the winter near the foodplant or in a tough cocoon on the bark of trees.

1994 Buff-tip *Phalera bucephala* 50mm Common. May–Jul. Unmistakable, markings mimic a broken twig. Throughout Britain in woods, parks, hedges, gardens. Female much larger than male. **FP** Sallows, birch, hazel, oak, etc. NS
1995 Puss Moth *Cerura vinula* 70mm Common. May–Jul. Large, unmistakable, throughout Britain, in woods, hedges, gardens, heaths, moors. **FP** Poplars, including Aspen, sallows. CMM
1996 Alder Kitten *Furcula bicuspis* 35mm Local. May–Jul. Scattered in woodland in southern Britain. Central band and cross-lines much darker than Sallow and Poplar Kitten. **FP** Alder, birch. DGG
1997 Sallow Kitten *Furcula furcula* 35mm Common. May–Jun, Jul–Aug. Throughout Britain, more common in south. Similar size to Alder Kitten, but markings much paler. Outer edge of central band indented. **FP** Willows, poplars, including Aspen. CMM
1998 Poplar Kitten *Furcula bifida* 45mm Local. May–Jul.

Mainly southern England and Wales, in poplar woods. Similar to Sallow Kitten but larger, outer edge of central band smooth. **FP** Poplars, including Aspen, willows. NS
1999 Lobster Moth *Stauropus fagi* 60mm Common. May–Jul. Common in mature woodland in southern Britain. Similar to Great Prominent but looks yellow-brown, not greenish. Occasional dark melanic form. **FP** Oak, hazel, birch, Beech. Larva looks a bit like a lobster. CMM
2000 Iron Prominent *Notodonta dromedarius* 43mm Common. May–Jun, Jul–Aug. Throughout Britain, in woods, heaths, gardens. **FP** Birch, Alder, hazel, oak. NS
2001 Large Dark Prominent *Notodonta torva* 50mm Vagrant/Accidental. Very scarce migrant from central Europe. Two records only, 1882, 1979. **FP** Poplars, including Aspen. DM
2002 Three-humped Prominent *Notodonta tritophus* 50mm Rare migrant. Apr–Aug. Similar to above, appears from Europe about once every 10 years. **FP** Poplars, including Aspen. MSP

1994

1996

1995

PROMINENTS AND KITTENS: NOTODONTIDAE (cont.)

2003 Pebble Prominent *Notodonta ziczac* 43mm
Common. May–Jun, Jul–Aug. Throughout Britain, in
woods, hedges, gardens, etc. **FP** Aspen, other poplars,
sallows and other willows. TJN, DGG, NS

2004 Tawny Prominent *Harpyia milhauseri* 50mm
Vagrant/Accidental. May–Jun. Two records in Britain,
1966 and 1993. Woodland in central Europe. **FP** Oaks,
including evergreens. CMM

2005 Great Prominent *Peridea anceps* 60mm Local.
Apr–Jun. Can be frequent where mature oaks occur in
southern half of Britain. Somewhat similar to Lobster
Moth but looks khaki coloured. **FP** Oaks. CMM, CMM

2003

2003

aberration   2003

2004

2005

2005

2006 Lesser Swallow Prominent *Pheosia gnoma* 44mm
Common. Apr–Jun, Aug. Throughout Britain. Similar
to Swallow Prominent but white wedge in corner of
forewing is shorter, broader and whiter. **FP** Birches.
CMM

2007 Swallow Prominent *Pheosia tremula* 50mm
Common. Apr–Jun, Aug. Throughout Britain. Similar
to Lesser Swallow Prominent, but generally larger and
slimmer. White wedge in corner of forewing is longer,
slimmer, duller. **FP** Aspen, other poplars, willows,
including sallows. CMM

2008 Coxcomb Prominent *Ptilodon capucina* 40mm
Common. Apr–Jun, Aug–Sep. Throughout Britain.
FP Many broadleaved trees. CMM

2009 Maple Prominent *Ptilodontella cucullina* 40mm
Local. May–Jul. Scattered in southern England and
Wales, on calcareous soils where foodplant grows.
FP Field Maple. CMM

2010 Scarce Prominent *Odontosia carmelita* 40mm
Local. Apr–May. In mature birch woods but local
throughout. White mark on forewing is diagnostic.
FP Silver and Downy Birch. CMM

PROMINENTS AND KITTENS: NOTODONTIDAE (cont.)

2011 Pale Prominent *Pterostoma palpina* 43mm
Common. May–Jun, Jul–Aug. Common from Yorkshire
southwards, scarcer in north. Resembles piece of dry,
rotten wood. **FP** Aspen, other poplars, willow. CMM

2012 White Prominent *Leucodonta bicoloria* 35mm
Extinct. Jun. Not seen for over a century, scarce even
then. **FP** Birch. GF

2013 Plumed Prominent *Ptilophora plumigera* 38mm Na.
Nov–Dec. Huge feathery antennae of males and flight
period make this unmistakable. In mature maple woods
on calcareous soils in south and south-east England.
FP Field Maple. CMM, CMM

2014 Marbled Brown *Drymonia dodonaea* 38mm
Common. May–Jun. Throughout Britain in mature oak
woods. Similar to Lunar Marbled Brown but without
black crescent on forewing. **FP** Oaks. CMM

2015 Lunar Marbled Brown *Drymonia ruficornis* 36mm
Local. Apr–May. Common in central and southern
England, scarcer northwards. In oak woods and hedges.
Black 'lunar' crescent on forewing. **FP** Oaks. CMM

2016 Dusky Marbled Brown *Gluphisia crenata vertunea*
32mm Vagrant/Accidental. Apr, Jun–Jul. Only three
records, last in 1853. From central and southern Europe.
FP Poplars. MSP

2017 Small Chocolate-tip *Clostera pigra* 25mm Nb. May,
Aug. Scarce throughout, on open, damp heaths, moors,
dunes. **FP** Creeping and Eared Willow, low Aspen. JSB

2018 Scarce Chocolate-tip *Clostera anachoreta* 33mm
RDB1. Apr–May, Aug–Sep. Resident only at Dungeness,
Kent, otherwise migrant. Similar to Chocolate-tip but
dark blotch is both sides of outer white cross-line; two
dark spots in trailing corner. **FP** Coastal shingle with
Grey Willow scrub. CS

2019 Chocolate-tip *Clostera curtula* 32mm Local.
Apr–May, Aug–Sep. Locally frequent in southern England,
fairly scarce elsewhere. In woods, hedges, gardens. **FP**
Aspen, other poplars, sallows, other willows. CMM, CMM

2020 Figure of Eight *Diloba caeruleocephala* 38mm
Common. Oct–Nov. Throughout Britain. Similar to
Figure of 80, which flies in spring. In gardens, hedges,
woods, scrub. **FP** Blackthorn, Hawthorn, Crab Apple,
Wild Rose, Bullace, etc. CMM

2011

2013 ♂

2012

2013 ♂

PROCESSIONARIES: THAUMETOPOEIDAE

There are just two processionary moths on the British list, both rare migrants that are abundant in mainland Europe. The larvae live in communal webs, emerging at night in procession to feed, causing considerable damage to forests.

2021 Pine Processionary *Thaumetopoea pityocampa* 35mm Vagrant/Accidental. May–Jul. Very rare migrant from European pine forests. Similar to Oak Processionary and Pale Eggar, which does not have central crescent mark. **FP** Pines. DE

2022 Oak Processionary *Thaumetopoea processionea* 33mm Vagrant/Accidental. Jul–Sep. Rare migrant from central and southern Europe. In oak woodlands. **FP** Oaks. MC

TUSSOCKS: LYMANTRIIDAE

Although a large family of around 2,700 species worldwide, there are only 11 tussock moths on the British list, two of which are extinct former residents. The name relates to the tufts of hair on the backs of the larvae, which can irritate. Larvae of the Brown-tail can reach pest status, as they live communally and shed hairs into the wind causing severe skin rashes. Adults do not feed, but will come to light except for the two Vapourer females, which are flightless. The larvae live on shrubs or reeds, spinning a silk cocoon to pupate on the foodplant.

2024 Reed Tussock *Laelia coenosa* 50mm Extinct. Jul–Aug. Last seen in Wicken Fen, Cambridge in 1879. Habitats destroyed. **FP** Common Reed, Great Fen-sedge, Branched Bur-reed. DM, DM

2025 Scarce Vapourer *Orgyia recens* 32mm (♂), 16mm (♀) RDB2. Jun–Jul. Scarce, in Yorkshire, Lincolnshire and Norfolk only. Similar to Vapourer but chocolate brown with white marks at wingtip. Female is wingless. In bogs, heath, woods, hedgerows. **FP** Deciduous trees and shrubs, Meadowsweet, Water Dock, heather, sorrel. DGG, DGG

2026 Vapourer *Orgyia antiqua* 28mm (♂), 12mm (♀) Common. Jul–Oct. Throughout Britain, in woods, gardens, parks, heathland, scrub. **FP** Most broadleaved trees and shrubs. PGC

2027 Dark Tussock *Dicallomera fascelina* 45mm (♂), 55mm (♀) Local. Jul–Aug. Local on lowland heaths of central southern England, also coastal dunes and northern moors. **FP** Heather, Creeping Willow, sallows, Broom, Bramble, Hawthorn. CMM

2028 Pale Tussock *Calliteara pudibunda* 42mm (♂), 60mm (♀) Common. May–Jun. Common from Cumbria southwards. Female much larger than male. In urban gardens, parks, hedges, woods, etc. **FP** Deciduous trees and shrubs, including Hop. CMM, TJN, NS

2029 Brown-tail *Euproctis chrysorrhoea* 35mm Local. Jul–Aug. White with diagnostic brown upper abdomen. Near coasts in south and east England, can be abundant in scrub, hedges, gardens. **FP** Bramble, Hawthorn, Blackthorn. CMM

2030 Yellow-tail *Euproctis similis* 33mm Common. Jul–Aug. Similar to above, but with yellow abdomen, often raised when disturbed. Male with light mark in trailing corner of forewing, female without mark and larger. Common anywhere throughout southern Britain. **FP** Broadleaved trees and shrubs. CMM

♂ 2025

♀, egg-laying on cocoon 2025

♀
♂
2026

♂ 2027

melanic
♂ 2028

♂ 2028

♀
♂
2028

♂ 2029

♂ 2030

TUSSOCKS: LYMANTRIIDAE (cont.)

2031 White Satin *Leucoma salicis* 45mm Local. Jul–Aug. Larger than Yellow and Brown Tails, with white abdomen and creamy white sheen, black bands on forelegs. Southern UK in damp woods, parks, scrub. **FP** Poplar, sallows and other willows. CMM

2032 Black V Moth *Arctornis l-nigrum* 50mm Migrant. Jun–Aug. Scarce migrant, with green veins when fresh and distinctive black V mark. **FP** Elm, lime. CMM, CMM

2033 Black Arches *Lymantria monacha* 44mm (♂), 52mm (♀) Local. Jul–Aug. Mostly southern Britain in mature oak woods. **FP** Oaks and other trees. NS, NS

2034 Gypsy Moth *Lymantria dispar* 45mm (♂), 64mm (♀) Vagrant/Accidental. Jul–Aug. Extinct resident, male appears as migrant. Females rarely fly. **FP** Broadleaved trees, can be serious pest in Europe. CS, CMM

2031

2032

♂
2033

♂ freshly emerged and pupa
2032

♀
2033

♀ and pupa
2034

♂
2034

FOOTMEN: ARCTIIDAE

There are 20 footman moths, 17 species in the sub-family Lithosiinae and three in Arctiinae. Adults are mostly small, dull buff or grey, often with narrow wings wrapped around the body. They do come to light, and the immigrant Crimson Speckled flies in sunshine as well as at night. The hairy larvae of Lithosiinae feed on lichens and algae at night, and can be found by torchlight on rocks, tree trunks, posts, etc. Larvae of Arctiinae feed on herbaceous plants. Footmen overwinter as larvae.

2035 Round-winged Muslin *Thumatha senex* 20mm Local. Jun–Aug. Mainly south and east England in damp areas. Similar to Muslin Footman but without cross-lines. **FP** Lichens, moss, algae. CMM
2036 Dew Moth *Setina irrorella* 28mm Na. Jun–Jul. Mainly rocky and shingle coasts in south and west Britain, on calcareous hills inland and Isle of Man. **FP** Lichens on rocks. DF
2037 Rosy Footman *Miltochrista miniata* 25mm Local. Jun–Aug. Stunning little orange-pink moth (very occasionally yellow) in mature woods in southern Britain. **FP** Lichens on oaks and other trees. CMM, JSB
2038 Muslin Footman *Nudaria mundana* 20mm Local. Jun–Aug. Similar to Round-winged Muslin but with two cross-lines on near-transparent wings. Local throughout. **FP** Lichens on stone walls, bushes and fences. DF

2039 Red-necked Footman *Atolmis rubricollis* 28mm Local. Jun–Jul. In southern England and south-west Scotland, in deciduous and coniferous woods. **FP** Lichens and green algae on oak, birch, Beech, Larch, etc. RW
2040 Four-dotted Footman *Cybosia mesomella* 33mm Local. Jun–Aug. Mainly southern Britain, local in the north, on heaths, moors, fens, damp woods. Occasionally occurs without black dots. **FP** Lichens and algae on heather, sallows, etc. DF
2041 Dotted Footman *Pelosia muscerda* 28mm RDB3. Jul–Aug. Found only in fens in Norfolk Broads. Slender grey forewing with straight leading edge and five or six black dots. **FP** Lichens and algae. NS
2042 Small Dotted Footman *Pelosia obtusa* 25mm RDB2. Jul. Found only in fens in Norfolk Broads. Broad brown forewing with curved leading edge and four black dots. **FP** Lichens and algae. RL

2035

2036

2037

2038

2039

flava

2037

2040

2041

2042

FOOTMEN: ARCTIIDAE (cont.)

2043 Orange Footman *Eilema sororcula* 28mm Local. May–Jun. Mainly in southern Britain in mature oak and beech woods. Melanistic form is rare. **FP** Lichens on trees. PHS

2044 Dingy Footman *Eilema griseola* 35mm Common. Jul–Aug. Frequent in southern Britain, in damp woods, fens. Two forms, both with broad, curved forewing. Sometimes described as the Melon Pip. **FP** Lichens and algae on trees and bushes. DF, CMM

2045 Hoary Footman *Eilema caniola* 32mm Nb. Jul–Sep. Scarce, on rocky coasts and quarries. Very pale silky grey with faint cream forewing edge. **FP** Lichens and algae on rocks. CMM

2046 Pigmy Footman *Eilema pygmaeola* 23mm RDB3. Jul–Aug. Very local but common on coastal sandhills and shingle beaches in Kent and Norfolk. Much smaller than Hoary Footman. Can also be pale yellow, rather than grey. **FP** Lichens on rocks and vegetation. DF

2047 Scarce Footman *Eilema complana* 32mm Local. Jul–Aug. Similar to Common Footman but wings wrapped around body and stripe along forewing edge continues to end of wing. Common but local from Yorkshire south and east on heaths, downs, in woods, gardens. **FP** Lichens and algae on rocks, plant stems, branches. DF

2048 Northern Footman *Eilema complana* f. *sericea* RDB2. Jul. A form of Scarce Footman, differs only slightly, found only in peat bogs around Shropshire. **FP** Lichens. NOT ILLUSTRATED

2049 Buff Footman *Eilema depressa* 35mm Local. Jul–Aug. Wing edges straight rather than curved like Dingy Footman. Local, mainly in mature woods from Midlands southwards. **FP** Lichens and algae on tree trunks. NS, CMM

2050 Common Footman *Eilema lurideola* 32mm Common. Jul–Aug. Frequent anywhere in England and Wales, only local in Scotland. Wings held flat, stripe along forewing edge does not reach end. **FP** Lichens and algae on trees, walls, rocks. Hawthorn leaves. CMM

2051 Four-spotted Footman *Lithosia quadra* 40mm (♂), 50mm (♀) Migrant. Jul–Sep. Both sexes unmistakable. Usually migrant, but resident in south-west England on coasts and in mature woods. **FP** Dog Lichen and algae on tree trunks and rocks. CMM, DF

2052 Feathered Footman *Spiris striata* 40mm Vagrant/Accidental. May–Aug. Four records from 19th century. DGG

2053 Speckled Footman *Coscinia cribraria bivittata* 35mm RDB1. Jul. Extremely local on heaths in south-east Dorset. Variable markings usually blurred. **FP** Bristle Bent, heathers. CMM, CMM

2054 Crimson Speckled *Utetheisa pulchella* 42mm Migrant. Jul–Oct. Stunning scarce migrant from Mediterranean, flies by day or night. **FP** Herbaceous plants. CMM, MC

usual

2044

stramineola

2044

melanic

2043

2046

2045

2047

plumbia

2049

2049

2050

2051 ♂

2051 ♀

2052

2053 ♂

2053 ♀

2054

2054

TIGERS AND ERMINES: ARCTIIDAE, ARCTIINAE

Adult tiger moths are mostly strongly marked with contrasting dark and light patterns of stripes or spots, hence the name. The markings are also a warning that the moth is poisonous. Ermines tend to be white and are named after the stoat, which, when camouflaged in its white winter coat, is known as an ermine. Adults come to light, and some such as Scarlet Tiger and Cinnabar also fly by day. Larvae feed on herbaceous plants. Most are very hairy (known as woolly bears) and are sometimes seen moving rapidly across open ground, footpaths, etc., looking for somewhere to pupate.

2056 Wood Tiger *Parasemia plantaginis* 40mm Local. May–Jul. Throughout Britain but always local. Flies by day on moors, heaths, downs, open woods. **FP** Bell Heather, plantains, Rock-rose, Groundsel, etc. JPo
2057 Garden Tiger *Arctia caja* 70mm Common. Jul–Aug. Throughout Britain in open, rough ground, can be

abundant. Markings very variable so each moth is different. **FP** Herbaceous and garden plants. DGG, DJP, CMM, DF, DJP
2058 Cream-spot Tiger 55mm *Arctia villica britannica* Local. May–Jul. Can be common in south Britain, especially on coasts, mainly on open ground. **FP** Herbaceous plants. CMM

2056

2057

aberration

2057

2057

aberration 2057

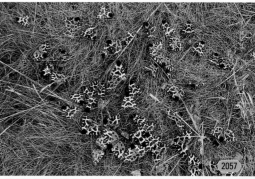

2057

2058

TIGERS AND ERMINES: ARCTIIDAE, ARCTIINAE (cont.)

2058a Patton's Tiger *Hyphoraia testudinaria* 40mm Vagrant/Accidental. May–Jul. Two records in Britain, in 2005, which is the one shown, and 2006. From mountainous regions of southern Europe. SP

2059 Clouded Buff *Diacrisia sannio* 40mm Local. Jun–Jul. Throughout Britain, but local, on heaths and moorland. Male comes to light, female flies in hot sun but is not attracted to light. **FP** Heathers, herbaceous plants, including sorrels, plantains, violets, scabious. CMM, PB

2060 White Ermine *Spilosoma lubricipeda* 40mm Common. May–Jul. Throughout Britain, almost anywhere. White background of southern examples tends to buff in Scotland. **FP** Sundry herbaceous plants. CMM

2061 Buff Ermine *Spilosoma luteum* 40mm Common. May–Jul. Throughout, but less common in north. **FP** Sundry herbaceous plants. DGG

2062 Water Ermine *Spilosoma urticae* 42mm Nb. Jun–Jul. Scarce, on coastal marshes of south-east England and in Devon. **FP** Marsh plants, including Yellow Loosestrife, Yellow Iris, Water Dock, Lousewort. DF

2063 Muslin Moth *Diaphora mendica* 35mm (♂), 40mm (♀) Common. May–Jun. Grey male is most often seen. Female, which occasionally comes to light, is slightly translucent with fewer spots than White Ermine. Found in most open habitats. **FP** Herbaceous plants and shrubs. CMM, CMM

2064 Ruby Tiger *Phragmatobia fuliginosa* 35mm Common. Apr–Jun, Jul–Sep. Throughout Britain, mostly in open habitats. **FP** Herbaceous plants and shrubs. CMM

2067 Jersey Tiger *Euplagia quadripunctaria* 65mm Nb. Jul–Sep. Resident in south-west, mainly coastal. Flies by day or night. **FP** Herbaceous plants, including nettle, Bramble, Hemp Agrimony. CMM

2068 Scarlet Tiger *Callimorpha dominula* 55mm Local. Jun–Jul. Local but can be abundant. Flies in sunshine. On marshy ground, river banks, water meadows in southern England. **FP** Comfrey, nettle, Bramble, Meadowsweet, Hemp Agrimony, etc. CMM

2069 Cinnabar *Tyria jacobaeae* 40mm Common. May–Aug. Throughout Britain, mostly on rough, open ground, wherever Ragwort grows. Flies by day or night. **FP** Flowers and leaves of Ragwort. CMM

2058a

2059 ♂

2059 ♀

2060

2061

2062

2063 ♂

2063 ♀

2064

2067

2068

2069

CTENUCHIDAE

Neither of these two day-flying moths have been seen in Britain since the 1870s but are common southern European species. With the onset of warmer summers, they could possibly occur again.

2070 Nine-spotted *Syntomis phegea* 40mm Vagrant/ Accidental. Jun–Jul. Southern European species, two British records from 1872 and 2000. CMM

2071 Handmaid *Dysauxes ancilla* 25mm Vagrant/ Accidental. One British record only, in 1876. CMM

ARCHES: NOLIDAE

All of the six members of this family on the British list are small, mostly black and white, with short rounded wings. They often have raised tufts of scales on the forewings. They fly at night and come to light. Larvae are hairy, herbaceous feeders and pupate in silk cocoons attached to the foodplant.

2075 Small Black Arches *Meganola strigula* 22mm Na. Jun–Jul. In mature oak woods, only in southern England. More brown on wings than Least Black Arches. **FP** Oak. CMM

2076 Kent Black Arches *Meganola albula* 24mm Nb. Jun–Aug. In southern Britain, mainly coastal. On heaths, salt marsh, beaches, chalk downs, open woods. **FP** Dewberry, Bramble, Raspberry, Wild Strawberry. CMM

2077 Short-cloaked Moth *Nola cucullatella* 20mm Common. Jun–Jul. In northern England and Wales southwards. Widespread in hedges, gardens, woods, scrub. **FP** Hawthorn, Blackthorn, Apple, Plum. DF

2078 Least Black Arches *Nola confusalis* 20mm Local. May–Jun. Local throughout, but more common in south, in woods, parks, hedges. **FP** Lime, Evergreen Oak, birch. CMM

2079 Scarce Black Arches *Nola aerugula* 16mm Extinct/Migrant. Jun–Aug. Resident in Kent up to 1898, now migrants only, along southern coasts. Cross-lines much straighter than Least Black Arches. **FP** Bird's-foot Trefoil, clovers. CMM

2079a Jersey Black Arches *Nola chlamitulalis* 16mm Vagrant/Accidental. Jun–Jul. First recorded in Jersey 1963; two mainland Britain records from Essex 2004, Dorset 2005. From southern Europe. MSP

NOCTUIDS: NOCTUIDAE

The Noctuids are members of the largest family of macro-moths in Britain. There are around 21,000 species worldwide, with over 400 British species, but these are split into 14 main sub-families. The taxonomy of the Noctuids is still subject to discussion, and the order of the British list differs from the European.

Adults are mainly medium sized and brown, though of course there are plenty of stunningly colourful exceptions such as the Merveille du Jour. They are usually stout-bodied with wings longer than they are wide for strong flight, unlike Geometers, for example. As always, there are exceptions: fan-foots, snouts and the Beautiful Hook-tip look very like Geometers. Many Noctuids have two obvious marks in the centre of the forewing, one kidney-shaped and one oval. The relative size, shape and colour of these can be important clues to identification. Antennae of males are generally ciliate (comb-like) whereas those of females are plain.

They fly at night, when they will all come to light as well as sugar baits, flowers and tree sap. Some also fly by day, and large numbers of Silver Y moths can be seen nectaring on Buddleia flowers in hot summers. Larvae feed at night and are usually fat, with smooth, round bodies like the clays and rustics, but again, the Beautiful Hook-tip is completely different. Some overwinter as larvae, others as eggs or pupae. There is usually one generation per year, though early arrivals of the migrant Silver Y will breed in hot summers.

NOCTUIDS: NOCTUIDAE, NOCTUINAE

This sub-family contains 65 species with long, narrow forewings that overlap when at rest, and includes the darts, yellow underwings, rustics and clays.

2080 Square-spot Dart *Euxoa obelisca grisea* 35mm Nb. Aug–Oct. On rocky coasts of south and west Britain. Very similar to other *Euxoa* species, but flight period is later. **FP** Common Rock-rose, Lady's Bedstraw. RL, PAD
2081 White-line Dart *Euxoa tritici* 35mm Common. Jul–Aug. Has black arrowhead marks at outer edge of forewing. Throughout Britain, on dunes, downs, heaths, moors, open woods. **FP** Herbaceous plants. NS, CMM
2082 Garden Dart *Euxoa nigricans* 32mm Common. Jul–Aug. Inhabits commons, sandhills, marshes, gardens. Generally plainer and browner than above species, without white lines. **FP** Herbaceous plants. DF

2080   2080   2082   2081   2081

NOCTUIDS: NOCTUIDAE, NOCTUINAE (cont.)

2083 Coast Dart *Euxoa cursoria* 35mm Nb. Jul–Aug. On coastal sandhills of northern Britain. Earlier flight period than Square-spot Dart, without arrowhead marks of White-line Dart. **FP** Various sand-dune plants, including Sea Sandwort, Sand Couch, Hound's Tongue. RL

2083a Wood's Dart *Agrotis graslini* 35mm Migrant. Aug–Oct. Coastal sand dunes of western Europe. Recorded and possible resident in Jersey. Similar to pale Archer's Dart, but pure white hind wing. **FP** Scabious, plantains. NOT ILLUSTRATED

2084 Light Feathered Rustic *Agrotis cinerea* 35mm Nb. May–Jun. Jagged cross-lines distinctive, though background colour can vary. Southern half of Britain on chalk downs, sea cliffs, quarries. **FP** Wild Thyme. DF

2085 Archer's Dart *Agrotis vestigialis* 35mm Local. Jul–Sep. Very distinctive, though background colour can vary. Mainly coastal dunes but also inland heaths. **FP** Bedstraws, Stitchwort, Sea Sandwort. CMM, DF

2087 Turnip Moth *Agrotis segetum* 40mm Common. May–Jun, Aug–Oct. Larger and narrower than Heart and Club. Kidney, spot and tooth marks usually outlined. Throughout Britain, in gardens, farmland, parks, woods. **FP** In roots and leaves of Turnip, Carrot, Beet, etc. Pest on root crops. CMM, CMM

2088 Heart and Club *Agrotis clavis* 35mm Common. Jun–Jul. Coastal dunes, chalk downs, rough ground. Throughout Britain, but more common in the south. **FP** Leaves and roots of dock, clover, Wild Carrot, Fat-hen. DF

2089 Heart and Dart *Agrotis exclamationis* 38mm Common. May–Aug, Sep. Abundant almost anywhere. Always has dark collar. **FP** Various herbaceous plants. CMM

2090 Crescent Dart *Agrotis trux lunigera* 40mm Local. Jul–Aug. On south and west coastal cliffs from Dorset round to Wales. Distinct white central spot. **FP** Thrift, Rock Sea-spurrey. DF, DF

2091 Dark Sword-grass *Agrotis ipsilon* 45mm Migrant. Any month. Common throughout Britain, most in south in late summer. Larger than other similar moths, with dark arrow mark beyond kidney mark. **FP** Herbaceous plants. NS

2091a Spalding's Dart *Agrotis herzogi* One British record only, from Cornwall in 1995. Slightly like a pale Archer's Dart. NOT ILLUSTRATED

2092 Shuttle-shaped Dart *Agrotis puta* 30mm Common. Apr–Oct. Found in most habitats, from Yorkshire southwards. Pale oval 'shuttle' is distinctive. Female is darker than male. **FP** Dock, Dandelion, etc. CJS, CJS

2083

2084

2085

2085

2087

2087

2088

2089

2090

2091

2090

♂ 2092

♀ 2092

NOCTUIDS: NOCTUIDAE, NOCTUINAE (cont.)

2093 Sand Dart *Agrotis ripae* 36mm Nb. Jun–Jul.
Common locally on coastal sand dunes. Flight period
is earlier than Coast Dart. **FP** Prickly Saltwort, Sea
Rocket, Orache. SR, DF
2094 Great Dart *Agrotis crassa* 40mm Rare
migrant. Aug. The inner of two pale cross-lines
has deep outward-pointing notch at trailing edge.
Found in Channel Islands and Europe. **FP** Plant
roots. DF

2097 Purple Cloud *Actinotia polyodon* 32mm Rare
migrant. May–Aug. Unmistakable. Found throughout
Europe. **FP** St John's Wort flowers and seeds. CMM
2097a Pale-shouldered Cloud *Actinotia hyperici* 35mm
Vagrant/Accidental. May–Aug. Mainly Mediterranean
species. **FP** St John's Wort. NS
2098 Flame *Axylia putris* 34mm Common. Jun–Jul, Sep.
Common in most habitats, though local in Scotland.
FP Dock, Dandelion, nettle, etc. CJS

2093
2093
2094
2097
2097a
2098

2099 Portland Moth *Actebia praecox* 45mm Nb. Jul–Sep. Unmistakable. Found on coastal sand dunes but seems to be decreasing. **FP** Creeping Willow, sundry sandhill plants. RL
2101 Black Collar *Ochropleura flammatra* 40mm Vagrant/Accidental. Very scarce migrant from central and southern Europe, Asia and North Africa. **FP** Wild Strawberry. DM
2102 Flame Shoulder *Ochropleura plecta* 30mm Common. Apr–Sep. Found in almost any habitat throughout Britain. **FP** Various herbaceous plants. CMM
2102a Radford's Flame Shoulder *Ochropleura leucogaster* 35mm Vagrant/Accidental. Sep–Nov. Migrant, from southern Europe, similar to above species but larger, with longer, narrower wings, less red. **FP** Bird's-foot Trefoil. MC
2103 Plain Clay *Eugnorisma depuncta* 40mm Nb. Jun–Sep. Edges of broadleaved woodland in northern Britain. **FP** Nettle, Stitchwort, dock, etc. DGG
2104 Northern Rustic *Standfussiana lucernea* 44mm Local. Jun–Sep. On rocky coasts of western Britain from Dorset to Scotland. Flies by day or night, visits flowers. **FP** Harebell, Stonecrop, etc. DF
2105 Dotted Rustic *Rhyacia simulans* 45mm Local. Jun–Oct. Local throughout Britain, but numbers fluctuate. In open country and woods, moors, hedges. **FP** Unknown in the wild. RL

NOCTUIDS: NOCTUIDAE, NOCTUINAE (cont.)

2106 Southern Rustic *Rhyacia lucipeta* 55mm
Vagrant/Accidental. Jul. Resident of southern Europe.
One British record only, in 1968. DM

2107 Large Yellow Underwing *Noctua pronuba* 55mm
Common. Jun–Oct. Can be abundant almost anywhere
throughout Britain. Well-defined black dots near
wingtip. Male is dark, female pale. **FP** Many herbaceous
plants. CMM, CMM, CMM

2108 Lunar Yellow Underwing *Noctua orbona* 40mm
Nb. Jun–Sep. Mainly in Brecklands of East Anglia,
also sandy coasts of Northumberland and south
Scotland. Smaller than above species, has similar dark
mark near wingtip, but also dark 'lunar' crescent on
hind wing. **FP** Fine grasses and small herbaceous
plants. DGG

2109 Lesser Yellow Underwing *Noctua comes* 40mm
Common. Jul–Sep. Similar to above species, but without
well-defined dark mark at wingtip. Common throughout
Britain. Form *sagittifer* found in Scilly Isles. **FP** Many
bushes, shrubs and herbaceous plants. TD, CMM

2110 Broad-bordered Yellow Underwing *Noctua
fimbriata* 60mm Common. Jun–Sep. Female is paler than
male. Throughout Britain, mostly in woodland. **FP**
Many bushes, shrubs and herbaceous plants. CMM, NS

2110a Langmaid's Yellow Underwing *Noctua janthina*
36mm Migrant. Jul–Sep. Looks the same as following
species. Upperside of hind wing is nearly all black with
yellow centre. MC, MC

2111 Lesser Broad-bordered Yellow Underwing
Noctua janthe 40mm Common. Jul–Sep. Looks same as
above species, but common throughout, anywhere, and
hind wing more yellow. **FP** Many bushes, shrubs and
herbaceous plants. DF

2112 Least Yellow Underwing *Noctua interjecta
caliginosa* 32mm Common. Jul–Aug. Widespread in
southern Britain, local in the north. In fens, sandhills
and open ground. **FP** Grasses, herbaceous plants. DF

2113 Stout Dart *Spaelotis ravida* 40mm Local. Jun–Sep.
Scarce, but numbers fluctuate. East Anglia and central
England, in damp meadows. **FP** Unknown in the wild. JPo

2106

2107 ♀

2107 ♂

2107 ♂

sagittifer 2109

2108

2109

2110 ♀

2110 ♂

2110a

2110a

2112

2111

2113

NOCTUIDS: NOCTUIDAE, NOCTUINAE (cont.)

2114 Double Dart *Graphiphora augur* 42mm Common. Jun–Jul. Local throughout in woods, parks, gardens. **FP** Sallows, birch, Hawthorn, Blackthorn, herbaceous plants. DGG

2115 Rosy Marsh Moth *Eugraphe subrosea* 36mm RDB2. Jul–Aug. Extremely scarce, from west Wales only, in acid bogs. **FP** Bog Myrtle, Crowberry. RPJ, IT

2116 Cousin German *Paradiarsia sobrina* 35mm RDB3. Jul–Aug. Very scarce, in Highlands of central Scotland, in birch woods with Bilberry. **FP** Birch, Bilberry. DGG

2117 Autumnal Rustic *Paradiarsia glareosa* 35mm Common. Aug–Oct. Common throughout on heaths, moors, downs, open ground. **FP** Heathers, bedstraws, etc. DGG

2118 True Lover's Knot *Lycophotia porphyrea* 30mm Common. Jun–Aug. Common on heaths and moors throughout Britain. **FP** Heathers. MSP

2119 Pearly Underwing *Peridroma saucia* 45mm Migrant. Any month. Can appear throughout the year, though mostly in autumn. Grey crest on thorax. **FP** Breeds in summer on herbaceous plants. CMM, CMM

2120 Ingrailed Clay *Diarsia mendica* 35mm Common. Jun–Aug. Very variable, darker in north. Small black spot in centre of forewing between oval and trailing edge is constant. **FP** Herbaceous and woody plants. CMM, PAD

2121 Barred Chestnut *Diarsia dahlii* 35mm Local. Aug–Sep. Male is deep orange-brown, well-barred with hints of purple. Female is sligly less well-defined. In northern Britain on acid heaths, moors, in woods. **FP** Birch, Bilberry, Bramble. PGC

2122 Purple Clay *Diarsia brunnea* 36mm Common. Jun–Aug. Woods and heaths throughout Britain. Purple sheen is distinctive. **FP** Woody and herbaceous plants. CMM

2123 Small Square-spot *Diarsia rubi* 32mm Common. May–Jun, Aug–Sep. Found anywhere throughout Britain, especially damp woods. Has dark dot in centre of forewing between oval and trailing edge, like Ingrailed Clay. **FP** Various herbaceous plants. NS

2124 Fen Square-spot *Diarsia florida* Local. Jun–Jul. Local form of above species. In fens and acid bogs, especially in East Anglia. **FP** Various herbaceous plants. NOT ILLUSTRATED

2125 Northern Dart *Xestia alpicola alpina* 38mm Na. Jun–Aug. Found only on mountain tops in northern England and Scotland above 450m. Most populations hatch together in alternate years, so numbers vary annually. **FP** Crowberry, maybe also heather. RL

2126 Setaceous Hebrew Character *Xestia c-nigrum* 36mm Common. May–Jul, Aug–Oct. Pale, shallow V-shaped mark in centre of forewing is distinctive. Throughout Britain, can be abundant in south. **FP** Various herbaceous plants. CMM

2127 Triple-spotted Clay *Xestia ditrapezium* 40mm Local. Jun–Aug. Local but widespread in damp woods and parkland. **FP** Shrubs and plants, including Bramble, sallows, Primrose. NS

2114

♂ 2115

♀ 2115

2116

2117

NOCTUIDS: NOCTUIDAE, NOCTUINAE (cont.)

2128 Double Square-spot *Xestia triangulum* 42mm
Common. Jun–Jul. Found throughout in woods, gardens,
hedges. **FP** Shrubs and plants, including Primrose, Cow
Parsley, Bramble, Hawthorn. CMM

2129 Ashworth's Rustic *Xestia ashworthii* 38mm Na.
Jun–Aug. Only on slate and limestone mountains in
north Wales. **FP** Herbaceous plants, including Thyme,
sorrel, bedstraw, Hawkweed. DGG

2130 Dotted Clay *Xestia baja* 40mm Common. Jul–Aug.
Small black dots near outer tip of forewing give this
moth its name. In woods, heaths and scrubby downland.
FP Herbaceous plants, including Nettle, also Bog
Myrtle, willows. CMM

2131 Square-spotted Clay *Xestia rhomboidea* 40mm Nb.
Jul–Aug. Scattered throughout but local, in mature
woods. Thick, dark band near outer edge of forewing
and purple sheen are distinctive. **FP** Nettle, Dog's
Mercury, Oxlip. NS

2132 Neglected Rustic *Xestia castanea* Local.
Aug–Sep. Two forms, grey or red-brown. Indistinct
markings, but dark in corner of kidney mark is
constant. On heaths and moorland throughout.
FP Heathers. CMM, CMM

2133 Six-striped Rustic *Xestia sexstrigata* 36mm
Common. Jul–Aug. Common throughout on damp
ground but also gardens, hedges. **FP** Bedstraw, plantain,
Bluebell, Bramble. CMM

2134 Square-spot Rustic *Xestia xanthographa* 36mm
Common. Jul–Oct. Almost square kidney mark is
diagnostic. Common to abundant throughout Britain.
FP Grasses. CJS

2135 Heath Rustic *Xestia agathina* 32mm Local.
Aug–Sep. Later flight period and more colourful than
True Lover's Knot. On acid heaths and moorland.
FP Heather. CMM

2136 Gothic *Naenia typica* 44mm Local. Jun–Jul. In
damp, lowland areas scattered throughout Britain.
Has broader forewings than scarce Bordered Gothic.
FP Herbaceous and woody plants, including Comfrey,
willowherbs, cleavers, sallows. NS

2137 Great Brocade *Eurois occulta* 55mm Na/Migrant.
Jul–Aug. Resident in Scottish Highlands, migrant
elsewhere. A large moth with significant pale oval in
centre of forewing. **FP** Bog Myrtle. MC

2138 Green Arches *Anaplectoides prasina* 48mm
Common. Jun–Jul. Unmistakable. Common throughout
Britain in woodland. **FP** Honeysuckle, Bilberry,
Primrose, dock. CMM

2139 Red Chestnut *Cerastis rubricosa* 35mm Common.
Mar–Apr. Common in woods, scrub, gardens and boggy
heaths. **FP** Herbaceous plants. CMM

2140 White-marked *Cerastis leucographa* 33mm Local.
Mar–Apr. Similar to above but oval and kidney marks
are pale and distinct. In open woods, scrub, hedges in
central southern England. **FP** Unknown in the wild. SH

2141 Pale Stigma *Mesogona acetosellae* 40mm
Vagrant/Accidental. Aug–Oct. From central and
southern Europe. One British record only, in 1895. NS

2133

2134

2135

2136

2137

2138

2139

2140

2141

NOCTUIDS: NOCTUIDAE, HADENINAE

This sub-family contains 68 species, usually with well-marked wings, but also includes wainscots with larvae that feed on leaves of grasses.

2142 Beautiful Yellow Underwing *Anarta myrtilli* 24mm Common. Apr–Aug. Throughout Britain on heaths and moors. Flies by day or night. **FP** Heather. DE, DGG

2143 Small Dark Yellow Underwing *Anarta cordigera* 24mm Na. Apr–May. Flies in sunshine on high, stony moors from 200–650m in central Highlands of Scotland. **FP** Bearberry. SR

2144 Broad-bordered White Underwing *Anarta melanopa* 26mm RDB3. May–Jun. Flies in sunshine on high moors above 650m in central Highlands of Scotland. **FP** Crowberry, Bilberry, Cowberry, Bearberry. RL

2145 Nutmeg *Discestra trifolii* 36mm Common. Apr–Jun, Aug–Sep. Throughout Britain, but more local from Midlands north, in many habitats. Kidney mark is dark nearest trailing edge and outer cross-line has white 'W' in corner. **FP** Goosefoot, Orache. DF

2147 Shears *Hada plebeja* 35mm Common. May–Jul, Aug. Throughout Britain, on heaths, downs, dunes, open woodland. White or pale double-pointed mark like open scissors (shears) in center of forewing is distinctive. **FP** Hawk's Beard, Hawkweed, Dandelion, Chickweed. CJS, CMM

2142

2142

2143

2144

2145

2147

2147

2148 Pale Shining Brown *Polia bombycina* 50mm RDB. Jun–Jul. Formerly widespread, now mainly confined to Salisbury Plain, on scrubby chalk downland. Pale brown with shiny sheen. **FP** Unknown in the wild but may include flowers of Hawkbit, Sow-thistle, scabious. CMM

2149 Silvery Arches *Polia trimaculosa* 50mm Nb. Jun–Jul. On heaths, moors and open woods of Scotland and south-east England. Southern forms with reddish tint, northern forms are silvery or blueish. **FP** Birch, sallows, Bog Myrtle. GAC

2150 Grey Arches *Polia nebulosa* 50mm Common. Jun–Jul. Throughout Britain. Ground colour variable from near-white to near-black. **FP** Birch, sallows, Honeysuckle, Hawthorn, dock, etc. CMM

2151 Feathered Ear *Pachetra sagittigera britannica* 40mm Extinct. May–Jun. Formerly on chalk downs of south-east England, last seen in 1963. **FP** Grasses. CMM

2152 White Colon *Sideridis albicolon* 38mm Nb. May–Jun, Jul–Aug. Mainly coastal on dunes and salt marshes around Britain, also Brecks of East Anglia. Two white marks (colon) in corner of kidney mark are distinctive. **FP** Leaves and flowers of Goosefoot, Orache, Sea Bindweed, Restharrow, etc. CMM

2153 Bordered Gothic *Heliophobus reticulata* 40mm RDB. Jun–Jul. Smaller and with narrower wings than Gothic. Feathered Gothic is paler, slightly larger and flies later in the year. Formerly on chalk downs, Breckland. **FP** Unknown in wild. CMM

2154 Cabbage Moth *Mamestra brassicae* 45mm Common. May–Oct. Throughout lowland Britain. White outline of kidney mark is noticeable. **FP** Eats almost anything, but especially Cabbages. CMM

2155 Dot Moth *Melanchra persicariae* 40mm Common. Jun–Aug. Unmistakable, though Black Rustic is also dark but with only small pale mark in kidney. Widespread but more local in north in gardens, hedges, woods. **FP** Many herbaceous and woody plants. DF

2156 Beautiful Brocade *Lacanobia contigua* 36mm Local. Jun–Jul. Local throughout on heaths, moors and acid woodland. Diagonal pale bar from central dot mark is distinctive. **FP** Birch, sallows, Bog Myrtle, heather, Bracken, oak. CMM

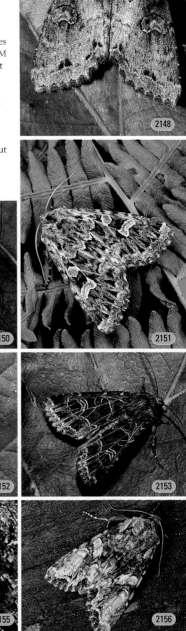

2148

2149

2150

2151

2152

2153

2154

2155

2156

NOCTUIDS: NOCTUIDAE, HADENINAE (cont.)

2157 Light Brocade *Lacanobia w-latinum* 42mm Local. May–Jul. Widespread, mainly in southern England, on heaths and downs. **FP** Broom, Dyer's Greenweed, Bramble, etc. CMM

2158 Pale-shouldered Brocade *Lacanobia thalassina* 40mm Common. May–Jul. Throughout britain, in woods, gardens, moors. There is a distinct, large, tooth-like mark on forewing. **FP** Oak, Hawthorn, Apple, sallows, Honeysuckle, etc. CMM

2159 Dog's Tooth *Lacanobia suasa* 40mm Local. May–Jul, Jul–Sep. Damp heaths, salt marshes, river valleys, mostly in southern Britain. Small tooth-like mark on forewing. **FP** Sea Lavender, Greater Plantain, Goosefoot. CMM, NS

2160 Bright-line Brown-eye *Lacanobia oleracea* 38mm Common. May–Jul, Aug–Sep. Common in most habitats throughout Britain. Kidney mark is 'brown eye'. **FP** Many herbaceous and woody plants. CMM

2160a Splendid Brocade *Lacanobia splendens* 35mm Immigrant. Jun–Jul. First recorded 2003 from Portland, Dorset, previously overlooked. From damp woods in Europe. **FP** Bindweed, Bittersweet. MC

2162 Glaucous Shears *Papestra biren* 38mm Local. May–Jun. On moorland in south-west England, Wales, northern England and Scotland. **FP** Heather, Meadowsweet, Bilberry, sallows, Bog Myrtle. DGG

2163 Broom Moth *Melanchra pisi* 40mm Common. May–Jul. Throughout Britain, particularly on heaths and moorland. Variable colour and markings but creamy, irregular, outer cross-line is diagnostic. **FP** Various plants and trees, including Broom, heather, Bracken, Bramble, sallows. CMM, CMM

2164 Broad-barred White *Hecatera bicolorata* 30mm Common. Jun–Aug. Widespread in southern Britain, local from Midlands north. On dunes, shingle, downs. **FP** Flowers of Hawkweed, Hawk's Beard, Sow Thistle. DF

2165 Small Ranunculus *Hecatera dysodea* 30mm RDBK. Jun–Aug. Thought extinct for 50 years before re-appearing in Kent, Essex and south Wales. Similar to Feathered and Large Ranunculus but smaller, and hind wing has wide tawny border. Found in chalk pits, rough ground, road verges. **FP** Flowers and seeds of wild and cultivated Lettuce. NS

2166 Campion *Hadena rivularis* 34mm Common. May–Jun, Aug–Sep. Purple tint when fresh but fades. Similar to Lychnis, but oval and kidney mark either joined or pointing together. Widespread in meadows and open land. **FP** Seeds of campions, Ragged Robin. CMM

2167 Tawny Shears *Hadena perplexa* 30mm Common. May–Jul, Aug. On dry, open downs, shingle beaches, breckland in England, Wales and southern Scotland. Very variable, but usually with outlined oval, kidney and tooth marks. Also with three small, dark, arrowhead marks near outer edge of forewing. **FP** Seeds of campions, Nottingham Catchfly, Rock Sea-spurrey. PAD, DF

2167 Pod Lover *Hadena perplexa capsophila* 30mm Local. May–Jul. A subspecies of Tawny Shears. Similar but on rocky western coasts only, from Cornwall to Scotland. **FP** Campion seeds. JBH

2168 Viper's Bugloss *Hadena irregularis* 32mm Presumed extinct. May–Jul. Formerly on Brecks of East Anglia, not seen since 1968. **FP** Spanish Catchfly seeds. DGG

2169 Barrett's Marbled Coronet *Hadena luteago barrettii* 38mm Nb. Jun–Jul. Only found on coasts of Devon, Cornwall and south Wales. Pale area runs towards trailing edge from oval mark. **FP** Roots of Sea Campion, Rock Sea-spurrey. DF, NS

2170 Varied Coronet *Hadena compta* 30mm Common. Jun–Jul. In gardens and downland in south and east England up to Yorkshire. Central white bar crosses forewing. **FP** Seeds of Sweet William, Bladder Campion. NS

2157

2158

aberration

2159

2159

2160

2160a

2162

2163

2163

2164

2166

2165

capsophila 2167

2167

2167

2169

2169

2170

2168

NOCTUIDS: NOCTUIDAE, HADENINAE (cont.)

2171 Marbled Coronet *Hadena confusa* 34mm Local. May–Jul, Aug. Throughout Britain, on calcareous coasts, downs and gardens. White blotch near wingtip, central band incomplete. **FP** Seeds of campions, Rock Sea-spurrey, etc. RL

2172 White Spot *Hadena albimacula* 35mm RDB2. May–Jun. Scarce, on scarce foodplant, usually found growing just over the edge of chalk cliffs in southern England. Also on shingle at Dungeness, Kent. **FP** Nottingham Catchfly seeds. CMM

2173 Lychnis *Hadena bicruris* 35mm Common. May–Jul, Aug–Sep. Similar to Campion, but without purple. Oval and kidney marks are well separated. Common throughout Britain. **FP** Seeds of campions, Sweet William. NS

2174 Grey *Hadena caesia mananii* 35mm RDB3. May–Aug. On rocky coasts of west Scotland, Hebrides and Isle of Man. **FP** Sea Campion. JPo

2175 Silurian *Eriopygodes imbecilla* 27mm (♂), 25mm (♀) RDB2. Jun–Jul. Flies on sunny afternoons and at night. On high moors in Monmouthshire, Wales.

FP Unknown in wild. CMM, CMM, CMM

2176 Antler *Cerapteryx graminis* 28mm (♂), 38mm (♀) Common. Jul–Sep. Throughout Britain, particularly in northen acid uplands, moors and downs. Flies on warm days and at night. **FP** Hard grasses, including Sheep's Fescue, Mat-grass, Purple Moor-grass. NS, DGG

2177 Hedge Rustic *Tholera cespitis* 40mm Common. Aug–Sep. Throughout Britain, but local in Scotland, in open areas with rough grass. **FP** Hard grasses, including Mat-grass, Wavy Hair-grass. CMM

2178 Feathered Gothic *Tholera decimalis* 44mm Common. Aug–Sep. Flies later than Gothic or Bordered Gothic, and looks paler. Throughout Britain in rough grassland, downs, parks. **FP** Hard grasses, including Mat-grass, Sheep's Fescue. CMM

2179 Pine Beauty *Panolis flammea* 33mm Common. Mar–May. Throughout Britain, wherever pines grow. Unmistakable. **FP** Pine needles. CMM, NS, CMM (right)

2181 Silver Cloud *Egira conspicillaris* 37mm Na. Apr–May. Very local, only in Severn Valley. **FP** Unknown in wild, but possibly dock and elm. CMM

2171

2173

2172

NOCTUIDS: NOCTUIDAE, HADENINAE (cont.)

2182 Small Quaker *Orthosia cruda* 27mm Common. Feb–May. Throughout Britain, very frequent in south, in woods, hedgerows, gardens, wet heaths. **FP** Oak, sallows, hazel, birch. CMM, NS

2183 Blossom Underwing *Orthosia miniosa* 34mm Local. Mar–Apr. In woods and hedgerows with mature oaks, in southern Britain. **FP** Oak. CMM

2184 Northern Drab *Orthosia opima* 32mm Local. Apr–May. Widespread but local throughout. Ground colour is grey to brown. Found in damp areas, on marshes, dunes, river valleys. **FP** Woody and herbaceous plants, including sallows, birch, Ragwort, Mugwort, Common Sea Lavender. PB

2185 Lead-coloured Drab *Orthosia populeti* 35mm Local. Mar–Apr. Throughout Britain but local, in woods and parks with poplars. **FP** Catkins and leaves of Aspen, Black Poplar. CMM, NS

2186 Powdered Quaker *Orthosia gracilis* 40mm Common. Apr–May. Ground colour variable, but fairly plain with curved row of dark dots between kidney mark and outer cross-line. Throughout Britain, in damp woods, marshes and heaths. **FP** Woody and herbaceous plants, including willows, poplars, Bog Myrtle, Purple Loosestrife, Meadowsweet. CMM

2187 Common Quaker *Orthosia cerasi* 35mm Common. Mar–May. Frequent throughout Britain in woodland. Usually well-defined, large oval and kidney marks and outer cross-line. **FP** Various trees, including oak, sallows, birch, elm. CMM, DGG, CMM, DGG, DGG

2188 Clouded Drab *Orthosia incerta* 40mm Common. Mar–May. Extremely variable, but larger than Common Quaker and outer cross-line usually with dark patch at tip. Frequent throughout Britain in woodland. **FP** Various trees, including oak, sallows, birch, elm, Hawthorn, hazel. CMM, CMM, NS, CMM, DGG

2186

2187

2187

2187

2187

2187

2188

2188

2188

2188

highland form

2188

NOCTUIDS: NOCTUIDAE, HADENINAE (cont.)

2189 Twin-spotted Quaker *Orthosia munda* 40mm
Common. Mar–Apr. Usually unmistakable with pair of
dark spots, but these can be absent. In woodland
throughout Britain, but most common in the south.
FP Trees and shrubs, including oak, sallows, Aspen,
Honeysuckle, Hop. CMM, CMM
2190 Hebrew Character *Orthosia gothica* 34mm
Common. Mar–May. Variable but always with dark
saddle mark. Common absolutely anywhere. **FP** Trees,
shrubs and plants. CMM, CMM

2191 Double Line *Mythimna turca* 44mm Nb. Jun–Jul.
Local in southern Britain. In damp, open woodland and
acid grassland. **FP** Grasses, including Common Bent,
Cock's-foot, Wood Meadow-grass. DF
2192 Brown-line Bright Eye *Mythimna conigera* 35mm
Common. Jun–Aug. Widespread throughout in rough
grassland. Bright 'eye' is distinctive, with V-shaped
inner cross-line. **FP** Grasses, including Common Couch,
Cock's-foot. DF

2193 Clay *Mythimna ferrago* 38mm Common. Jun–Aug. Rather plain with irregular, indistinct pale mark. Found throughout in open woods, gardens, grassland. **FP** Grasses, including meadow-grass, Cock's-foot. DGG

2194 White-point *Mythimna albipuncta* 34mm Migrant. May–Nov. Usually migrant but breeds on south coast of England. Darker orange-brown than Clay, with bright clear white mark. **FP** Grasses, including Common Couch, Cock's-foot. CMM

2195 Delicate *Mythimna vitellina* 40mm Migrant. May–Nov. Migrant, but can breed in hot summers. Variable ground colour, but three wavy cross-lines generally visible. **FP** Grasses, including meadow-grass, Cock's-foot. CMM, RW

2196 Striped Wainscot *Mythimna pudorina* 40mm Local. Jun–Jul. Southern Britain on marshes and wet, acid heaths. The pink-tinged forewing is broad, brown-streaked and dusted with scattered black scales. **FP** Grasses, including Common Reed, Purple Moor-grass, Reed Canary-grass. DF

2197 Southern Wainscot *Mythimna straminea* 35mm Local. Jul–Aug. Southern Britain on marshes, fens and wet ditches. Similar to Smoky Wainscot but outer edge of forewing slightly concave to produce pointed tip, and hind-wing upper is white. **FP** Common Reed, Reed Canary-grass. CMM

2198 Smoky Wainscot *Mythimna impura* 34mm Common. Jun–Aug. Throughout Britain, in grassland, open woods, gardens. Similar to Southern Wainscot but outer forewing edge is rounded and hind-wing upper is smoky grey. **FP** Grasses, including Common Reed, Cock's-foot, Hairy Wood-rush. DF

NOCTUIDS: NOCTUIDAE, HADENINAE (cont.)

2199 Common Wainscot *Mythimna pallens* 36mm
Common. Jun–Oct. Throughout Britain, in grassy
areas, very common in the south. Paler than Southern
and Smoky Wainscot, without streaks. Ground colour
can be reddish or straw. **FP** Grasses, including Tufted
Hair-grass, Cock's-foot, Common Couch. CMM

2200 Mathew's Wainscot *Mythimna favicolor* 36mm
Nb. Jun–Jul. On coastal salt marshes in southern
and eastern England. Very similar to Common
Wainscot but has a silky sheen. **FP** Common
Saltmarsh-grass. CMM

2201 Shore Wainscot *Mythimna litoralis* 36mm Nb.
Jun–Aug. On coastal dunes and beaches very close to
the sea in southern Britain. **FP** Marram. CMM

2202 L-album Wainscot *Mythimna l-album* 36mm Nb.
Jul, Sep–Oct. Unmistakable. Found on coasts of
southern England. **FP** Marram. CMM

2203 White-speck *Mythimna unipuncta* 40mm Migrant.
Aug–Oct. Regular migrant, usually on southern coasts.
Similar to Clay but larger, narrower, with dark streak
pointing into wing corner. **FP** Grasses. CMM

2204 Obscure Wainscot *Mythimna obsoleta* 36mm
Local. May–Jul. Similar to Smoky Wainscot but there is
central white dot at end of main vein and brown streak
along vein is much less prominent. In reed-beds on
marshes, estuaries, ponds, rivers in southern England.
FP Common Reed. DF

2205 Shoulder-striped Wainscot *Mythimna comma* 36mm
Common. May–Jul. Widespread and unmistakable. In
marshes and damp woods. **FP** Cock's-foot Grass. CMM

2206 Devonshire Wainscot *Mythimna putrescens* 34mm
Na. Jul–Sep. Squat, dark Wainscot, with central white
dot. Found on coasts of Devon, Cornwall and
Pembrokeshire only. **FP** Grasses. RPJ

2208 Cosmopolitan *Mythimna loreyi* 38mm Migrant.
Aug–Oct. Similar to White-speck but dark streak down
centre of wing contrasts with pale either side. Rare
migrant, usually on south coast. **FP** Grasses. MC

2209 Flame Wainscot *Mythimna flammea* 34mm Na.
May–Jul. A very local moth found in reed-beds in East
Anglia, Sussex, Kent and around Poole Harbour in
Dorset. **FP** Common Reed. CMM

2202

2203

2204

2205

2206

2208

2209

NOCTUIDS: NOCTUIDAE, CUCULLIINAE

This sub-family contains 45 species, including the sharks, named after the crest on the thorax, which resembles a shark's dorsal fin. They often have long, pointed wings.

2211 Wormwood *Cucullia absinthii* 38mm Nb. Jul–Aug. Scattered colonies from Yorkshire southwards, mainly coastal but also in quarries, slag heaps, Brecks of East Anglia. **FP** Flowers and seeds of Wormwood, Mugwort. NS

2214 Chamomile Shark *Cucullia chamomillae* 44mm Local. Apr–May. Very similar to Shark but flies earlier, is smaller, and hind-wing margin has two dark and two light fringes. Local throughout, mostly southern, on rough grass, commons, etc. **FP** Flowers of chamomiles, Scentless Mayweed, Feverfew. CMM

2216 Shark *Cucullia umbratica* 52mm Common. Jun–Jul. Similar to Chamomile Shark but more common, larger, flies later in the year, and hind-wing margin with one dark and one light fringe only. Throughout Britain on rough ground, downs, beaches, commons, gardens. **FP** Flowers and leaves of Sow Thistles, Wild Lettuce, Hawk's Beard, hawkweeds. NS

2217 Star-wort *Cucullia asteris* 50mm Nb. Jun–Aug. Local in south-east England on coastal salt marsh and in woodland, also found in Wales. Similar to Mullein but outer margins not scalloped, oval and kidney marks usually visible, and flies later in year. **FP** Flowers of Sea Aster, Sea Wormwood, in woods on Goldenrod, in gardens on Michaelmas Daisy. NS

2218 Cudweed *Cucullia gnaphalii occidentalis* 40mm Presumed extinct. May–Jul. Formerly in warm woods in south-east England. Not seen since 1979. **FP** Goldenrod flowers. GF

2219 Striped Lychnis *Shargacucullia lychnitis* 44mm Na. Jun–Jul. Similar to Mullein, but smaller, later flight period, and faint V or zig-zag mark usually visible on forewing leading edge. Scarce, on chalk downs and open sites in central southern England. **FP** Flowers of Dark Mullein, occasionally other mulleins. DF

2221 Mullein *Shargacucullia verbasci* 48mm Common. Apr–May. Widespread in central and southern Britain. Larger and flies earlier than similar Star-wort and Striped Lychnis. Outer wing margins are scalloped. Found anywhere, the gregarious larvae being very noticeable on mulleins in gardens, roadsides, woods, downs. **FP** Leaves of mulleins, figworts, Buddleias. CMM

2223 Toadflax Brocade *Calophasia lunula* 28mm RDB3. May–Jun, Aug. Very scarce on vegetated shingle beaches at Dungeness, Kent, and along south-eastern coasts. Occasional migrant. **FP** Toadflax. DGG

2225 Minor Shoulder-knot *Brachylomia viminalis* 30mm Common. Jul–Aug. Usually pale in the south, darker forms in Midlands and north. Dark streak at shoulder always visible. Found in damp woods, fens, marshes. **FP** Willows, Aspen. DF

2226 Beautiful Gothic *Leucochlaena oditis* 30mm RDB3. Aug–Oct. Found on southern coasts of England from Isle of Wight to Cornwall on grassy cliffs. Common where it does occur. **FP** Grasses, including Common Couch, Annual Meadow-grass. CMM

NOCTUIDS: NOCTUIDAE, CUCULLIINAE (cont.)

2227 Sprawler *Brachionycha sphinx* 42mm Common. Oct–Dec. Widespread in woodland and scrub, mainly in southern Britain in late autumn. **FP** Many trees, including oak, Hawthorn, hazel, Blackthorn. CMM

2228 Rannoch Sprawler *Brachionycha nubeculosa* 50mm RDB3. Mar–Apr. Found only in four areas in Scottish Highlands in mature birch woods. **FP** Birch. DGG

2229 Brindled Ochre *Dasypolia templi* 50mm Local. Sep–Oct, Mar–Apr. Throughout Britain, but mainly coastal on rough cliffs and grassland. Mated female

overwinters. **FP** Wild Angelica, Hogweed, in stems and roots. CMM, CMM

2230 Feathered Brindle *Aporophyla australis pascuea* 37mm Nb. Aug–Oct. On southern coasts of Britain. Ground colour varies from pale to brown. **FP** Sea Campion, Wood Sage, sorrel. CMM

2231 Deep-brown Dart *Aporophyla lutulenta* 37mm Common. Sep–Oct. Common in southern Britain on heaths, downs, meadows. **FP** Sundry plants and shrubs, including Tufted Hair-grass, dock, sorrel, Broom, Hawthorn. CMM

2227
2228
2229
2229
2230
2231

2231a Northern Deep-brown Dart *Aporophyla lueneburgensis* 37mm Common. Aug–Sep. Variable. Found on moorland and rocky coasts in north Wales, Isle of Man, northern England and Scotland. **FP** Heather, Bilberry, Bird's-foot Trefoil. RL, RL

2232 Black Rustic *Aporophyla nigra* 42mm Common. Sep–Oct. Throughout most of Britain but not eastern England. On heaths, moors, chalk grassland, gardens. Similar to Dot Moth but later flight period and kidney mark only pale at outer edge. **FP** Various plants, including heather, Tufted Hair-grass, clovers. CMM, CMM

2233 Golden-rod Brindle *Lithomoia solidaginis* 45mm Local. Aug–Sep. In northern Britain only, on moors and in open woods. **FP** Heather, Bilberry, Bearberry, Cowberry, Bog Myrtle, willow. IK

2235 Tawny Pinion *Lithophane semibrunnea* 40mm Local. Oct–Nov, Mar–May. Spring flight is after hibernation. Differs from Pale Pinion in having tawny dark crest and dark bar from centre of forewing to trailing corner. Local in southern Britain in woods, parks, gardens. **FP** Ash. CMM

NOCTUIDS: NOCTUIDAE, CUCULLIINAE (cont.)

2236 Pale Pinion *Lithophane hepatica* 40mm Local. Oct–Nov, Mar–May. Similar to above species in lifestyle, habitat and looks, but without the dark bar or crest. **FP** Various trees and shrubs, including oak, sallows, birch, Apple, Horse Chestnut, Privet. CMM

2237 Grey Shoulder-knot *Lithophane ornitopus lactipennis* 38mm Common. Sep–Nov, Feb–Apr. Spring flight is after hibernation. Antler mark at base of forewing is distinctive. In woodland in southern Britain. **FP** Oak. CMM

2238 Conformist *Lithophane furcifera* 42mm Rare migrant. Extremely scarce migrant from Denmark and Scandinavia. Similar to a richly-marked Grey Shoulder-knot. Recorded in 1946 and 2007. TT

2240 Blair's Shoulder-knot *Lithophane leautieri hesperica* 40mm Common. Sep–Nov. First established on Isle of Wight in 1951, now resident throughout Britain in woods, parks, gardens. **FP** Leyland, Lawson's and Monterey Cypress. CMM

2241 Red Sword-grass *Xylena vetusta* 60mm Local. Sep–Oct, Mar–Apr. Spring flight is after hibernation. Large, rich red-brown and straw-coloured, with black sword-shaped streak on outer half of wing. Always local, mainly northern on moorland, damp heaths, woods and marshes, but also on heaths of southern England. **FP** Heather, Bog Myrtle, Yellow Iris, sedges. CMM

2242 Sword-grass *Xylena exsoleta* 60mm Nb. Sep–Oct, Mar–Apr. Similar to Red Sword-grass but grey. On moorland and open woodland in northern Britain. **FP** Heather, Bog Myrtle, Yellow Iris, sedges as above but also Restharrow, Creeping Cinquefoil, Groundsel, dock. DGG

2243 Early Grey *Xylocampa areola* 34mm Common. Mar–May. Common throughout Britain in woods, hedges, gardens. Usually grey, but can be purple-tinged. **FP** Honeysuckle. CJS, CMM

2245 Green-brindled Crescent *Allophyes oxyacanthae* 40mm Common. Sep–Nov. Throughout Britain in woods, hedges, gardens, scrub. Dark form usually found in industrial areas. **FP** Blackthorn, Hawthorn, Crab Apple, Dog Rose, Plum, Rowan. CMM, CJS

2246a Oak Rustic *Dryobota labecula* 30mm Rare migrant. Oct–Dec. Usually migrant but can breed on south coast of England. Kidney mark is ochre or white. **FP** Evergreen (Holm) Oak. CMM

2247 Merveille du Jour *Dichonia aprilina* 45mm Common. Sep–Oct. Unmistakable autumn moth, found throughout Britain in woods, parks, hedges, gardens. **FP** Broadleaved oaks. CMM, CMM, CMM

2248 Brindled Green *Dryobotodes eremita* 35mm Common. Aug–Sep. Throughout Britain in oak woodland, only local in Scotland. Pale mark in centre of wing alongside angled black line. **FP** Broadleaved oaks. CMM, PAD

2249 Beautiful Arches *Blepharita satura* 40mm Unconfirmed. Jul–Oct. Very rare migrant from Europe. DGG

2250 Dark Brocade *Blepharita adusta* 40mm Common. Jun–Jul. Local in southern Britain, more common in the north. On downs, heaths, moors, sand dunes, grassland, woods. **FP** Heather, Bog Myrtle, Alder, Hawthorn, etc. JPo

2251 Flame Brocade *Trigonophora flammea* 50mm Migrant. Sep–Nov. Regular but scarce migrant to south coast. DF

2242

2243

2243

2245

2245 *capucina*

2247

2246a

2247

2247

2248

2248

2249

2250

2251

NOCTUIDS: NOCTUIDAE, CUCULLIINAE (cont.)

2252 Large Ranunculus *Polymixis flavicincta* 45mm Local. Sep–Oct. Southern Britain in gardens, rough ground, sea cliffs. Larger than either Black-banded or Feathered Ranunculus. **FP** Leaves of many wild and cultivated plants, including Michaelmas Daisy, Valerian, plantain, Ragwort. CMM

2252a Cameo *Polymixis gemmea* 35mm Vagrant/Accidental. Jul–Sep. One British record only, from Berkshire in 1979. JV

2253 Black-banded *Polymixis xanthomista statices* 35mm Na. Aug–Sep. Very local on rocky coasts of Cornwall, Devon and south-west Wales, as well as Anglesey and Isle of Man. Greyer than Feathered Ranunculus, with dark central band. **FP** Flowers and leaves of Thrift,

close enough to the sea to get splashed by waves. DGG, DGG

2254 Grey Chi *Antitype chi* 36mm Common. Aug–Sep. Central Britain northwards, on moors, grassy uplands, parks. Elongated X mark on forewing (like Greek letter chi) is diagnostic. **FP** Flowers and leaves of dock, sorrel, etc. DF

2255 Feathered Ranunculus *Polymixis lichenea* 35mm Local. Aug–Oct. Coastal species, most frequent from Isle of Wight westwards around to Scotland, scarce on east coasts and inland. More greenish than Black-banded without dark central band. **FP** Various, including Biting Stonecrop, Sea Plantain, Thrift, Wild Cabbage, Hound's Tongue. CMM

NOCTUIDS: NOCTUIDAE, ACRONICTINAE

This sub-family contains 40 species including chestnuts, sallows and daggers. Daggers have distinctive wing markings and colourful caterpillars, as also are the larvae of Sycamore, Alder and Knot Grass.

2256 Satellite *Eupsilia transversa* 40mm Common. Sep–Apr. Widespread throughout in woods, parks, gardens. Kidney mark with two satellite dots, either fawn or white, is diagnostic. **FP** Leaves of various trees and shrubs, also carnivorous, eating larvae of other moths. CMM, CMM

2257 Orange Upperwing *Jodia croceago* 35mm RDB1. Sep–Nov, Feb–May. Spring flight after hibernation. Very scarce, in open oak woods in southern Britain only, last seen in 1994 in Cardiganshire, Wales. **FP** Oak leaves on coppiced trees and low branches. DM, DM

2258 Chestnut *Conistra vaccinii* 32mm Common. Sep–May. Throughout Britain in woods, hedges, gardens. With or without dark spot in kidney mark, and outer edge of forewing rounded. **FP** Oak, elm, Blackthorn, Hawthorn, birch, dock. CMM, CMM

2259 Dark Chestnut *Conistra ligula* 32mm Common. Oct–Feb. Throughout Britain in woods, farmland, gardens. Similar to Chestnut but darker and forewing outer edge comes to slight hook-tip. **FP** Hawthorn, sallows, oak, dock, Dandelion. CMM

NOCTUIDS: NOCTUIDAE: ACRONICTINAE (cont.)

2260 Dotted Chestnut *Conistra rubiginea* 36mm Nb.
Oct–Nov, Mar–Apr. Spring flight after hibernation.
Found in woods, thick hedges and wooded heaths in
central southern and south-western England and Wales.
FP Unknown in wild but possibly including Apple.
CMM, PGC

2261 Red-headed Chestnut *Conistra erythrocephala*
38mm Rare migrant. Sep–Nov. Scarce migrant, though
breeds in northern France. Red thorax and three black
dots in kidney mark are distinctive. **FP** Oak, elm,
Hornbeam. SN, DF

2262 Brick *Agrochola circellaris* 36mm Common.
Sep–Dec. Throughout Britain, in woods, parks, gardens.
FP Leaves and flowers of Wych Elm, Aspen and other
poplars, sallows, ash. CMM

2263 Red-line Quaker *Agrochola lota* 37mm Common.
Sep–Nov. Throughout in woods, parks, gardens, hedges,
heaths. Grey-looking, with dark spot in kidney mark,
and red outer cross-line. **FP** Catkins and leaves of
willows. CMM

2264 Yellow-line Quaker *Agrochola macilenta* 34mm
Common. Sep–Nov. Throughout Britain in woods,
parks, gardens, hedges, heaths. Yellow-looking, with or
without dark spot in kidney mark, yellow outer cross-
line. **FP** Oak, poplar, Beech, sallows, etc. NS, CMM

2264a Southern Chestnut *Agrochola haematidea* 35mm
RDB2. Sep–Nov. On heathland in central southern
England. Flies for a very short time just at dusk. **FP**
Flowers of Bell Heather. CMM, CMM

2265 Flounced Chestnut *Agrochola helvola* 40mm
Common. Sep–Oct. Throughout, but more common in
south. In woods, scrub, heaths, moors. **FP** Oak, elm,
birch, willow, heather, Bilberry. NS, SH

2266 Brown-spot Pinion *Agrochola litura* 35mm
Common. Aug–Oct. Throughout Britain in woods,
parks, gardens, heaths, hedges. Dark bar at base of
forewing is diagnostic. **FP** Meadowsweet, sorrel, Bladder
Campion, low-growing leaves of oak, Hawthorn,
sallows. DGG

2267 Beaded Chestnut *Agrochola lychnidis* 35mm
Common. Sep–Nov. Common in England and Wales in
woods, hedges, scrub, gardens, heaths. Variable, can be
melanistic in Midlands. **FP** Herbaceous plants, low-
growing tree leaves. CMM, CMM

2268 Suspected *Parastichtis suspecta* 30mm Local.
Jul–Aug. Widespread but local throughout Britain. In
woodland and wooded heaths. **FP** Birch, possibly
sallows. CMM

2264

obsoleta 2264

2265

2264a

2265

2264a

2267

2267

2266

2268

NOCTUIDS: NOCTUIDAE, ACRONICTINAE (cont.)

2269 Centre-barred Sallow *Atethmia centrago* 33mm
Common. Aug–Sep. Common in England and Wales,
but local in Scotland. In woods, hedges, parks with ash
trees. **FP** Buds and flowers of ash. CMM, CMM
2270 Lunar Underwing *Omphaloscelis lunosa* 33mm
Common. Aug–Oct. Common to abundant in southern
Britain, only local in the north. On downs, commons,
rough ground, gardens. **FP** Leaves, stems and roots of
grasses, including Yorkshire Fog, Annual Meadow-grass.
CMM, CMM, CMM
2271 Orange Sallow *Xanthia citrago* 36mm Common.
Aug–Sep. Widespread throughout Britain in urban and
rural areas with mature limes. No dark spot in kidney
mark, unlike Angle-striped Sallow. **FP** Lime. NS
2272 Barred Sallow *Xanthia aurago* 30mm Common.
Sep–Oct. From Yorkshire southwards, in woods, hedges,
farmland, etc. **FP** Field Maple, Beech. DGG, DGG

2273 Pink-barred Sallow *Xanthia togata* 30mm
Common. Sep–Oct. Throughout Britain in damp woods
and marshy places. Red head and shoulders are
distinctive. **FP** Catkins of sallows, poplar, later on leaves
of docks and other herbaceous plants. NS
2274 Sallow *Xanthia icteritia* 35mm Common. Sep–Oct.
Throughout Britain in damp woods and marshy places,
heaths, gardens, hedges. Markings very variable or
almost absent, but with dark spot in kidney mark. Outer
edge of forewing pointed or slightly hooked. **FP** Catkins
of sallows, poplar, later on leaves of docks and other
herbaceous plants. CMM, CMM, CMM
2275 Dusky-lemon Sallow *Xanthia gilvago* 35mm Local.
Aug–Oct. Throughout Britain, but always local, in
woods with mature elms. Markings variable, similar to
Sallow but outer edge of forewing rounded. **FP** Seeds
and leaves of Wych Elm, English Elm. MC

2269　2269　2270
2270　2270

2271

2272

2272

2273

2274

2274

2274

2275

NOCTUIDS: NOCTUIDAE, ACRONICTINAE (cont.)

2276　Pale-lemon Sallow *Xanthia ocellaris* 38mm Na. Sep–Oct. Local in south-east England and East Anglia in parks, urban areas, river banks with poplars. **FP** Catkins, then leaves of Black and other Poplars, as well as vegetation under the trees. RL

2277　Scarce Merveille du Jour *Moma alpium* 38mm RDB3. Jun–Jul. Unmistakable. Very local in mature oak woods in the very south of England. **FP** Pedunculate and Sessile Oak. DGG, SR

2278　Poplar Grey *Acronicta megacephala* 40mm Common. May–Aug. Throughout Britain in woods, commons, parks. Has noticeable pale patch beyond kidney mark. **FP** Aspen, Black and other Poplars, willows. DGG

2279　Sycamore *Acronicta aceris* 45mm Local. Jun–Aug. Mostly in southern Britain, in urban parks, gardens, woods, scrub. Distinctive S-shaped white zig-zag outer cross-line. **FP** Sycamore, Horse Chestnut, Field Maple, oak. CMM

2280　Miller *Acronicta leporina* 40mm Common. May–Aug. Throughout, in woods, heaths, moors, urban areas. White form is usual but grey occurs in the Midlands. **FP** Birch, Alder, willow, Aspen and other poplars, oak. CMM

2281　Alder Moth *Acronicta alni* 35mm Local. May–Jun. Throughout Britain in damp woods and scrub, but not common. **FP** Alder, birch, Goat Willow, etc. NS, CMM

2283　Dark Dagger *Acronicta tridens* 40mm Common. May–Jul. In southern Britain in woods, gardens, etc. Visually identical to Grey Dagger, but different genitalia and caterpillars. **FP** Various trees and shrubs, including Hawthorn, Blackthorn, Rose, sallows, Pear, Apple. DGG

2284　Grey Dagger *Acronicta psi* 44mm Common. May–Jul. In southern Britain in woods, gardens, etc. Visually identical to Dark Dagger, but with different genitalia and caterpillars. **FP** Various trees and shrubs, including Hawthorn, Blackthorn, Apple, birch, lime, elm. NS

2276

2277

2277

2278

2279

2280

suffusa 2281

2281

2284

2283

NOCTUIDS: NOCTUIDAE, ACRONICTINAE (cont.)

2285 Marsh Dagger *Acronicta strigosa* 28mm Extinct. Jun–Jul. Formerly in Cambridgeshire but not seen since 1933. **FP** Hawthorn. CS

2286 Light Knot Grass *Acronicta menyanthidis* 35mm Local. May–Jul. Northern Britain on moors, damp heaths, bogs. Kidney mark has dark outline, very small oval also outlined. **FP** Bog Myrtle, Bilberry, heather, sallows. DGG

2287 Scarce Dagger *Acronicta auricoma* 36mm Migrant. May–Jul. Formerly resident of Sussex, Surrey and Kent, but not seen since around 1920. Scarce migrant since.

Oval mark has central dot. **FP** Oaks. JV, JV

2288 Sweet Gale Moth *Acronicta euphorbiae myricae* 36mm Na. Apr–Jun. Found on moorland in Scotland and Ireland. Lacks 'dagger' mark at base of forewing. **FP** Bog Myrtle, heathers, Eared and Creeping Willow, plantains. RL

2289 Knot Grass *Acronicta rumicis* 38mm Common. May–Jun, Aug–Sep. Throughout Britain in most habitats. Bright white zig-zag at trailing edge where wings meet is diagnostic. **FP** Many herbaceous and woody plants. CMM, DF

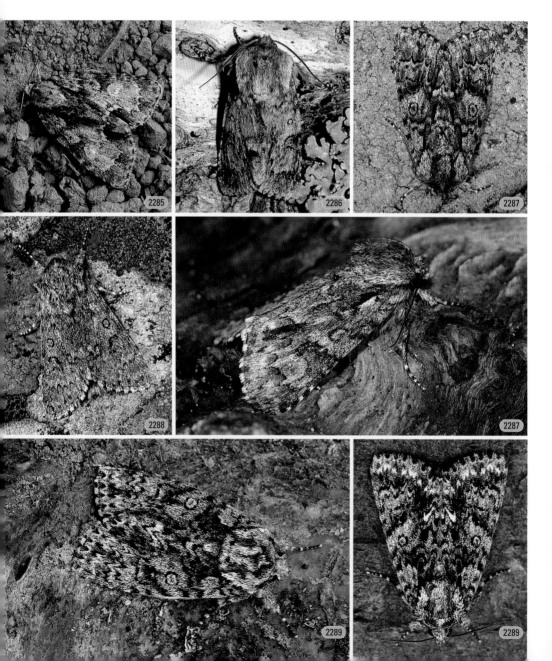

2290 Reed Dagger *Simyra albovenosa* 36mm Nb.
May–Jul, Aug–Sep. In reed-beds in East Anglia. Has a
pure white hind wing. **FP** Common Reed. NS
2291 Coronet *Craniophora ligustri* 37mm Local. Jun–Jul.
Throughout Britain, but more common in south. Found
anywhere. Has crown-like area beyond kidney mark. White
marked form is usual. **FP** Ash, Wild Privet. CMM
2292 Tree-lichen Beauty *Cryphia algae* 28mm Rare
migrant. Jul–Sep. Usually recorded from southern coasts.
Broad, lichen-coloured band near forewing base is
distinctive. NS
2293 Marbled Beauty *Cryphia domestica* 25mm

Common. Jul–Aug. Throughout Britain, often urban but
almost anywhere. Has pale band with black wavy cross-
line right across forewing near base. **FP** Lichens on rocks,
walls, trees, roofs. CMM
2294 Marbled Grey *Cryphia raptricula* 30mm Rare
migrant. Jul–Aug. Occasional records from south-east
coast. **FP** Lichens on rocks, walls, trees, roofs. AMF
2295 Marbled Green *Cryphia muralis* 30mm Local.
Jul–Aug. Found in southern England, mainly coastal.
Variable ground colour, without continuous band and
cross-line of Marbled Beauty. **FP** Lichens on rocks, walls,
roofs. CMM, PAD

NOCTUIDS: NOCTUIDAE, AMPHIPYRINAE

A varied and confused group of 100 species, often with rather descriptive names. It includes the wainscots whose larvae feed inside stems of foodplants.

2296 Levant Blackneck *Tathorhynchus exsiccata* 30mm Rare migrant. African species, occasionally arrives on warm southerly winds, even in February. MC

2297 Copper Underwing *Amphipyra pyramidea* 50mm Common. Jul–Oct. Widespread in southern Britain as far north as Yorkshire. In woods, parks, gardens. Very similar to Svensson's Copper Underwing. Viewed from underneath (in a clear container), underwing has minimal copper marking beside body. **FP** Many low-growing trees and shrubs. CMM, NS

2298 Svensson's Copper Underwing *Amphipyra berbera svenssoni* 50mm Common. Jul–Sep. Widespread in southern Britain as far north as Yorkshire. In woods, parks, gardens. Very similar to Copper Underwing. Viewed from underneath (in a clear container), underwing has copper marking extending full length of body. **FP** Pedunculate Oak, lime, Hornbeam, sallows, Rhododendron. CMM, NS

2299 Mouse Moth *Amphipyra tragopoginis* 35mm

Common. Jul–Sep. Throughout Britain in woods, gardens, dunes, moors. Mouse-coloured and runs to hide when exposed. **FP** Leaves and flowers of various herbaceous plants. CMM

2300 Old Lady *Mormo maura* 70mm Local. Jul–Sep. Throughout but local in woods, marshes, gardens, hedges. Sometimes found roosting in sheds. **FP** Herbaceous and woody plants, including Ivy, dock, Hawthorn. CMM

2301 Bird's Wing *Dypterygia scabriuscula* 38mm Local. May–Jul. Mainly in central and south-east England, in woods, scrub, rough ground. **FP** Dock, sorrel, Knotgrass, etc. CMM

2302 Brown Rustic *Rusina ferruginea* 38mm Common. Jun–Jul. Throughout Britain, in woods, heaths, grassland, suburban gardens. **FP** Herbaceous plants, including docks, plantains, vetches. CMM

2302a Guernsey Underwing *Polyphaenis sericata* 35mm Channel Islands. Jun–Aug. In sheltered coastal valleys on Jersey and Guernsey only. **FP** Honeysuckle. CMM

2297

2296

2297

2298

2298

2299

2300

2301

2302a

2302

NOCTUIDS: NOCTUIDAE, AMPHIPYRINAE (cont.)

2303 Straw Underwing *Thalpophila matura* 40mm
Common. Jul–Aug. Throughout, but local in north.
In gardens, parks, dunes, sea cliffs, open grassland.
FP Various grasses. CMM

2304 Orache Moth *Trachea atriplicis* 42mm Rare migrant.
Jun–Jul. Formerly resident in East Anglia, last seen in
1915. Now resident in Channel Islands, migrant on
south coast, potential resident. **FP** Orache, Goosefoot,
Knotgrass, etc. MC

2305 Small Angle Shades *Euplexia lucipara* 33mm
Common. Jun–Jul. Rests with forewing edge folded and
head slightly down, similar to Angle Shades. Prominent
cream kidney-mark. Throughout Britain in parks, woods,
heaths, moors. **FP** Woody and herbaceous plants, espially
Bracken. Also ferns, Foxglove, nettle, Mallow, etc. CMM

2306 Angle Shades *Phlogophora meticulosa* 50mm
Common. May–Oct. Unmistakable, with similar resting
pose to Small Angle Shades. Found anywhere
throughout Britain. **FP** Many wild and cultivated woody
and herbaceous plants. CMM

2308 Latin *Callopistria juventina* 33mm
Vagrant/Accidental. Scarce migrant from southern
Europe. **FP** Bracken. DF

2309 Latreille's Latin *Callopistria latreillei* 28mm

Migrant. One specimen in Natural History Museum,
London, from 1856, marked 'Bred'. Second record from
Kent, 26 Oct 2006. Resident of southern Europe and
Canary Isles. NOT ILLUSTRATED

2310 Cumberland Gem *Eucarta amethystina* 30mm
Unconfirmed. Dubious old record from Cumberland.
CMM

2310a Silvery Gem *Eucarta virgo* 28mm Migrant.
Herefordshire 2006. Possible import. From south-east
Europe but range is expanding. RDJ

2311 Double Kidney *Ipimorpha retusa* 28mm Local.
Jul–Sep. Southern Britain only, in damp woods and
marshes. Cross-lines parallel, pointing back, with hooked
wingtip. Oval mark roughly kidney shaped.
FP Sallows and other willows, Black Poplar. CMM

2312 Olive *Ipimorpha subtusa* 28mm Local. Jul–Sep.
Local through Britain to southern Scotland in damp
woods, parks, gardens. **FP** Aspen and other poplars. DF

2313 Angle-striped Sallow *Enargia paleacea* 38mm Nb.
Aug–Sep. In Midlands and central Scotland in woods
and heathland with mature birch. Markings vary from
strong to almost plain, but dark spot in kidney is
constant, which Orange Sallow does not have.
FP Silver and Downy Birch. RL

2303   2305   2304   2306

2310

2310a

2308

2311

2312

2313

NOCTUIDS: NOCTUIDAE, AMPHIPYRINAE (cont.)

2314 Dingy Shears *Parastichtis ypsillon* 38mm Local. Jun–Aug. Rather plain with tooth mark and dark marks between oval and kidney. Local, mainly southern, in damp woods, marshes. **FP** Leaves and catkins of sallows and other willows, poplars. NS

2315 Heart Moth *Dicycla oo* 32mm RDB3. Jun–Jul. In very mature, open, oak woods and parks around Surrey and Berkshire. **FP** Pedunculate Oak. CMM

2316 Lesser-spotted Pinion *Cosmia affinis* 30mm Local. Jul–Aug. Widespread from Yorkshire southwards in elm

woods and hedges. White forewing leading-edge marks are smaller than on White-spotted Pinion. **FP** Elms. JPo

2317 White-spotted Pinion *Cosmia diffinis* 30mm Na. Jul–Aug. In central southern England on mature elms. Bolder and brighter markings than Lesser-spotted Pinion. **FP** Elms. DGG

2318 Dun-bar *Cosmia trapezina* 34mm Common. Jul–Sep. Throughout Britain, anywhere with trees or shrubs. Variable colour, but constant markings. **FP** Most trees and shrubs. CMM, CJS

2319 Lunar-spotted Pinion *Cosmia pyralina* 30mm Local. Jul–Aug. Widespread from Yorkshire southwards in parks, gardens, woods and hedges. Leading forewing edge is curved. **FP** Elms, Apple, Bullace, Hawthorn, Blackthorn. CMM

2320 Saxon *Hyppa rectilinea* 40mm Nb. May–Jun. In Scotland and northern England in open woods and moorland. **FP** Sallows, Bramble, Raspberry, Bilberry, Bearberry, Cowberry. RPJ

2321 Dark Arches *Apamea monoglypha* 50mm Common. Jun–Aug, Sep–Oct. Common to abundant throughout Britain, occurs almost anywhere. **FP** Grasses, including Cock's-foot, Couch. CJS, CJS

2322 Light Arches *Apamea lithoxylaea* 45mm Common. Jun–Aug. Throughout Britain, in grassy areas. Dark scythe-shaped mark in centre is distinctive. **FP** Grasses, including Annual Meadow-grass. DF

2323 Reddish Light Arches *Apamea sublustris* 42mm Local. Jun–Jul. Local in southern and central England in downland, breckland, vegetated dunes. **FP** Probably on grasses. DF

NOCTUIDS: NOCTUIDAE, AMPHIPYRINAE (cont.)

2324 Exile/Northern Arches *Apamea zeta* 40mm Na. Jul–Aug. In Highlands of Scotland on high moorland. Form from Shetland Isles known as Exile. **FP** Probably on grasses. RL, DF

2325 Crescent Striped *Apamea oblonga* 44mm Nb. Jun–Aug. Coastal on salt marshes, estuaries, tidal river banks. Indistinct markings, with a silky sheen. **FP** Roots and stems of Saltmarsh-grass, Red Fescue. NS, RL

2326 Clouded-bordered Brindle *Apamea crenata* 42mm Common. May–Jul. Throughout Britain in gardens, downland, moors, coastal vegetated dunes. Two regular colour forms. **FP** Cock's-foot and other grasses. CMM, CMM

2327 Clouded Brindle *Apamea epomidion* 40mm Common. Jun–Jul. Throughout Britain, but more common in the south. Found in open woods, scrub, parks. Markings more distinct than Clouded-bordered Brindle, with dark outline to oval. **FP** Grasses, including Tufted Hair-grass, Cock's-foot. NS, DF

2328 Scarce Brindle *Apamea lateritia* 42mm Rare migrant. Jul–Aug. Mostly east-coast records, from northern Europe. **FP** Grasses. DM

2329 Confused *Apamea furva britannica* 36mm Local. Jul–Sep. Mainly northern on rocky coasts and high moorland in Wales, Midlands and into Scotland. Similar to Dusky Brocade but greyer, markings less distinct. **FP** Grasses, including Rough and Wood Meadow-grass. RL

2330 Dusky Brocade *Apamea remissa* 40mm Common. Jun–Jul. Throughout Britain in gardens, grassland, open woods. Very variable but distinct W on outer pale cross-line, and rounded tip to forewing. **FP** Grasses, including Reed Canary-grass, Common Couch. CMM

2331 Small Clouded Brindle *Apamea unanimis* 33mm Common. May–Jul. Throughout Britain in damp areas. Kidney mark is defined with white. **FP** Grasses, including Reed Canary-grass, Wavy Hair-grass. PAD

2333 Large Nutmeg *Apamea anceps* 43mm Local. Jun–Jul. On chalk downs, farms, in gardens and woods, mainly in southern Britain. Markings clear but weak, including fine cross-lines and white outlines to oval and kidney marks. **FP** Grasses, including cereals, Cock's-foot, Common Couch. DF

2334 Rustic Shoulder-knot *Apamea sordens* 40mm Common. May–Jul. Throughout Britain in grassland, open woods, gardens. **FP** Grasses, including cereals, Cock's-foot, Common Couch. CMM

2324   2324   2325

2326   *combusta*   2326   2325

NOCTUIDS: NOCTUIDAE, AMPHIPYRINAE (cont.)

2335 Slender Brindle *Apamea scolopacina* 35mm Local. Jun–Aug. In woodland from Yorkshire southwards. Dark patch on back of thorax is obvious. **FP** Grasses, including Wood Millet, Wood Mellick, Wood Meadow-grass, False Brome, Quaking-grass. CMM, NS

2336 Double Lobed *Apamea ophiogramma* 30mm Local. Jun–Aug. Unmistakable. Throughout Britain in damp woods, fens, marshes, gardens. **FP** Wild and cultivated forms of Reed Canary-grass, Pampas-grass. CMM

2337 Marbled Minor *Oligia strigilis* 25mm Common. May–Jul. Frequent throughout Britain in grassy habitats. Variable, can be very similar to Rufous and Tawny Marbled Minor, but usually with distinct white outer

band and dark central band. Genitalia examination required for certainty. **FP** Grasses. CMM

2338 Rufous Minor *Oligia versicolor* 25mm Local. Jun–Jul. Throughout Britain, but local. Variable, *see above* species. Oval and kidney marks often pale brown. **FP** Grasses. DGG

2339 Tawny Marbled Minor *Oligia latruncula* 25mm Common. May–Jul. Throughout Britain. Variable, *see above* species, but usually with coppery outer band. **FP** Grasses. CMM

2340 Middle-barred Minor *Oligia fasciuncula* 22mm Common. Jun–Jul. Throughout Britain in damp woods, grassland, gardens. **FP** Grasses, including Tufted Hair-grass. CMM

2341 Cloaked Minor *Mesoligia furuncula* 22mm
Common. Jul–Sep. Throughout, but local in
northern Britain. On coastal cliffs, dunes, downs with
short grass. Extremely variable but central bar, if
present, is narrow, and ground colour not pink as in
Rosy Minor. **FP** Grasses, including Tufted Hair-grass,
Sheep's Fescue, False Oat-grass. CMM, CMM, RW

2342 Rosy Minor *Mesoligia literosa* 25mm Common.
Jul–Aug. Throughout, but more local in northern
Britain. On coastal cliffs, dunes, downs with short grass.
Variable but central bar is narrow, ground colour pink or
red-brown with grey. **FP** Grasses, including Sheep's
Fescue, False Oat-grass, Marram. DF, CMM

2343 Common Rustic *Mesapamea secalis* 32mm
Common. Jul–Aug. This and Lesser Common Rustic
virtually identical visually, and both variable. Only
reliably separated by genitalia examination. Common to
abundant throughout. **FP** Grasses, including Cock's-foot
and fescues. CMM, DGG

2343a Lesser Common Rustic *Mesapamea didyma*
32mm Common. Jul–Aug. This and Common Rustic
virtually identical visually, and both variable, though
black with white kidney mark usually indicates Lesser
Common Rustic. Only reliably separated by genitalia
examination. Common to abundant throughout. **FP**
Grasses, including Cock's-foot and fescues. CJS

2343b Remm's Rustic *Mesapamea remmi* Local.
Probably a different form of Common and Lesser
Common Rustic. NOT ILLUSTRATED

NOCTUIDS: NOCTUIDAE, AMPHIPYRINAE (cont.)

2344 Least Minor *Photedes captiuncula* 16mm RDB3. Jun–Aug. Very scarce, restricted to open limestone grassland areas of northern England, mainly coastal. Flies in afternoon sunshine. **FP** Glaucous Sedge. DGG

2345 Small Dotted Buff *Photedes minima* 28mm (♂), 22mm (♀) Common. Jun–Aug. Throughout Britain in damp woods and meadows. **FP** Tufted Hair-grass. CMM, DF

2346 Morris's Wainscot *Chortodes morrisii* 30mm RDB1. Jun–Jul. Extremely local, from 25km of coast from west Dorset to Devon on undercliffs. **FP** Tall Fescue. DF

2346 Bond's Wainscot *Chortodes morrisii bondii* RDB1. Jun–Jul. A local form of Morris's Wainscot, formerly on a cliff at Folkestone, Kent, but not seen since 1970. **FP** Tall Fescue. NOT ILLUSTRATED

2347 Concolorous *Chortodes extrema* 26mm RDB3. Jun–Jul. Extremely local in the counties of Huntingdon, Northampton, Lincoln and Leicester. Found in marshy woods and fens. Has conspicuous row of black dots near outer edge of forewing. **FP** Purple and Wood Small-reed. AM, AM

2348 Lyme Grass *Chortodes elymi* 35mm Nb. Jun–Aug. In coastal sand dunes and salt marsh from Suffolk north to Scotland, and at Camber Sands, Sussex. Two colour forms. **FP** Lyme-grass. SR, SR

2349 Mere Wainscot *Chortodes fluxa* 25mm Nb. Jul–Aug. In damp, ancient woods and rough, wet meadows in central and southern England. Kidney mark has grey patch. **FP** Wood Small-reed. SR, DF

2350 Small Wainscot *Chortodes pygmina* 25mm Common. Aug–Sep. Throughout Britain, in damp woods, marshes, etc. Colours vary. **FP** Sedges, rushes, grasses. CMM, CMM, NS

2351 Fenn's Wainscot *Chortodes brevilinea* 34mm RDB3. Jul–Aug. In reed-beds in East Anglia. Wings dusted black, with row of black dots for outer cross-line. **FP** Common Reed. AF

2352 Dusky Sallow *Eremobia ochroleuca* 34mm Common. Jul–Sep. On grassland in southern and eastern England from Yorkshire southwards. Unmistakable. **FP** Grasses, including Cock's-foot, False Oat-grass, Couch. CMM, NS

2353 Flounced Rustic *Luperina testacea* 35mm Common. Aug–Sep. Throughout Britain on grassland, especially coastal dunes. Colour varies, but pattern fairly constant. **FP** Grasses, including Couch, fescues. CJS, CMM

NOCTUIDS: NOCTUIDAE, AMPHIPYRINAE (cont.)

2354 Sandhill Rustic *Luperina nickerlii* 30mm Na. Jul–Sep. Scarce, on coastal beaches in Kent, Essex, Cornwall, north Wales and Lancashire. Oval is tiny, kidney chalky white. **FP** Sand Couch, Saltmarsh-grasses. NS

2355 Dumeril's Rustic *Luperina dumerilii* 32mm Migrant. Aug–Sep. A few records from south coast. **FP** Grass roots. NS, MSP

2357 Large Ear *Amphipoea lucens* 36mm Local. Aug–Sep. All four 'ear' moths are very similar and can only be reliably distinguished by genitalia examination. Large Ear is found on wet acid moors and marsh in western and northern Britain. Kidney mark is often orange-red. **FP** Roots and stems of Purple Moor-grass, Common Cottongrass. DF

2358 Saltern Ear *Amphipoea fucosa paludis* 35mm Local. Aug–Sep. On salt marshes, sand dunes and wet moors around coasts of southern Britain. Kidney mark usually white and crescent shaped, but *see* above species. **FP** Probably grass stems and roots. DF

2359 Crinan Ear *Amphipoea crinanensis* 30mm Local. Aug–Sep. On moors and damp meadows in northern Britain. Both kidney and oval marks usually orange. **FP** Probably grass stems and roots. RL

2360 Ear Moth *Amphipoea oculea* 30mm Common. Jul–Sep. Throughout Britain on damp meadows, moors, marshes, in damp, open woods. Kidney and oval marks usually orange or white. **FP** Roots and stems of grasses, including Annual Meadow-grass, Tufted Hair-grass. PAD

2361 Rosy Rustic *Hydraecia micacea* 40mm Common. Aug–Oct. Throughout Britain in gardens, hedges, fields, open woods. Variable size and ground colour, but usually pink-brown tinge. **FP** Various low plants, including dock, plantain, Woundwort, Potato, Strawberry, Hop. CMM

2362 Butterbur *Hydraecia petasitis* 50mm Local. Aug–Sep. Local throughout, but mostly in northern England. Larger and browner than Rosy Rustic, with pointed forewing. **FP** Butterbur. MD

2363 Marsh Mallow Moth *Hydraecia osseola hucherardi* 45mm RDB1. Sep. Very local in two locations in Kent and East Sussex in saline marshy meadows. First discovered in 1951. **FP** Marsh Mallow. DGG

2364 Frosted Orange *Gortyna flavago* 40mm Common. Aug–Oct. Throughout Britain in woods, hedges, pastures, dunes. **FP** Thistles, Burdock, Foxglove, Ragwort, mullein, etc. CMM

2365 Fisher's Estuarine Moth *Gortyna borelii lunata* 50mm RDB2. Sep–Oct. Similar to above species, but unlikely to be found casually. Easy to see sitting on foodplant after dark in Essex and Kent marshes, as long as you can find the foodplant in the first place! **FP** Stems and roots of Hog's Fennel. CMM, CMM

2366 Burren Green *Calamia tridens* 40mm RDB2. Jul–Aug. Only in limestone Burren area of Ireland. **FP** Blue Moor-grass. GF

2367 Haworth's Minor *Celaena haworthii* 25mm Local. Aug–Sep. Local in northern Britain, very local in south, on boggy acid moors and marsh. **FP** Cottongrass. TJN

NOCTUIDS: NOCTUIDAE, AMPHIPYRINAE (cont.)

2368   Crescent *Celaena leucostigma* 36mm Local.
Jul–Sep. Throughout in reed-beds, marshes, moors.
Crescent-shaped pale kidney mark, sometimes with
white streaks. **FP** Yellow Iris, Great Fen-sedge. PAD, NS
2369   Bulrush Wainscot *Nonagria typhae* 45mm
Common. Jul–Sep. Throughout Britain but local in
Scotland. Dark marks along outer edge of forewing with
fine dark streaks just in from the edge. Female larger and
paler than male. **FP** Bulrush (Giant Reedmace) and
Lesser Bulrush. DF
2370   Twin-spotted Wainscot *Archanara geminipuncta*
25mm Local. Aug–Sep. Found mainly in southern
Britain, sometimes common. In reed-beds, reedy
ditches, ponds. Pale to dark brown with, ideally, two
white spots in kidney mark, but can be one or none.
FP Inside stems of Common Reed. NS, PAD, CMM
2371   Brown-veined Wainscot *Archanara dissoluta*
26mm Local. Jul–Sep. In reed-beds in southern Britain.
Dark streak down centre of forewing, kidney mark
usually outlined with white. **FP** Inside stems of
Common Reed. DF

2372   White-mantled Wainscot *Archanara neurica* 26mm
RDB3. Jul–Aug. Very scarce, from 15km stretch of
coastal reed-beds in Suffolk only. Has faint white collar
(mantle) behind head and three faint white marks along
central vein. **FP** Inside stems of Common Reed. NS
2373   Webb's Wainscot *Archanara sparganii* 42mm Nb.
Aug–Oct. Southern Britain in ponds, lakes, ditches,
mostly near coasts. Usually with dark central mark and
row of black dots at outer margin. **FP** In stems of Giant
Reedmace (Bulrush), also Lesser Reedmace, Yellow Iris,
Common Club-rush, Branched Bur-reed. PAD, DF
2374   Rush Wainscot *Archanara algae* 32mm RDB3.
Aug–Sep. Very local, in East Anglia, Surrey and
Sussex in lakes, gravel pits, broads. Pointed forewing
tip, without black dots along edge. **FP** Inside stems of
Bulrushes (Reedmace), Yellow Iris, Common Club-
rush. RL
2375   Large Wainscot *Rhizedra lutosa* 45mm Common.
Aug–Oct. Throughout Britain, but local in Scotland. In
damp, but not wet, reed-beds, ditches. **FP** Inside roots
and stem bases of Common Reed. CMM, CMM, CMM

2372

2373 ♂

2373 ♀

2374 ♂

2375

2375

2375

NOCTUIDS: NOCTUIDAE, AMPHIPYRINAE (cont.)

2376 Blair's Wainscot *Sedina buettneri* 26mm RDB1. Sep–Oct. Flies briefly at dusk in early October. Very scarce, in stands of sedge in east Dorset, where it was re-discovered in 1996 after being thought extinct since 1952. Small, brownish with very pointed wingtip, dark hind wing. **FP** Inside stems of Lesser Pond-sedge. CMM

2377 Fen Wainscot *Arenostola phragmitidis* 32mm Local. Jul–Aug. In reed-beds in south and east England, Midlands and north Wales. Plain wing sometimes darker towards outer edge, slightly silky look. **FP** Inside stems of Common Reed. DF

2378 Brighton Wainscot *Oria musculosa* 30mm pRDB. Jul–Aug. Discovered near Brighton in late 19th century, now confined to Salisbury Plain. Possibly extinct. **FP** In stems of grasses and cereals. DGG

2379 Small Rufous *Coenobia rufa* 20mm Local. Jul–Aug. Mainly in southern Britain, in fens, bogs, marshy fields. Outer cross-line represented by a few small dark dots. **FP** Inside stems of Jointed, Sharp-flowered and Soft Rush. DGG

2380 Treble Lines *Charanyca trigrammica* 35mm Common. May–Jul. Common in England and Wales in gardens, hedges, heaths, grassland, open woods. **FP** Low plants, including plantains, Dandelion, Knapweed, thistles. CMM, CMM

2381 Uncertain *Hoplodrina alsines* 33mm Common. Jun–Aug. Throughout, but local in Scotland. In woods,

meadows, gardens, etc. Named because of similarity to Rustic. Cross-lines scalloped, with narrow dark central bar, hind wing brown. **FP** Low plants, including Primrose, Chick-weed, dock, Dead-nettle. DF

2382 Rustic *Hoplodrina blanda* 33mm Common. Jun–Aug. Throughout Britain in most lowland habitats. Similar to Uncertain but cross-lines and central bar less distinct, and hind wing paler. **FP** Low plants, including dock, plantain. DF

2383 Powdered Rustic *Hoplodrina superstes* 30mm Vagrant/Accidental. Jun–Aug. Only seven British records. Very similar to above species, but greyer. **FP** Low plants, including dock, plantain. CS

2384 Vine's Rustic *Hoplodrina ambigua* 30mm Local. May–Jul, Aug–Sep. In England and Wales, mainly southern. In grassland, open woods, gardens. Smaller, paler and greyer than Uncertain and Rustic. **FP** Low plants, including dock, plantain, knotgrass. DGG

2385 Small Mottled Willow *Spodoptera exigua* 26mm Migrant. Jun–Oct. Regular migrant, usually in south. Rests with wings wrapped around body; oval and kidney marks are orange. **FP** Various herbaceous plants. CMM

2386 Mediterranean Brocade *Spodoptera littoralis* 40mm Migrant. Jun–Oct. Scarce migrant and import from Africa, southern Mediterranean, Canary Islands. **FP** Wide variety of fruit and vegetables, including Banana, Maize, Potato, Chrysanthemum. NO

2379

2380

2381

2382

bilinea 2380

2383

2384

2385

2386

NOCTUIDS: NOCTUIDAE, AMPHIPYRINAE (cont.)

2386c Dark Mottled Willow *Spodoptera cilium* 30mm Rare migrant. African species, also present in southern Spain and France, Canary Islands. **FP** Short grass on lawns, golf courses. TD

2387 Mottled Rustic *Caradrina morpheus* 32mm Common. Jun–Aug. Throughout Britain, in gardens, woods, farmland, scrub. No outline to kidney mark or oval. **FP** Various plants, including nettle, dock, Dandelion. DF

2387a Clancy's Rustic *Platyperigea kadenii* 30mm Migrant. Sep–Oct. First recorded 2002, many records since. Pale grey and plain, only kidney mark shows. CMM

2388 Lorimer's Rustic *Paradrina flavirena* Oct. One British record from Middlesex in 1967. Similar to Pale Mottled Willow, but rests with wings wrapped around body like Small Mottled Willow. NOT ILLUSTRATED

2389 Pale Mottled Willow *Paradrina clavipalpis* 30mm Common. May–Jul, Aug–Oct. Throughout Britain, on farms, grassland, urban gardens. Dark marks along forewing edge and white marks in kidney distinguish this from similar moths. **FP** Seeds of grass, cereals, plantains, Garden Peas. CMM

2391 Silky Wainscot *Chilodes maritimus* 28mm Local. Jun–Jul. In reed-beds from Yorkshire southwards. Variable, but curved forewing leading edge, pointed tip and absence of palps help identification. **FP** Feeds on live or dead invertebrates as well as in stems of Common Reed. DF, CMM, DF

2386c

2387

2387a

2389

bipunctata　2391

2391

wismariensis　2391

2392 Marsh Moth *Athetis pallustris* 35mm RDB3. May–Jun. Known from two sites on Lincolnshire coast only, on damp meadow just behind sand dunes. Female is much smaller than male. **FP** Meadowsweet, Ribwort Plantain. LG

2392a Porter's Rustic *Proxenus hospes* 25mm Vagrant/Accidental. May–Sep. Southern European species, occasionally recorded along south coast. CMM

2393 Reddish Buff *Acosmetia caliginosa* 30mm RDB1. May–Jun. Named after its colour. Found in one spot on Isle of Wight only, on open heath. Female is smaller than male. **FP** Saw-wort. TJN

2394 Anomalous *Stilbia anomala* 35mm Local. Aug–Sep. Found in Scotland, Wales, Midlands, south-west and southern England on heaths and moors, and Brecks of East Anglia. Female is smaller and browner with markings less clearly defined than in male. **FP** Wavy and Tufted Hair-grass. CMM

2396 Rosy Marbled *Elaphria venustula* 18mm Nb. May–Jul. Occurs mainly in south-east England from Dorset to East Anglia in open woods and heaths on acid soils. **FP** Probably Tormentil, Creeping Cinquefoil. CMM, TJN

NOCTUIDS: NOCTUIDAE, STIRIINAE

The day-flying Small Yellow Underwing is the only British member of this sub-family.

2397 Small Yellow Underwing
Panemeria tenebrata 18mm Local. May–Jun. Widespread in England, Wales, south-east Scotland. Very small, flies busily in sunshine in flowery meadows, rests immediately if shaded. **FP** Seeds of Common and Field Mouse-ear. SR

NOCTUIDS: NOCTUIDAE, HELIOTHINAE

A small group of fast-flying moths on the wing by day or night. Most have a broad, dark, outer band on the hind wing.

2399 Bordered Sallow *Pyrrhia umbra* 35mm Local. Jun–Jul. Throughout Britain, mainly on costal dunes and cliffs, but also on downland in south. **FP** Common and Spiny Restharrow. JSB

2400 Scarce Bordered Straw *Helicoverpa armigera* 40mm Migrant. Sep–Oct. Variable, similar to smaller, scarcer, Eastern Bordered Straw, but only weak or no dark dots on outer edge of forewing. **FP** Pest on cultivated plants, including Cotton, Maize, Tomato. NS, CMM

2401 Marbled Clover *Heliothis viriplaca* 33mm RDB3. Jun–Jul, Aug. Found in Brecklands of East Anglia, downs and meadows of south-east England. Also a migrant. Similar to Shoulder-striped Clover but front of central cross-band does not reach thorax. Flies in sunshine. **FP** Flowers and seeds of various plants, including Restharrow, campion, Carrot, clover, Groundsel. CMM

2402 Shoulder-striped Clover *Heliothis maritima* 33mm RDB3. Jun–Jul. Very local on damp, acid, southern heaths. Similar to Marbled Clover, but front of central cross-band reaches thorax. Flies in sunshine. Subspecies *bulgarica* recorded once in Britain by the author's uncle in Kent in 1947. **FP** Flowers of Cross-leaved Heath, heather, Bog Asphodel. DF

2403 Bordered Straw *Heliothis peltigera* 35mm Migrant. Jun–Sep. Regular migrant. Dark mark between kidney and leading edge and single black dot in trailing corner are diagnostic. **FP** Restharrow, Ploughman's Spikenard, Scentless Mayweed, Groundsel. DGG, CMM

2404 Eastern Bordered Straw *Heliothis nubigera* 37mm Vagrant/Accidental. Scarce migrant from eastern Mediterranean, Canary Islands. Smaller than Scarce Bordered Straw, with bold black dots along outer edge of forewing. PAD

2405 Spotted Clover Moth *Schinia scutosa* 33mm Rare migrant. Jun–Aug. European species. **FP** Wormwood, Goosefoot. DM

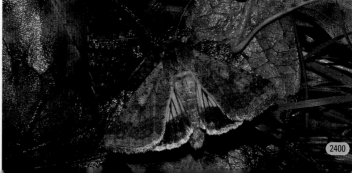

NOCTUIDS: NOCTUIDAE, ACONTIINAE

A largely tropical sub-family, so includes several migrant species. Most have small, rounded wings, unlike most other noctuids.

2407 Purple Marbled *Eublemma ostrina* 20mm Migrant. May–Oct. Scarce, from southern Europe and North Africa. **FP** Flowers and seedheads of thistles. PGC, MC
2407a Beautiful Marbled *Eublemma purpurina* 25mm Migrant. May–Oct. First recorded in 2004 in Dorset. From mainland Europe on dry, open grassland. **FP** Flowers and seedheads of thistles. DF, NS
2408 Small Marbled *Eublemma parva* 15mm Migrant. Mar–Oct. Scarce migrant from southern Europe, North Africa, India. **FP** Flowers of Common Fleabane, Ploughman's Spikenard. CMM, DF

NOCTUIDS: NOCTUIDAE, ACONTIINAE (cont.)

2410 Marbled White Spot *Protodeltote pygarga* 23mm Common. May–Jul. Common in southern England, local in Wales and Midlands. In woods, heaths and moors. **FP** Grasses, including Purple Moor-grass, False Brome. CMM

2411 Pretty Marbled *Deltote deceptoria* 25mm Migrant. Apr–Jul. Scarce, from central Europe. **FP** Grasses. DGG, CMM

2412 Silver Hook *Deltote uncula* 22mm Local. May–Jul. Scattered throughout Britain in fens, marshes, boggy heathland and moors. **FP** Grasses and sedges, including Tufted Hair-grass, Wood-sedge. DGG

2413 Silver Barred *Deltote bankiana* 22mm RDB3. May–Jul, Aug. Resident in Chippenham and Wicken Fens in Cambridgeshire, migrant elsewhere. **FP** Purple Moor-grass, Smooth Meadow-grass. CMM

2413a Shining Marbled *Pseudeustrotia candidula* 22mm Vagrant/Accidental. May–Sep. One British record on 28 Oct 2006 from Hereford. Occurs in eastern Europe from Sweden down to Iran. Likely to have been imported as larva or egg in fruit

plants. **FP** Grasses, bur-reeds, docks, sorrels. CMM

2414 Spotted Sulphur *Emmelia trabealis* 20mm Presumed extinct. Jun–Jul. Formerly resident in Brecklands of East Anglia but not seen since 1960. **FP** Field Bindweed. NS

2415 Pale Shoulder *Acontia lucida* 28mm Rare migrant. Jun–Aug. From hot, dry parts of southern Europe and North Africa. CMM, MC

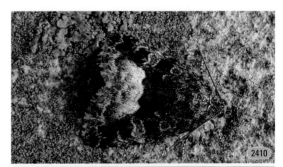
2410

2411

2411

2412

2413a

2413

2415 · 2415 · 2414

NOCTUIDS: NOCTUIDAE, EARIADINAE

Mainly tropical or sub-tropical; many are agricultural pests. One British resident only.

2418 Cream-bordered Green Pea *Earias clorana* 22mm Nb. May–Jul, Aug.
Widespread but local from Yorkshire southwards, in fens, marshes, damp woods,
riversides, damp heaths in Dorset. **FP** Sallows and other willows, including
Creeping Willow. CMM
2420a Bollworm *Earias vittella* 24mm Import. From Asia. The one shown came to
light at Swanage, Dorset, in a period of high migration activity. **FP** Okra. SN

2420a

2418

NOCTUIDS: NOCTUIDAE, CHLOEPHORINAE

Only three British residents.
The other members are
tropical.

2421 Scarce Silver-lines
Bena bicolorana 45mm Local.
Jun–Jul. Occurs in woodland
from southern Britain up to
Yorkshire. **FP** Oaks. CMM,
PGC

2421

2421

NOCTUIDS: NOCTUIDAE, CHLOEPHORINAE (cont.)

2422 Green Silver-lines *Pseudoips prasinana britannica* 36mm Common. Jun–Jul, Aug–Sep. Frequent in woodland in south, more local in northern England and Scotland. **FP** Oak, birch, Beech, hazel, Aspen, etc. JV, NS

2423 Oak Nycteoline *Nycteola revayana* 24mm Local. Sep–Nov, Mar–May. Spring flight is after hibernation. Can be common in oak woodland in southern England, more local elsewhere. Extremely variable, but shape and long palps are distinctive. **FP** Oak. CMM, CMM, NS, CMM

NOCTUIDS: NOCTUIDAE, PANTHEINAE

The widespread Nut-tree Tussock is the only British member of this sub-family.

2425 Nut-tree Tussock *Colocasia coryli* 35mm Common. Apr–Jun, Jul–Sep. Throughout Britain, in broadleaved woodland. **FP** Hazel, birch, Beech, oak, Field Maple, Hornbeam. CMM

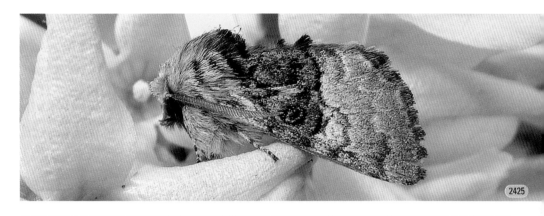

NOCTUIDS: NOCTUIDAE, PLUSIINAE

This sub-family contains 20 or so species, often with shiny Y-marks, gold spots or brassy patches as well as conspicuous tufts on the thorax and abdomen.

2428 Golden Twin-spot *Chrysodeixis chalcites* 40mm Migrant. Scarce visitor from southern Europe, North Africa, Canary Islands. Gold sheen and dark spot in centre of outer edge of forewing as well as (usually) twin spots help identification. **FP** Tobacco, Sage, Chrysanthemum, etc. NS, DGG

2429 Tunbridge Wells Gem *Chrysodeixis acuta* Very scarce, from North Africa. Similar to above species, but less golden. First recorded Tunbridge Wells, Kent, in 1870. NOT ILLUSTRATED

2430 Scar Bank Gem *Ctenoplusia limbirena* 38mm Rare migrant. Very scarce, from Africa, Canary Islands, Madeira. Similar to Ni, Silver Y (*see* photos), but has small dark oval near outer edge of forewing. MC

2432 Ni Moth *Trichoplusia ni* 33mm Migrant. May–Oct. From southern Europe and North Africa. Similar to more common Silver Y but marked less like Y, often white tip is separate. Has white mark in trailing corner of forewing. PAD

NOCTUIDS: NOCTUIDAE, PLUSIINAE (cont.)

2433 Slender Burnished Brass *Trysanoplusia orichalcea* 40mm Migrant. Aug–Oct. Scarce, from Canary Islands, Azores, Africa. TD

2434 Burnished Brass *Diachrysia chrysitis* 40mm Common. Jun–Jul, Aug–Sep. Throughout Britain on rough ground, commons, hedges, gardens. Has dark central band across forewing. **FP** Common Nettle, also Dead-nettle, Marjoram, Spear Thistle. CMM

2434a Cryptic Burnished Brass *Diachrysia stenochrysitis* 40mm Details as for Burnished Brass, but with dark bar across centre of wing split by 'brass' colour. MSP, CMM

2435 Scarce Burnished Brass *Diachrysia chryson* 45mm Na. Jul–Aug. Local in southern England and Wales in damp, open woods, marshes, fens, river valleys. **FP** Hemp-agrimony, mostly on plants growing in shade. JSB

2436 Dewick's Plusia *Macdunnoughia confusa* 36mm Rare migrant. Jul–Oct. Scarce. Widespread in Europe. Elongated silvery mark is diagnostic. Similar to resident Gold Spangle, which has much shorter, thicker, more golden mark.

FP Common Nettle, Yarrow, Chamomile. CMM

2437 Golden Plusia *Polychrysia moneta* 44mm Common. Jun–Aug. Garden species mainly in southern Britain. **FP** Flowers and leaves of Delphinium, Monk's-hood, Larkspur. PGC

2438 Purple-shaded Gem *Euchalcia variabilis* 40mm Vagrant/Accidental. A very few records from the 18th century. From mountainous areas of Europe. GF

2439 Gold Spot *Plusia festucae* 38mm Common. Jun–Jul, Aug–Sep. Throughout Britain in damp woods, fens, ditches, river banks, heaths, moors. Similar to scarcer Lempke's Gold Spot. **FP** Sedges, Yellow Iris, Water-plantain. CMM

2440 Lempke's Gold Spot *Plusia putnami gracilis* 35mm Local. Jul–Aug. Found in fens of East Anglia and northern Britain. Similar to Gold Spot, but paler, smaller, outer of two central white marks is rounder, apical streaks at forewing tip are shorter. **FP** Wood and Purple Small-reed. RPJ

2433　2434a　2434　2434a　2435

2436

2437

2438

2439

2440

aberration

2439

NOCTUIDS: NOCTUIDAE, PLUSIINAE (cont.)

2441 Silver Y *Autographa gamma* 40mm Migrant. May–
Oct. Usually a common to abundant breeding migrant,
but does not overwinter. Flies by day visiting flowers, at
sunset and at night. Similar to scarce Ni Moth but 'Y'
more pronounced, without white mark in trailing corner.
FP Various wild and cultivated plants, including Cabbage,
Runner Bean, bedstraws, clover, nettle. NS, CMM
2442 Beautiful Golden Y *Autographa pulchrina* 40mm
Common. May–Aug. Throughout Britain in woods,

hedges, gardens, heaths, moors. Deeper, richer colour
and more ornate than Plain Golden Y, with faintly
outlined kidney mark. **FP** Herbaceous plants, including
nettle, Honeysuckle, Ragwort. MSP, DGG
2443 Plain Golden Y *Autographa jota* 40mm Common.
Jun–Aug. Throughout Britain in woods, hedges,
gardens, heaths, moors. Plainer than above species.
FP Herbaceous plants, including Common Nettle,
Dead-nettle, Honeysuckle. PAD, CMM

gammina   2441

2442

2441

2442

2443

2443

2444 Gold Spangle *Autographa bractea* 42mm Common. Jul–Aug. Widespread in northern Britain, in woods, gardens, hedges, moors, meadows. Similar to migrant Dewick's Plusia but pale central mark much more condensed. **FP** Herbaceous plants, including Common Nettle, Dead-nettle, Honeysuckle, Bilberry, Ground-ivy. CMM

2445 Stephen's Gem *Megalographa biloba* 38mm Vagrant/Accidental. An abundant North American species recorded as an immigrant about five times. The one shown came to light on the Gower Peninsula, Wales, in 2002. **FP** Pest on Tobacco, Cabbage, Lettuce. DJP

2447 Scarce Silver Y *Syngrapha interrogationis* 35mm Local. Jun–Aug. Resident in northern Britain on moorland. Occasional immigrants occur in south. **FP** Heather, Bilberry. JV

2448 Essex Y *Cornutiplusia circumflexa* 40mm Vagrant/Accidental. Two British records. One in Essex in 1802, another in Hampshire in 1979. RPJ

2449 Dark Spectacle *Abrostola triplasia* 36mm Common. Jun–Jul, Aug–Sep. Widespread throughout but more common in western Britain. In gardens, hedgerows, cliffs, marshes. Similar to Spectacle but generally larger and dark red-brown rather than grey. **FP** Common Nettle, Hop. CMM

2450 Spectacle *Abrostola tripartita* 33mm Common. May–Jul, Jul–Sep. Throughout Britain in gardens, hedges, fields, open woods, waste ground. Named after markings on front of thorax that resemble spectacles. Similar to above species but greyer. **FP** Common Nettle. CMM, DGG

2445

2444

2447

2448

2450

2449

2450

NOCTUIDS: NOCTUIDAE, CATOCALINAE

There are only 12 species in this sub-family, which includes the large red or blue underwing moths. Their larvae are flattened to be camouflaged on a twig (*see* Caterpillars section, pp.322 and 324).

2451 Clifden Nonpareil *Catocala fraxini* 95mm Migrant. Aug–Oct. Usually on eastern coasts of Britain, from north-east Europe. Large and unmistakable. **FP** Aspen and other poplars. DGG

2451a Minsmere Crimson Underwing *Catocala conjuncta* 70mm Migrant. One British record from Minsmere, Suffolk, in September 2004. Resident of southern Europe, North Africa, Middle East. **FP** Holm (Evergreen) Oak. JBH

2452 Red Underwing *Catocala nupta* 80mm Common. Aug–Oct. Widespread in south-east and central England, more local in south-west and Wales. Inhabits woodland, parks, riverbanks, gardens. **FP** Black and White Poplar, Aspen, Crack and White Willow. CMM

2453 Rosy Underwing *Catocala electa* 80mm Vagrant/Accidental. Sep. Six British records only. From southern European forests. **FP** Willow, Aspen. DM

2454 Light Crimson Underwing *Catocala promissa* 60mm RDB3. Jul–Sep. Confined to large mature oak woods of New Forest, Hampshire. Smaller and greyer than Dark Crimson Underwing. **FP** Oak. DGG, DGG

2455 Dark Crimson Underwing *Catocala sponsa* 70mm RDB2. Jul–Sep. Confined to large mature oak woods of New Forest, Hampshire. **FP** Oak. DGG

2455a Oak Yellow Underwing *Catocala nymphagoga*

42mm Vagrant/Accidental. Jul–Aug. Very rare migrant from oak woods of central and southern Europe. **FP** Oak. DGG

2456 Lunar Double-stripe *Minucia lunaris* 60mm Migrant. May–Jun. Immigrant and occasional resident, in open managed oak woodland. **FP** Coppiced Pedunculate and Evergreen Oak. TJN

2460 Passenger *Dysgonia algira* 42mm Vagrant/Accidental. Aug–Sep. Scarce migrant from southern Europe. **FP** Castor-oil, Pomegranate, Bramble. NS

2461 Geometrician *Prodotis stolida* 30mm Vagrant/Accidental. Sep. Scarce migrant from southern Europe. **FP** Oak, Bramble. RPJ

2462 Mother Shipton *Callistege mi* 32mm Common. May–Jul. Named after 16th-century Yorkshire witch because of wing markings. Flies in sunshine in open meadows, heaths, downs, verges. Throughout, but local in Scotland. **FP** Clovers, Black Medick, Lucerne, Bird's-foot Trefoil. CMM

2463 Burnet Companion *Euclidia glyphica* 30mm Common. May–Jul. Common in southern England, local in rest of Britain. Flies on warm days in grassland, meadows, downs, verges. **FP** Clovers, Black Medick, Lucerne, Bird's-foot Trefoil, Tufted Vetch. DF

2451

2451a

2452

2453

NOCTUIDS: NOCTUIDAE, OPHIDERINAE

This grouping includes a dozen or so varied species that just do not fit anywhere else.

2464 Alchymist *Catephria alchymista* 44mm Rare migrant. Jun–Sep. From open woods of Europe. **FP** Oak. CMM
2464a Sorcerer *Aedia leucomelas* 38mm Rare migrant. First British record 11 Sep 2006 from Isle of Wight. From southern Europe, around Mediterranean. RH
2465 Four-spotted *Tyta luctuosa* 25mm Na. May–Jun, Jul–Aug. Very local, mainly confined to Portland, Dorset and main east-coast railway line in Northamptonshire. Likes hot, dry, south-facing slopes. **FP** Field Bindweed. CMM, CMM
2466 Blackneck *Lygephila pastinum* 40mm Local. Jun–Jul. Local, from Yorkshire southwards. In damp meadows and open woods, fens, marsh and downland. **FP** Tufted Vetch. DGG
2467 Scarce Blackneck *Lygephila craccae* 40mm RDB3.

Jul–Aug. Similar to Blackneck, but has dark marks along leading edge of forewing, pale veins and incomplete kidney mark. Found on rocky cliffs of north coasts of Cornwall, Devon and Somerset. **FP** Wood Vetch. CMM
2469 Herald *Scoliopteryx libatrix* 46mm Common. Aug–Nov, Mar–Jun. Unmistakable. Spring flight is after hibernation in a shed, cave, or hollow tree. Throughout Britain in woods, hedges, gardens, etc. **FP** Willows, Aspen and other poplars. NS
2470 Small Purple-barred *Phytometra viridaria* 18mm Local. May–Jul. Widespread, but mainly in southern Britain. Flies in sunshine and at night. Usually as shown but also occurs as more unifomly olive-brown. On heathland, downs, open woods, sandhills. **FP** Common and Heath Milkwort. DF, CMM

2464 · 2464a · 2465 · 2467 · 2466 · 2465 · 2469 · 2470 · 2470

NOCTUIDS: NOCTUIDAE, RIVULINAE

Members of this sub-family resemble Geometers, especially the Waved Black. The larva of the Beautiful Hook-tip resembles a lichen (*see* Caterpillars section, p.324).

2472 Lesser Belle *Colobochyla salicalis* 28mm Presumed extinct. May–Jul. Formerly resident at Hamstreet, Kent, but last seen in 1977. Smaller than other Belles, with outer cross-line curving into wingtip. **FP** Leaves of Aspen and on young shoots and suckers. DGG
2473 Beautiful Hook-tip *Laspeyria flexula* 30mm Local. Jun–Aug. Found in southern Britain in woods, parks, old orchards, mature gardens. **FP** Lichens growing on various trees. CMM, DGG

2474 Straw Dot *Rivula sericealis* 23mm Common. Jun–Jul, Aug–Sep. Throughout Britain, in damp grassland, damp woods, heaths, moors. Also occurs as migrant. **FP** False Brome, Tor-grass, Purple Moor-grass. DF
2475 Waved Black *Parascotia fuliginaria* 30mm Nb. Jun–Jul. Mainly in central southern Britain, in boggy woodland. Rests with wings spread like a Geometer. **FP** Damp fungi on rotting wood, especially birch and pines. DGG

SNOUTS: NOCTUIDAE, HYPENINAE

The long palps resemble a snout, hence the vernacular name. The wings are always delta-shaped at rest.

2476 Beautiful Snout *Hypena crassalis* 30mm Local. May–Aug. On heathland, moors, open woodland in southern Britain. **FP** Bilberry. Possibly also heathers. DF

2477 Snout *Hypena proboscidalis* 38mm Common. Jun–Aug, Sep–Oct. Throughout Britain in most habitats wherever foodplant occurs. **FP** Common Nettle. CMM

2478 Bloxworth Snout *Hypena obsitalis* 32mm RDB3. Sep–Oct, May–Jun. Hibernates for 6 months over winter. First recorded as immigrant at Bloxworth, Dorset, in 1884. Breeds on rocky southern coasts from Dorset to Cornwall. Also occurs as darker form than shown. **FP** Pellitory-of-the-wall. SH

2479 Paignton Snout *Hypena obesalis* 40mm Vagrant/Accidental. Aug–Oct. Rare. First recorded at Paignton, Devon, in 1908. Larger, plainer, with slimmer and more pointed wing than Bloxworth Snout. **FP** Common Nettle. MB

2480 Buttoned Snout *Hypena rostralis* 30mm Nb. Aug–Oct, Apr–Jun. Spring flight after hibernation. In southern Britain in hedgerows, gardens, river valleys. Found over winter in sheds, garages, etc. **FP** Hop. NS

NOCTUIDS: NOCTUIDAE, STREPSIMANINAE

The four members of this sub-family are known as snouts, like the members of the Hypeninae sub-family, on account of their enlarged palps (sensory mouth parts projecting in front of the head). They are smaller than the Hypeninae and are easily overlooked as Micros.

2482 White-line Snout *Schrankia taenialis* 20mm Nb. Jul–Aug. Found in damp woods, open heaths and shady hedgebanks in southern Britain. **FP** Unknown in wild. DGG

2483 Autumnal Snout *Schrankia intermedialis* RDB3. Sep–Oct. Found in Hertfordshire. Probable rare hybrid (six records) of White-line and Pinion-streaked Snouts. **FP** Unknown in wild. NOT ILLUSTRATED

2484 Pinion-streaked Snout *Schrankia costaestrigalis* 20mm Local. Jun–Aug, Sep–Oct. Throughout Britain, more common in south. Inhabits damp woods, boggy heaths, riversides, marshy meadows. **FP** Unknown in wild. DGG

2485 Marsh Oblique-barred *Hypenodes humidalis* 15mm Nb. Jun–Aug. Throughout Britain. Inhabits damp woods, boggy heaths and moors, riversides, marshy meadows. Tiny. Outer oblique bar extends to wingtip. **FP** Unknown in wild. DGG

FAN-FOOTS: NOCTUIDAE, HERMINIINAE

Members of this sub-family are similar to snouts, but bland-looking. The brown larvae feed on withered leaves.

2488 Common Fan-foot *Pechipogo strigilata* 32mm Na. May–Jun. Scarce, in ancient woods in southern Britain. Flight period is earlier than other Fan-foots. Cross-lines all diffuse, kidney-mark faint. **FP** Withered leaves of damaged oak. TJN

2488a Plumed Fan-foot *Pechipogo plumigeralis* 28mm Vagrant/Accidental. Jul–Oct. Possibly resident on coasts of Kent and Sussex. Outer cross-line white-edged, distinct kidney-mark. **FP** Roses, Broom, Ivy. CMM

FAN-FOOTS: NOCTUIDAE, HERMINIINAE (cont.)

2489 Fan-foot *Zanclognatha/Herminia tarsipennalis* 30mm Common. Jun–Aug. Throughout, but local in northern Britain. In woods, thick hedges, gardens. Three cross-lines distinct, outermost does not reach into wingtip. Male antennae have a bulge. **FP** Withered leaves of oak, Beech, Bramble. DF

2490 Jubilee Fan-foot *Zanclognatha lunalis* 32mm Vagrant/Accidental. Jul–Aug. Similar to Plumed Fan-foot but outer cross-line indistinct. **FP** Withered leaves. NS

2491 Shaded Fan-foot *Herminia tarsicrinalis* 28mm RDB3. Jun–Jul. Inhabits dense Bramble thickets in East Anglia. Similar to Fan-foot, but slightly smaller and with diffuse, faint, shaded central bar running through weak crescent mark. **FP** Withered leaves of Bramble. NS

2491a Dusky Fan-foot *Zanclognatha zelleralis* 32mm Vagrant/Accidental. One British record only, from Pembrokeshire in 1982. DM

2492 Small Fan-foot *Herminia grisealis* 25mm Common. Jun–Aug. Throughout Britain in woods, hedgerows, scrub, gardens. Smaller than Fan-foot, outer cross-line runs into wingtip. **FP** Healthy, withered and fallen leaves of various trees, including oak, Hawthorn, birch, hazel, Cherry, etc. NS

2493 Dotted Fan-foot *Macrochilo cribrumalis* 28mm Nb. Jun–Aug. In south-east England, especially East Anglia, in fens, bogs, marshy areas. **FP** Wood-sedge, Hairy and Field Wood-rush. CMM

2494 Clay Fan-foot *Paracolax tristalis* 32mm Na. Jun–Aug. Inhabits coppiced open woodland in south-east England. Has only two cross-lines. **FP** Damp, fallen oak leaves. CMM

2495 Olive Crescent *Trisateles emortualis* 28mm RDB3. Jun–Jul. Very local in mature woods in north Essex and the Chilterns, Buckinghamshire. Only two pale cross-lines. Occurs as migrant along south coast from Dorset eastwards. **FP** Withered leaves of oak, Beech. CMM

CATERPILLARS, EGGS AND PUPAE

Lepidopterans are egg-layers. The eggs (or ova) incubate for varying periods, depending on the species, and may be a matter of days, or several months over the winter so that eggs laid in autumn hatch in spring as fresh plant growth emerges for caterpillars to feed on.

The eggs hatch into caterpillars (or larvae), which come in various shapes, sizes and colours. Some are camouflaged, whereas some possess warning coloration. The larvae simply eat and grow. As they get larger they change their skin to allow for more growth, usually four times before pupation – these stages are known as 'instars'. Early instars can look very different from later ones.

Pupation may be after weeks, months over the winter, or years in the case of Goat Moth. The larva of this species feeds inside live trees, which are low in nourishment so larval development is slow. The hard, protective cover of the pupa (or chrysalis) allows the insect to develop inside before it splits open allowing the adult insect to pump up its wings and (usually) fly off to seek a mate. There are some wingless female moths that hatch in winter and conserve energy by letting the males do all the flying, and there is even one micro-moth female, *Acentria ephemerella*, that lives under water and does not fly.

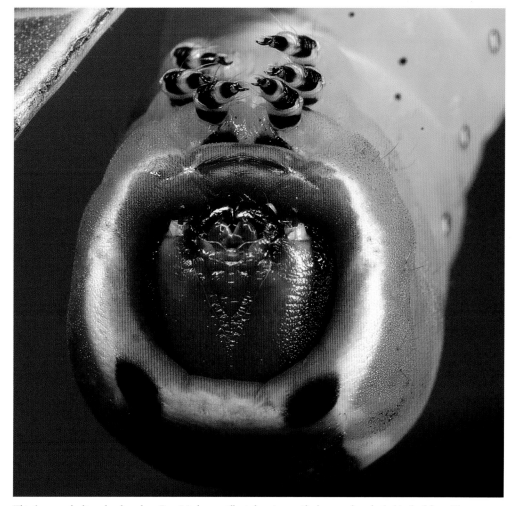

This fearsome looking, but harmless, Puss Moth caterpillar is hanging upside down under a leaf of its foodplant. The head-on view shows mouth parts and the true legs on the thoracic segments that will be the legs of the adult moth. JV

BUTTERFLIES

1539 Swallowtail *Papilio machaon* 50mm PE (all photos) (ADULT: P. 78)
1546 Brimstone *Gonepteryx rhamni* 35mm PE, PE (ADULT: P. 78)
1548 Black-veined White *Aporia crataegi* 35mm PE, PE (ADULT: P. 78)
1549 Large White *Pieris brassicae* 45mm CMM (ADULT: P. 80)
1553 Orange-tip *Anthocharis cardamines* 30mm PE, PE (ADULT: P. 80)
1556 Brown Hairstreak *Thecla betulae* 18mm PE, PE (ADULT: P. 81)
1562 Large Copper *Lycaena dispar* 20mm PE, PE (ADULT: P. 82)
1567a Geranium Bronze *Cacyreus marshalli* PE (ADULT: P. 83)

1539

early instar – pupating   1539

pupating   1539

pupa   1539

1546

1548

pupa   1548

pupa   1546

1549

1553

1556

egg 1553

egg 1556

1562

pupa 1567a

pupa 1562

BUTTERFLIES (cont.)

1575 Chalk-hill Blue *Lysandra coridon* 15mm PE
(ADULT: P. 84)
1576 Adonis Blue *Lysandra bellargus* PE (ADULT: P. 84)
1580 Holly Blue *Celastrina argiolus* 15mm PE
(ADULT: P. 86)
1582 Duke of Burgundy Fritillary *Hamearis lucina* PE
(ADULT: P. 87)
1584 White Admiral *Limenitis camilla* 27mm PE, PE
(ADULT: P. 87)

1585 Purple Emperor *Apatura iris* 40mm PE, PE, JV
(ADULT: P. 88)
1590 Red Admiral *Vanessa atalanta* PE (ADULT: P. 88)
1593 Small Tortoiseshell *Aglais urticae* 30mm PE
(ADULT: P. 88)
1594 Large Tortoiseshell *Nymphalis polychloros* 40mm
PE, PE (ADULT: P. 88)
1597 Peacock *Inachis io* 40mm KP-G (ADULT: P. 88)
1598 Comma *Polygonia c-album* PE, PE (ADULT: P. 90)

1575
pupa 1576
1580
1584
pupa 1582
egg 1584

1585

pupa 1585

1585

pupa 1590

1594

1593

pupa 1594

1597

1598

pupa 1598

BUTTERFLIES (cont.)

1599 European Map *Araschnia levana* 25mm PE, PE, PE
(ADULT: P. 90)
1603 Queen of Spain Fritillary *Issoria lathonia* 30mm
PE, PE (ADULT: P. 90)
1606 High Brown Fritillary *Argynnis adippe* 40mm PE,
PE (ADULT: P. 92)
1607 Dark Green Fritillary *Argynnis aglaja* 40mm PE
(ADULT: P. 92)

1608 Silver-washed Fritillary *Argynnis paphia* 42mm PE
(ADULT: P. 92)
1610 Marsh Fritillary *Eurodryas aurinia* 30mm PE
(ADULT: P. 92)
1612 Glanville Fritillary *Melitaea cinxia* 26mm PE, PE,
PE (ADULT: P. 92)
1613 Heath Fritillary *Mellicta athalia* 25mm PE, PE, PE
(ADULT: P. 92)

eggs 1599

1599

pupa 1599

pupa 1603

1603

pupa 1606

1606

1607

1608

1610

eggs 1612

1612

pupa 1612

eggs 1613

1613

pupa 1613

BUTTERFLIES (cont.)

1614 Speckled Wood *Pararge aegeria* 28mm PE, PE, PE
(ADULT: P. 94)
1615 Wall *Lasiommata megera* 25mm PE (ADULT: P. 94)
1618 Scotch Argus *Erebia aethiops* 25mm PE
(ADULT: P. 94)
1620 Marbled White *Melanargia galathea* 30mm PE
(ADULT: P. 94)
1621 Grayling *Hipparchia semele* 30mm JV (ADULT: P. 94)

1626 Meadow Brown *Maniola jurtina* 27mm PE
(ADULT: P. 94)
1627 Small Heath *Coenonympha pamphilus* 20mm PE
(ADULT: P. 94)
1628 Large Heath *Coenonympha tullia* 25mm PE
(ADULT: P. 94)
1629 Ringlet *Aphantopus hyperantus* 22mm PE, PE
(ADULT: P. 96)

1614

pupa 1614

adult ready to emerge 1614

1615

1618

1620

pupa 1620

1621

1626

1627

1628

1629

pupa 1629

GOAT, BURNETS, FESTOON AND CLEARWINGS

eggs and young larvae 173

173

underside 173

174

374

emerged pupa 374

EGGARS: LASIOCAMPIDAE

1631 **December Moth** *Poecilocampa populi* 45mm NS (ADULT: P. 106)
1633 **Small Eggar** *Eriogaster lanestris* 47mm SH, NS (ADULT: P. 106)
1634 **Lackey** *Malacosoma neustria* 50mm DGG (ADULT: P. 106)
1635 **Ground Lackey** *Malacosoma castrensis* 50mm DGG, JV, JV (ADULT: P. 106)
1636 **Grass Eggar** *Lasiocampa trifolii trifolii* 65mm JV (ADULT: P. 106)

1631

1633

larval web   1633

1634

1635

1635

1636

eggs   1635

EGGARS: LASIOCAMPIDAE (cont.)

1637 Oak Eggar *Lasiocampa quercus* 80mm JV, NS
(ADULT: P. 106)
1638 Fox Moth *Macrothylacia rubi* 70mm DGG, NS
(ADULT: P. 108)
1639 Pine Tree Lappet *Dendrolimus pini* 60mm JV
(ADULT: P. 108)
1640 Drinker *Euthrix potatoria* 65mm , DGG, NS
(ADULT: P. 108)
1642 Lappet *Gastropacha quercifolia* 80mm DGG
(ADULT: P. 108)

early instar　1637

1637

1638

young larva　1638

1639

early instar　1640

1640

1642

EMPEROR MOTH: SATURNIIDAE

1643 Emperor *Saturnia pavonia* 65mm MJ, SH (young larva), JV, NS, SH (ADULT: P. 109)

1643

pupating 1643

young larva 1643

first instar 1643

HOOK-TIPS: DREPANIDAE

1645 Scalloped Hook-tip *Falcaria lacertinaria* DGG
(ADULT: P. 111)
1646 Oak Hook-tip *Watsonalla binaria* 23mm DGG
(ADULT: P. 111)

1647 Barred Hook-tip *Watsonalla cultraria* 20mm JV
(ADULT: P. 111)
1651 Chinese Character *Cilix glaucata* 17mm DGG
(ADULT: P. 111)

early instar 1645 1646

1647 1651

THYATIRIDAE

1654 Figure of Eighty *Tethea ocularis octogesimea* 35mm JV (ADULT: P. 112)
1659 Yellow Horned *Achlya flavicornis* 30mm JV, JV (ADULT: P. 112)
1660 Frosted Green *Polyploca ridens* 33mm DGG (ADULT: P. 112)

1659

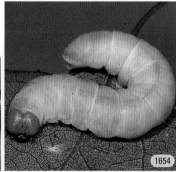

1654

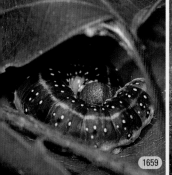

1659

1660

GEOMETERS: GEOMETRIDAE

1663 March Moth *Alsophila aescularia* 26mm DGG
(ADULT: P. 113)
1665 Grass Emerald *Pseudoterpna pruinata atropunctaria* 27mm DGG (ADULT: P. 114)
1666 Large Emerald *Geometra papilionaria* 33mm JV
(ADULT: P. 114)
1669 Common Emerald *Hemithea aestivaria* 28mm DGG
(ADULT: P. 114)

1672 Sussex Emerald *Thalera fimbrialis* 30mm JV
(ADULT: P. 114)
1674 Little Emerald *Jodis lactearia* 20mm JV, JV
(ADULT: P. 114)
1675 Dingy Mocha *Cyclophora pendularia* 22mm SH
(ADULT: P. 116)

GEOMETERS: GEOMETRIDAE (cont.)

1680 Maiden's Blush *Cyclophora punctaria* 24mm JV, DGG, DGG (ADULT: P. 117)

1704 Silky Wave *Idaea dilutaria* 13mm DGG (ADULT: P. 120)

1726 Large Twin-spot Carpet *Xanthorhoe quadrifasiata* 25mm NS (ADULT: P. 124)

1737 Small Argent and Sable *Epirrhoe tristata* 21mm JV, JV (ADULT: P. 126)

1741 Many-lined *Costaconvexa polygrammata* 25mm JV, JV (ADULT: P. 127)

1743 Yellow-ringed Carpet *Entephria flavicinctata* 22mm NS (ADULT: P. 127)

1747 Streamer *Anticlea derivata* 27mm DGG (ADULT: P. 127)

1756 Northern Spinach *Eulithis populata* 25mm DGG (ADULT: P. 128)

1759 Small Phoenix *Ecliptopera silaceata* 25mm JV, JV (ADULT: P. 128)

1761 Autumn Green Carpet *Chloroclysta miata* 25mm DGG (ADULT: P. 128)

1764 Common Marbled Carpet *Chloroclysta truncata* 25mm DGG (ADULT: P. 130)

1768 Grey Pine Carpet *Thera obeliscata* 22mm JV (ADULT: P. 130)

pupa 1680

1680

1680

1704

1726

1737

egg 1737

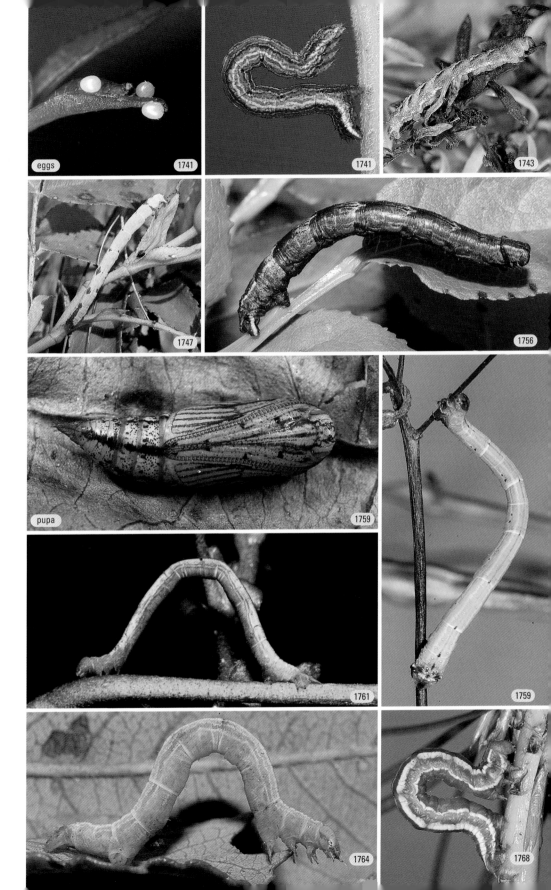

eggs 1741

1741

1743

1747

1756

pupa 1759

1759

1761

1764

1768

GEOMETERS: GEOMETRIDAE (cont.)

1769 Spruce Carpet *Thera britannica* 22mm DGG (ADULT: P. 132)

1771 Juniper Carpet *Thera juniperata* 22mm DGG (ADULT: P. 132)

1771a Cypress Carpet *Thera cupressata* 25mm DGG (ADULT: P. 132)

1772 Netted Carpet *Eustroma reticulata* 23mm DGG (ADULT: P. 132)

1773 Broken-barred Carpet *Electrophaes corylata* 25mm JV (ADULT: P. 132)

1775 Mottled Grey *Colostygia multistrigaria* 19mm JV, JV (ADULT: P. 133)

1776 Green Carpet *Colostygia pectinaria* 19mm NS (ADULT: P. 133)

1777 July Highflyer *Hydriomena furcata* 20mm DGG (ADULT: P. 133)

1789 Scallop Shell *Rheumaptera undulata* 21mm JV (ADULT: P. 134)

1790 Tissue *Triphosa dubitata* 30mm DGG (ADULT: P. 134)

1791 Brown Scallop *Philereme vetulata* 22mm JV (ADULT: P. 134)

1792 Dark Umber *Philereme transversata britannica* 27mm NS (ADULT: P. 136)

1795 November Moth *Epirrita dilutata* 21mm DGG, DGG (ADULT: P. 136)

1797 Autumnal Moth *Epirrita autumnata* 22mm JV (ADULT: P. 136)

1799 Winter Moth *Operophtera brumata* 20mm DGG, JV (ADULT: P. 136)

1800 Northern Winter Moth *Operophtera fagata* 20mm DGG (ADULT: P. 138)

1810 Marsh Carpet *Perizoma sagittata* 20mm NS (ADULT: P. 139)

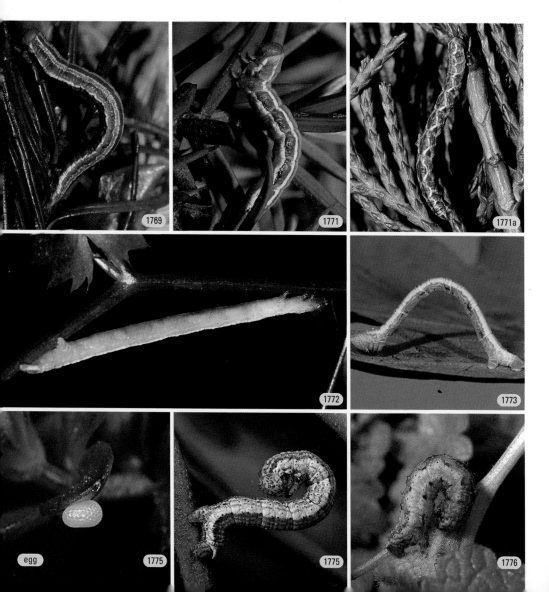

1769

1771

1771a

1772

1773

egg

1775

1775

1776

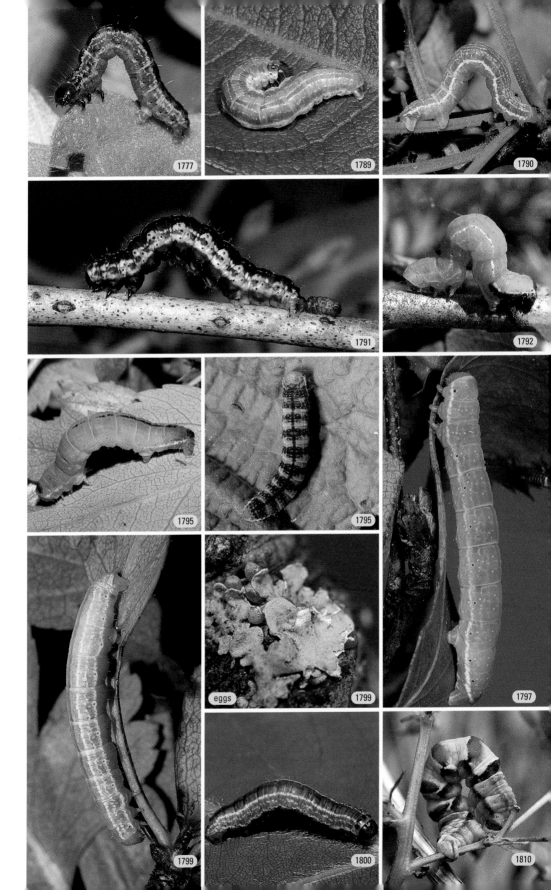

1777

1789

1790

1791

1792

1795

1795

1797

eggs

1799

1799

1800

1810

PUGS: GEOMETRIDAE, EUPITHECIA

1816 **Toadflax Pug** *Eupithecia linariata* 20mm DGG (ADULT: P. 140)

1819 **Mottled Pug** *Eupithecia exiguata* 25mm DGG (ADULT: P. 141)

1825 **Lime-speck Pug** *Eupithecia centaureata* 22mm DGG (ADULT: P. 141)

1828 **Satyr Pug** *Eupithecia satyrata* 23mm DGG (ADULT: P. 142)

1832 **Currant Pug** *Eupithecia assimilata* 23mm DGG (ADULT: P. 142)

1837 **Grey Pug** *Eupithecia subfuscata* 25mm NS (ADULT: P. 142)

1838 **Tawny-speckled Pug** *Eupithecia icterata* 25mm DGG (ADULT: P. 142)

1841 **Yarrow Pug** *Eupithecia millefoliata* 18mm NS (ADULT: P. 142)

1846 **Narrow-winged Pug** *Eupithecia nanata* 21mm JV, DGG, DGG (ADULT: P. 142)

1852 **Brindled Pug** *Eupithecia abbreviata* 25mm DGG (ADULT: P. 144)

1853 **Oak-tree Pug** *Eupithecia dodoneata* 23mm DGG (ADULT: P. 144)

1854 **Juniper Pug** *Eupithecia pusillata* 18mm DGG, DGG (ADULT: P. 144)

1859 **Sloe Pug** *Pasiphila chloerata* 11mm NS (ADULT: P. 144)

1860 **Green Pug** *Pasiphila rectangulata* 12mm DGG (ADULT: P. 144)

1862 **Double-striped Pug** *Gymnoscelis rufifasciata* 15mm DGG (ADULT: P. 144)

1816 1819 1825 1828 1838 1832 1837

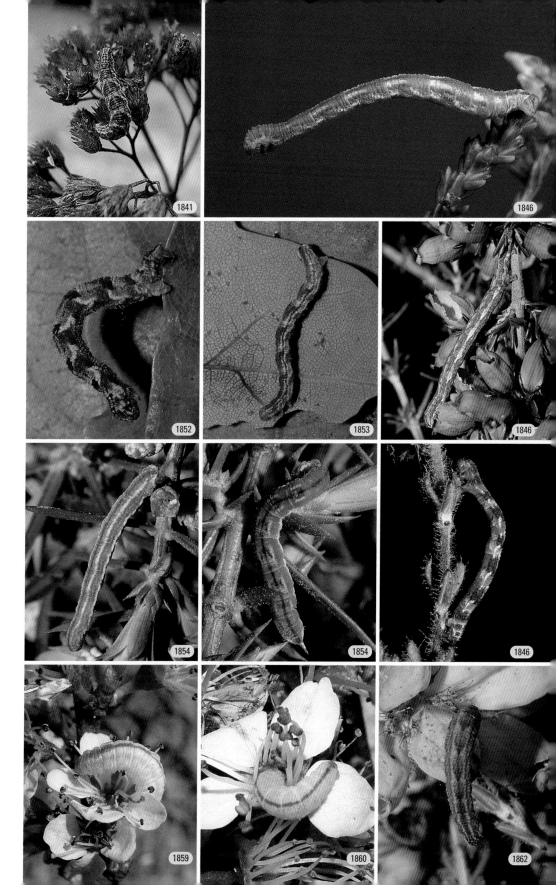

GEOMETERS: GEOMETRIDAE (cont.)

1864 **Streak** *Chesias legatella* 30mm DGG (ADULT: P. 146)
1878 **Drab Looper** *Minoa murinata* 15mm DGG
(ADULT: P. 146)
1880 **Barred Tooth-striped** *Trichopteryx polycommata*
22mm DGG (ADULT: P. 148)
1882 **Small Seraphim** *Pterapherapteryx sexalata* 25mm
DGG (ADULT: P. 148)
1885 **Clouded Magpie** *Abraxas sylvata* 30mm PB
(ADULT: P. 149)
1888 **Scorched Carpet** *Ligdia adustata* 22mm DGG
(ADULT: P. 149)
1890 **Sharp-angled Peacock** *Macaria alternata* 25mm
DGG (ADULT: P. 150)
1893 **Tawny-barred Angle** *Macaria liturata* 25mm JV
(ADULT: P. 150)

1899 **Frosted Yellow** *Isturgia limbaria* 25mm JV
(ADULT: P. 150)
1901 **Little Thorn** *Cepphis advenaria* 20mm JV, JV
(ADULT: P. 150)
1902 **Brown Silver-line** *Petrophora chlorosata* 30mm
DGG (ADULT: P. 150)
1904 **Scorched Wing** *Plagodis dolabraria* 38mm JV
(ADULT: P. 152)
1905 **Horse Chestnut** *Pachycnemia hippocastanaria*
28mm DGG (ADULT: P. 152)
1906 **Brimstone Moth** *Opisthograptis luteolata* 32mm
DGG (ADULT: P. 152)
1911 **Large Thorn** *Ennomos autumnaria* 50mm NS
(ADULT: P. 152)

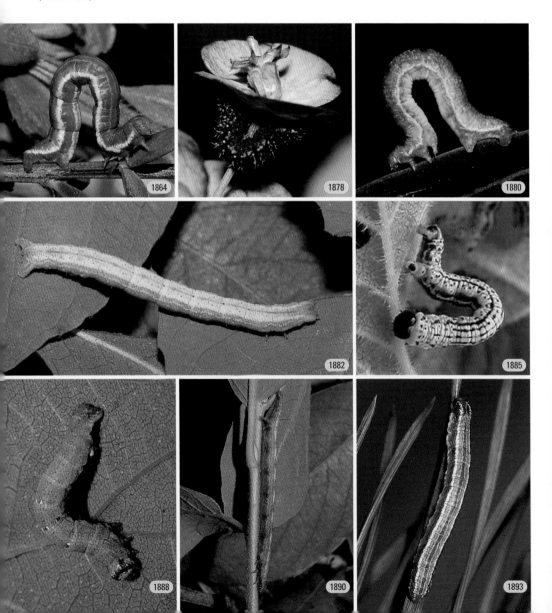

young larva 1901

GEOMETERS: GEOMETRIDAE (cont.)

1914 Dusky Thorn *Ennomos fuscantaria* 45mm JV (ADULT: P. 154)

1919 Purple Thorn *Selenia tetralunaria* 40mm DGG (ADULT: P. 154)

1920 Scalloped Hazel *Odontopera bidentata* 45mm DGG (ADULT: P. 154)

1921 Scalloped Oak *Crocallis elinguaria* 45mm DGG (ADULT: P. 154)

1922 Swallow-tailed Moth *Ourapteryx sambucaria* 52mm DGG (ADULT: P. 156)

1923 Feathered Thorn *Colotois pennaria* 42mm JV (ADULT: P. 156)

1926 Pale Brindled Beauty *Apocheima pilosaria* 40mm DGG (ADULT: P. 156)

1927 Brindled Beauty *Lycia hirtaria* 55mm DGG (ADULT: P. 158)

1928 Belted Beauty *Lycia zonaria* 40mm CMM, PB (ADULT: P. 158)

1929 Rannoch Brindled Beauty *Lycia lapponaria scotica* 40mm SH (ADULT: P. 158)

1931 Peppered Moth *Biston betularia* 55mm DGG (ADULT: P. 158)

1932 Spring Usher *Agriopis leucophaearia* 25mm JV, JV (ADULT: P. 160)

1933 Scarce Umber *Agriopis aurantiaria* 30mm DGG, DGG (ADULT: P. 160)

GEOMETERS: GEOMETRIDAE (cont.)

1934 **Dotted Border** *Agriopis marginaria* 30mm NS (ADULT: P. 161)
1935 **Mottled Umber** *Erannis defoliaria* 30mm DGG (ADULT: P. 161)
1938 **Bordered Grey** *Selidosema brunnearia* 30mm DGG (ADULT: P. 162)
1941 **Mottled Beauty** *Alcis repandata* 37mm NS (ADULT: P. 162)
1943 **Great Oak Beauty** *Hypomecis roboraria* 48mm DGG (ADULT: P. 162)
1944 **Pale Oak Beauty** *Hypomecis punctinalis* 43mm JV (ADULT: P. 164)
1945 **Brussels Lace** *Cleorodes lichenaria* 28mm DGG (ADULT: P. 164)
1947 **Engrailed** *Ectropis bistortata* 33mm DGG (ADULT: P. 164)
1948 **Small Engrailed** *Ectropis crepuscularia* 33mm JV (ADULT: P. 164)
1950 **Brindled White-spot** *Parectropis similaria* 40mm JV (ADULT: P. 164)
1952 **Common Heath** *Ematurga atomaria* 30mm DGG (ADULT: P. 164)
1955 **Common White Wave** *Cabera pusaria* 30mm NS (ADULT: P. 166)
1956 **Common Wave** *Cabera exanthemata* 30mm JV (ADULT: P. 166)
1958 **Clouded Silver** *Lomographa temerata* 25mm JV (ADULT: P. 166)
1960 **Early Moth** *Theria primaria* 25mm JV (all photos) (ADULT: P. 166)

1934

1935

1938

1941

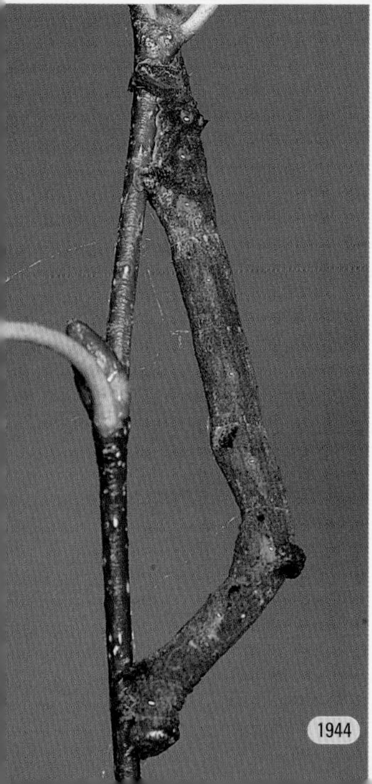

1944

1943

1945

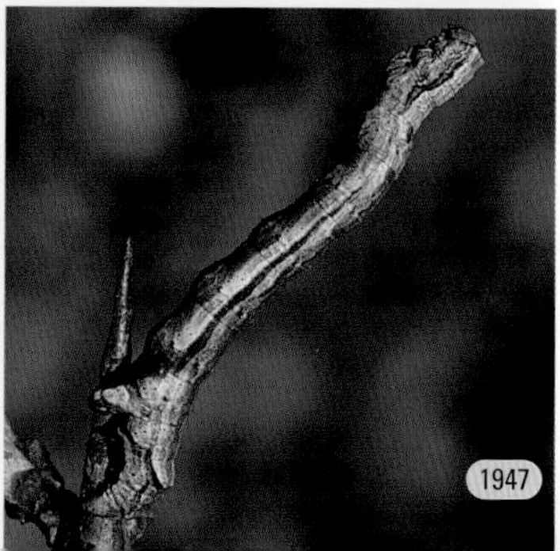

1947

1948

1950

1952

1955

1956

1958

1960

1960

eggs

1960

1960

GEOMETERS: GEOMETRIDAE (cont.)

1961 **Light Emerald** *Campaea margaritata* 38mm DGG (ADULT: P. 166)
1962 **Barred Red** *Hylaea fasciaria* 32mm JV (ADULT: P. 166)
1968 **Yellow Belle** *Semiaspilates ochrearia* 30mm NS (ADULT: P. 168)
1969 **Grey Scalloped Bar** *Dyscia fagaria* 33mm DGG (ADULT: P. 168)
1970 **Grass Wave** *Perconia strigillaria* 35mm JV (ADULT: P. 168)

HAWK-MOTHS: SPHINGIDAE

1972 Convolvulus Hawk-moth *Agrius convolvuli* 100mm DGG (ADULT: P. 169)
1973 Death's-head Hawk-moth *Acherontia atropos* 120mm DGG (ADULT: P. 169)
1978 Pine Hawk-moth *Hyloicus pinastri* 80mm NS (ADULT: P. 170)
1979 Lime Hawk-moth *Mimas tiliae* 65mm JV (ADULT: P. 170)
1980 Eyed Hawk-moth *Smerinthus ocellata* 70mm NS (ADULT: P. 170)

HAWK-MOTHS: SPHINGIDAE (cont.)

1981 Poplar Hawk-moth *Lathoe populi* 65mm SGC (ADULT: P. 170)
1982 Narrow-bordered Bee Hawk *Hemaris tityus* 45mm DGG
(ADULT: P. 172)
1983 Broad-bordered Bee Hawk *Hemaris fuciformis* 50mm NS
(ADULT: P. 172)
1984 Hummingbird Hawk-moth *Macroglossum stellatarum* 65mm MSP
(ADULT: P. 172)
1986 Spurge Hawk-moth *Hyles euphorbiae* 85mm DGG (ADULT: P. 174)
1987 Bedstraw Hawk-moth *Hyles galii* 80mm NS, DGG (ADULT: P. 174)
1991 Elephant Hawk-moth *Deilephila elpenor* 85mm NS, RPJ
(ADULT: P. 174)
1992 Small Elephant Hawk-moth *Deilephila porcellus* 55mm CMM
(ADULT: P. 174)
1993 Silver-striped Hawk-moth *Hippotion celerio* 75mm DGG
(ADULT: P. 174)

1987

1987

1991

penultimate instar 1991

1992

1993

KITTENS, PROMINENTS, TUSSOCKS, ETC.

1994 Buff-tip *Phalera bucephala* 70mm DGG
(ADULT: P. 176)
1995 Puss Moth *Cerura vinula* 60mm JV (all photos)
(ADULT: P. 176)
1997 Sallow Kitten *Furcula furcula* 35mm JV, NS, DGG,
(ADULT: P. 176)
1998 Poplar Kitten *Furcula bifida* 36mm NS, DGG

(ADULT: P. 176)
1999 Lobster Moth *Stauropus fagi* 60mm JV, JV
(ADULT: P. 176)
2001 Large Dark Prominent *Notodonta torva* 40mm JV
(ADULT: P. 176)
2003 Pebble Prominent *Notodonta ziczac* 40mm DGG
(ADULT: P. 178)

1994

egg 1995

1995

early instar 1995

1995

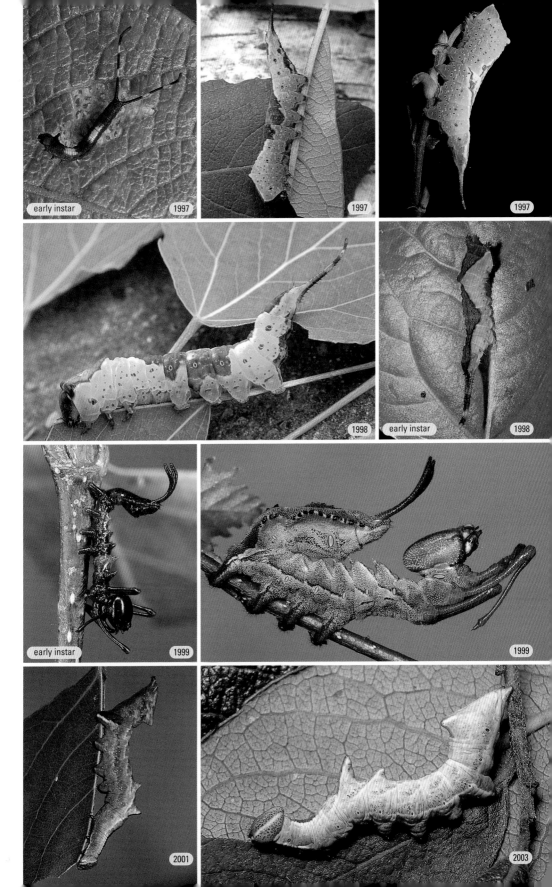

early instar   1997

1997

1997

1998

early instar   1998

early instar   1999

1999

2001

2003

KITTENS, PROMINENTS, TUSSOCKS, ETC. (cont.)

2004 **Tawny Prominent** *Harpyia milhauseri* 40mm JV (ADULT: P. 178)
2005 **Great Prominent** *Peridea anceps* 43mm NS (ADULT: P. 178)
2008 **Coxcomb Prominent** *Ptilodon capucina* 35mm JV, SH, DGG
(ADULT: P. 179)
2009 **Maple Prominent** *Ptilodontella cucullina* 32mm JV (ADULT: P. 179)
2011 **Pale Prominent** *Pterostoma palpina* 40mm JV (ADULT: P. 180)
2012 **White Prominent** *Leucodonta bicoloria* 35mm JV (ADULT: P. 180)
2013 **Plumed Prominent** *Ptilophora plumigera* 35mm NS (ADULT: P. 180)
2015 **Lunar Marbled Brown** *Drymonia ruficornis* 38mm DGG (ADULT: P. 180)
2016 **Dusky Marbled Brown** *Gluphisia crenata vertunea* 26mm JV
(ADULT: P. 180)
2018 **Scarce Chocolate-tip** *Clostera anachoreta* 35mm JV (ADULT: P. 180)
2019 **Chocolate-tip** *Clostera curtula* 32mm NS (ADULT: P. 180)
2020 **Figure of Eight** *Diloba caeruleocephala* 40mm CMM (ADULT: P. 180)

2004

2005

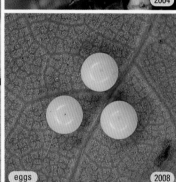

eggs 2008

2008

2008

2009

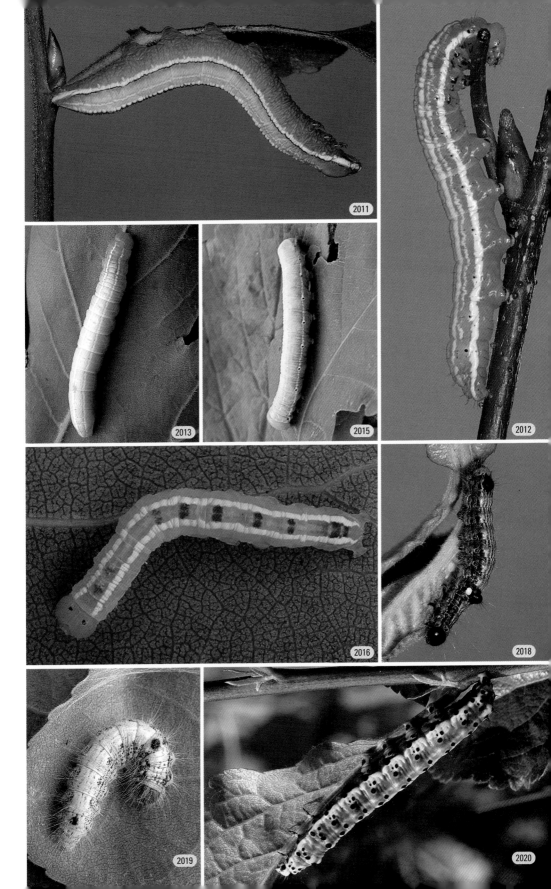

KITTENS, PROMINENTS, TUSSOCKS, ETC. (cont.)

2022 Oak Processionary *Thaumetopoea processionea* 25mm JV (ADULT: P. 182)
2025 Scarce Vapourer *Orgyia recens* 37mm DGG (ADULT: P. 182)
2026 Vapourer *Orgyia antiqua* 38mm PGC, DGG (ADULT: P. 182)
2027 Dark Tussock *Dicallomera fascelina* 42mm JV (ADULT: P. 182)
2028 Pale Tussock *Calliteara pudibunda* 44mm RW, SH, DGG (ADULT: P. 182)

2029 Brown-tail *Euproctis chrysorrhoea* 40mm DGG, JV (ADULT: P. 182)
2030 Yellow-tail *Euproctis similis* 42mm JV (ADULT: P. 182)
2031 White Satin *Leucoma salicis* 44mm JV (ADULT: P. 184)
2032 Black V Moth *Arctornis l-nigrum* 45mm CMM (ADULT: P. 184)
2033 Black Arches *Lymantria monacha* 40mm DGG (ADULT: P. 184)
2034 Gypsy Moth *Lymantria dispar* 45mm DGG (ADULT: P. 184)

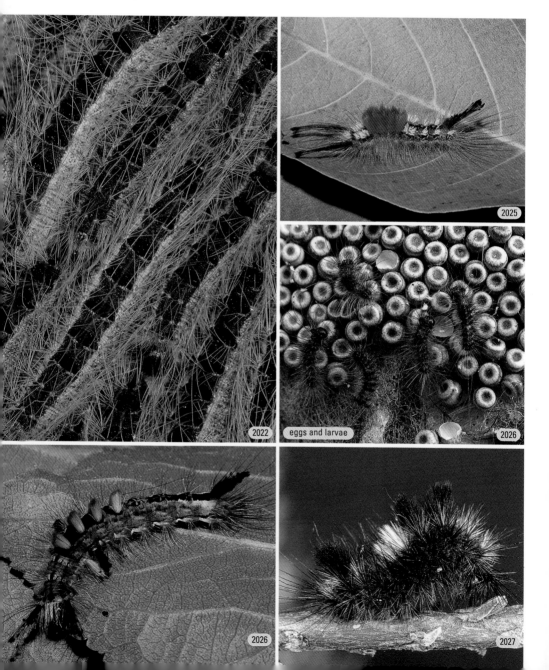

2022

2025

eggs and larvae

2026

2026

2027

2028

2028

2028

2029

2029

2030

2031

2032

2033

2034

FOOTMEN: ARCTIIDAE

2036 **Dew Moth** *Setina irrorella* 20mm DGG (ADULT: P. 185)
2043 **Orange Footman** *Eilema sororcula* 20mm NS (ADULT: P. 186)
2047 **Scarce Footman** *Eilema complana* 25mm DGG (ADULT: P. 186)
2049 **Buff Footman** *Eilema depressa* 22mm NS (ADULT: P. 186)
2051 **Four-spotted Footman** *Lithosia quadra* 34mm DGG (ADULT: P. 186)
2052 **Feathered Footman** *Spiris striata* 30mm JV (ADULT: P. 186)
2054 **Crimson Speckled** *Utetheisa pulchella* 30mm CMM (ADULT: P. 186)

TIGERS AND ERMINES: ARCTIIDAE, ARCTIINAE

2057 Garden Tiger *Arctia caja* 60mm RL (ADULT: P. 188)
2059 Clouded Buff *Diacrisia sannio* 37mm DGG, DGG
(ADULT: P. 190)
2061 Buff Ermine *Spilosoma luteum* 44mm DGG
(ADULT: P. 190)

2062 Water Ermine *Spilosoma urticae* 44mm JV
(ADULT: P. 190)
2063 Muslin Moth *Diaphora mendica* 37mm JV
(ADULT: P. 190)

TIGERS AND ERMINES: ARCTIIDAE, ARCTIINAE (cont.)

2064 Ruby Tiger
Phragmatobia fuliginosa 35mm
JV (ADULT: P. 190)
2068 Scarlet Tiger
Callimorpha dominula 44mm
DGG (ADULT: P. 190)
2069 Cinnabar *Tyria*
jacobaeae 28mm CMM
(ADULT: P. 190)
2077 Short-cloaked Moth
Nola cucullatella 15mm DGG
(ADULT: P. 192)

2068

2064

2069

2077

NOCTUIDS: NOCTUIDAE

2091 Dark Sword-grass *Agrotis ipsilon* 45mm DGG (ADULT: P. 194)
2107 Large Yellow Underwing *Noctua pronuba* 50mm DGG (ADULT: P. 198)
2108 Lunar Yellow Underwing *Noctua orbona* 40mm NS, DGG (ADULT: P. 198)

2110 Broad-bordered Yellow Underwing *Noctua fimbriata* 50mm DGG (ADULT: P. 198)
2115 Rosy Marsh Moth *Eugraphe subrosea* 40mm IT (ADULT: P. 200)
2117 Autumnal Rustic *Paradiarsia glareosa* 33mm NS (ADULT: P. 200)

NOCTUIDS: NOCTUIDAE (cont.)

2118 True Lover's Knot *Lycophotia porphyrea* 30mm DGG (ADULT: P. 200)
2128 Double Square-spot *Xestia triangulum* 38mm NS (ADULT: P. 202)
2129 Ashworth's Rustic *Xestia ashworthii* 40mm DGG (ADULT: P. 202)
2130 Dotted Clay *Xestia baja* 40mm JV (ADULT: P. 202)
2131 Square-spotted Clay *Xestia rhomboidea* 38mm NS (ADULT: P. 202)
2132 Neglected Rustic *Xestia castanea* 35mm DGG, DGG (ADULT: P. 202)

2134 Square-spot Rustic *Xestia xanthographa* 35mm JV (ADULT: P. 202)
2139 Red Chestnut *Cerastis rubricosa* 42mm NS (ADULT: P. 202)
2142 Beautiful Yellow Underwing *Anarta myrtilli* 26mm DGG, NS (ADULT: P. 204)
2145 Nutmeg *Discestra trifolii* 40mm NS (ADULT: P. 204)
2154 Cabbage Moth *Mamestra brassicae* 28mm JV (ADULT: P. 205)
2155 Dot Moth *Melanchra persicariae* 44mm JV (ADULT: P. 205)

NOCTUIDS: NOCTUIDAE (cont.)

2156 **Beautiful Brocade** *Lacanobia contigua* 40mm JV (ADULT: P. 205)
2157 **Light Brocade** *Lacanobia w-latinum* 43mm DGG (ADULT: P. 206)
2160 **Bright-line Brown-eye** *Lacanobia oleracea* 42mm PGC (ADULT: P. 206)
2163 **Broom Moth** *Melanchra pisi* 42mm DGG, DGG (ADULT: P. 206)
2173 **Lychnis** *Hadena bicruris* 40mm JV, DGG (ADULT: P. 208)
2177 **Hedge Rustic** *Tholera cespitis* 34mm NS (ADULT: P. 208)
2182 **Small Quaker** *Orthosia cruda* 30mm DGG (ADULT: P. 210)
2183 **Blossom Underwing** *Orthosia miniosa* 38mm DGG (ADULT: P. 210)
2187 **Common Quaker** *Orthosia cerasi* 38mm NS (ADULT: P. 210)
2188 **Clouded Drab** *Orthosia incerta* 40mm DGG (ADULT: P. 210)
2189 **Twin-spotted Quaker** *Orthosia munda* 38mm DGG (ADULT: P. 212)
2190 **Hebrew Character** *Orthosia gothica* 45mm DGG (ADULT: P. 212)

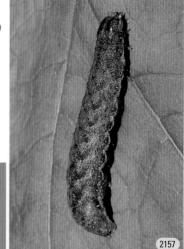

2157

2160

2156

2163

2163

young larva & egg

2173

NOCTUIDS: NOCTUIDAE (cont.)

2195 Delicate *Mythimna vitellina* 40mm SH
(ADULT: P. 213)
2198 Smoky Wainscot *Mythimna impura* 38mm DGG
(ADULT: P. 213)
2211 Wormwood *Cucullia absinthii* 40mm NS
(ADULT: P. 216)
2214 Chamomile Shark *Cucullia chamomillae* 44mm
DGG, JV (ADULT: P. 216)
2216 Shark *Cucullia umbratica* 50mm JV (ADULT: P. 216)
2217 Star-wort *Cucullia asteris* 45mm DGG (ADULT: P. 216)
2219 Striped Lychnis *Shargacucullia lychnitis* 44mm
DGG (ADULT: P. 216)

2221 Mullein *Shargacucullia verbasci* 48mm CMM
(ADULT: P. 216)
2223 Toadflax Brocade *Calophasia lunula* 35mm NS
(ADULT: P. 216)
2227 Sprawler *Brachionycha sphinx* 45mm NS
(ADULT: P. 218)
2228 Rannoch Sprawler *Brachionycha nubeculosa* 50mm
DGG (ADULT: P. 218)
2230 Feathered Brindle *Aporophyla australis pascuea*
40mm NS (ADULT: P. 218)
2231 Deep-brown Dart *Aporophyla lutulenta* 40mm NS
(ADULT: P. 218)

NOCTUIDS: NOCTUIDAE (cont.)

2235 **Tawny Pinion** *Lithophane semibrunnea* 40mm SH (ADULT: P. 219)
2241 **Red Sword-grass** *Xylena vetusta* 60mm SH (ADULT: P. 220)
2242 **Sword-grass** *Xylena exsoleta* 60mm DGG, PB (ADULT: P. 220)
2243 **Early Grey** *Xylocampa areola* 44mm JV (ADULT: P. 220)
2245 **Green-brindled Crescent** *Allophyes oxyacanthae* 45mm DGG, SH (ADULT: P. 220)
2247 **Merveille du Jour** *Dichonia aprilina* 48mm DGG (ADULT: P. 220)
2253 **Black-banded** *Polymixis xanthomista statices* 44mm DGG (ADULT: P. 222)
2255 **Feathered Ranunculus** *Polymixis lichenea* 38mm JV (ADULT: P. 222)
2256 **Satellite** *Eupsilia transversa* 50mm DGG (ADULT: P. 223)
2258 **Chestnut** *Conistra vaccinii* 35mm DGG (ADULT: P. 223)
2261 **Red-headed Chestnut** *Conistra erythrocephala* 44mm JV (ADULT: P. 224)
2262 **Brick** *Agrochola circellaris* 40mm JV (ADULT: P. 224)
2263 **Red-line Quaker** *Agrochola lota* 40mm DGG (ADULT: P. 224)
2264a **Southern Chestnut** *Agrochola haematidea* 35mm NS (ADULT: P. 224)

2241

2242

2235

2242

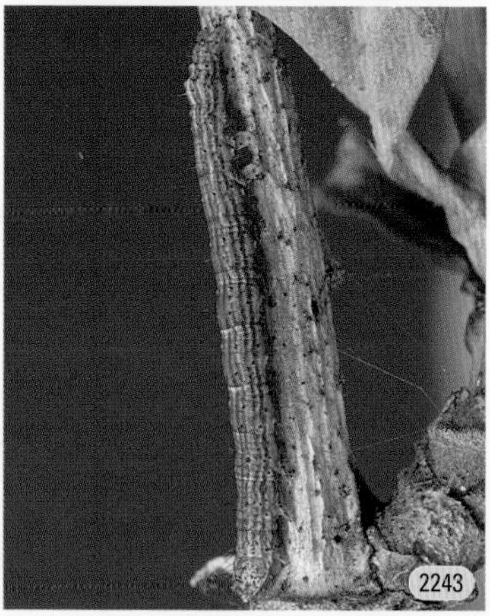

2243

2245

2245

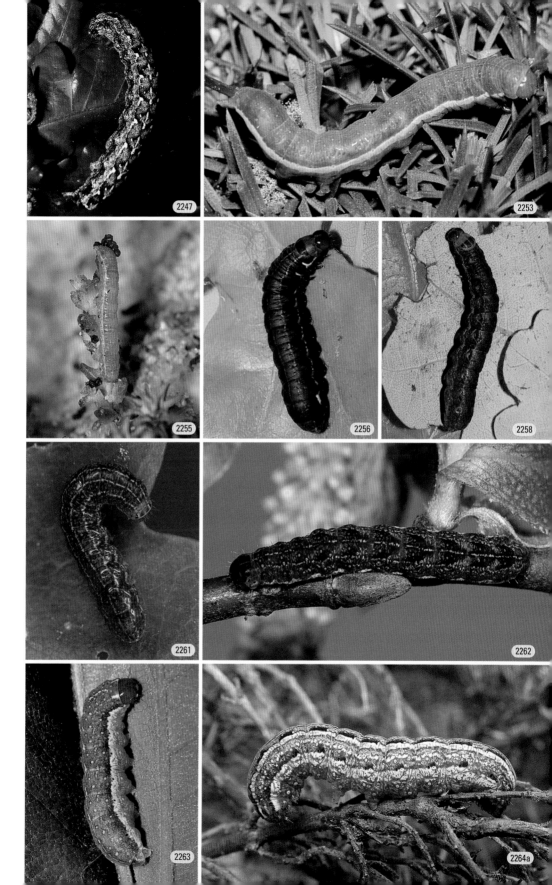

NOCTUIDS: NOCTUIDAE (cont.)

2269 Centre-barred Sallow *Atethmia centrago* 35mm NS
(ADULT: P. 226)
2270 Lunar Underwing *Omphaloscelis lunosa* 35mm NS
(ADULT: P. 226)
2273 Pink-barred Sallow *Xanthia togata* 30mm JV
(ADULT: P. 226)
2274 Sallow *Xanthia icteritia* 30mm DGG (ADULT: P. 226)
2275 Dusky-lemon Sallow *Xanthia gilvago* 30mm JV
(ADULT: P. 226)

2277 Scarce Merveille du Jour *Moma alpium* 30mm JV,
JV (ADULT: P. 228)
2279 Sycamore *Acronicta aceris* 40mm JV, JV, NS (right
photo) (ADULT: P. 228)
2281 Alder Moth *Acronicta alni* 35mm JV, JV
(ADULT: P. 228)
2284 Grey Dagger *Acronicta psi* 38mm DGG
(ADULT: P. 228)

eggs 2277

2277

early instar 2279

2279

2279

early instar 2281

2281

2284

NOCTUIDS: NOCTUIDAE (cont.)

2286 Light Knot Grass *Acronicta menyanthidis* 38mm DGG (ADULT: P. 230)
2287 Scarce Dagger *Acronicta auricoma* 38mm JV (ADULT: P. 230)
2289 Knot Grass *Acronicta rumicis* 38mm CMM (ADULT: P. 230)
2290 Reed Dagger *Simyra albovenosa* 40mm NS (ADULT: P. 231)
2291 Coronet *Craniophora ligustri* 38mm JV (ADULT: P. 231)
2295 Marbled Green *Cryphia muralis* 25mm SH (ADULT: P. 231)
2297 Copper Underwing *Amphipyra pyramidea* 40mm DGG (ADULT: P. 232)
2298 Svensson's Copper Underwing *Amphipyra berbera svenssoni* 36mm DGG (ADULT: P. 232)
2300 Old Lady *Mormo maura* 65mm DGG (ADULT: P. 232)
2305 Small Angle Shades *Euplexia lucipara* 35mm DGG (ADULT: P. 234)
2306 Angle Shades *Phlogophora meticulosa* 42mm DGG (ADULT: P. 234)
2313 Angle-striped Sallow *Enargia paleacea* 42mm DGG (ADULT: P. 234)
2316 Lesser-spotted Pinion *Cosmia affinis* 26mm JV (ADULT: P. 236)
2318 Dun-bar *Cosmia trapezina* 30mm DGG (ADULT: P. 236)

2286

2287 2289 2290

2291 2295 2297

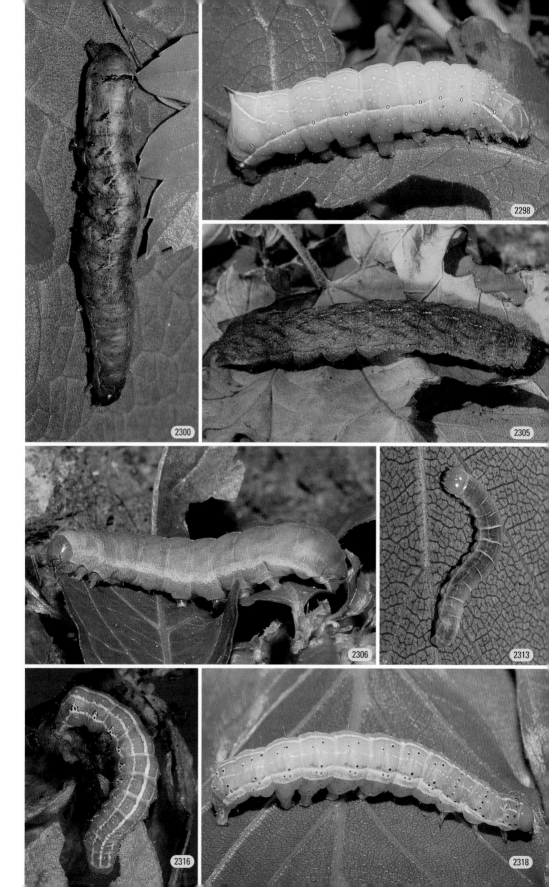

2298

2300

2305

2306

2313

2316

2318

NOCTUIDS: NOCTUIDAE (cont.)

2331 Small Clouded Brindle *Apamea unanimis* 30mm JV (ADULT: P. 238)
2369 Bulrush Wainscot *Nonagria typhae* 55mm NS (ADULT: P. 246)
2393 Reddish Buff *Acosmetia caliginosa* 30mm DGG (ADULT: P. 251)
2400 Scarce Bordered Straw *Helicoverpa armigera* 38mm SH (ADULT: P. 252)
2402 Shoulder-striped Clover *Heliothis maritima* 33mm TJN (ADULT: P. 252)
2421 Scarce Silver-lines *Bena bicolorana* 33mm DGG (ADULT: P. 255)
2422 Green Silver-lines *Pseudoips prasinana britannica* 36mm DGG (ADULT: P. 256)
2423 Oak Nycteoline *Nycteola revayana* 24mm JV (ADULT: P. 256)
2436 Dewick's Plusia *Macdunnoughia confusa* 35mm CMM (ADULT: P. 258)
2441 Silver Y *Autographa gamma* 35mm NS (ADULT: P. 260)
2450 Spectacle *Abrostola tripartita* 36mm NS (ADULT: P. 261)
2454 Light Crimson Underwing *Catocala promissa* 50mm DGG (ADULT: P. 262)

2331

2369

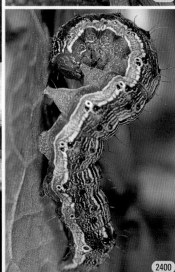

2400

2393

2402

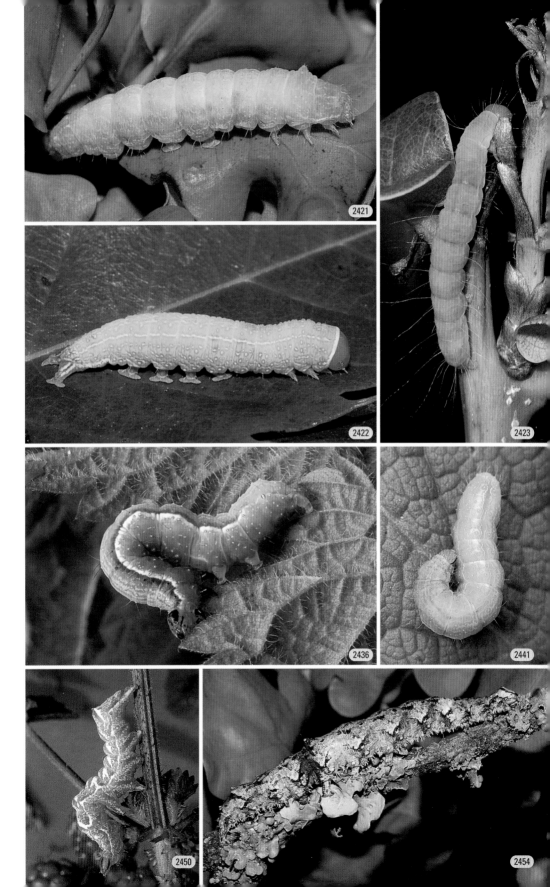

NOCTUIDS: NOCTUIDAE (cont.)

2455 Dark Crimson Underwing *Catocala sponsa* 55mm JV, JV (ADULT: P. 262)
2469 Herald *Scoliopteryx libatrix* 44mm NS (ADULT: P. 264)
2473 Beautiful Hook-tip *Laspeyria flexula* 25mm DGG (ADULT: P. 265)

2477 Snout *Hypena proboscidalis* 26mm DGG (ADULT: P. 266)
2480 Buttoned Snout *Hypena rostralis* 24mm NS (ADULT: P. 266)
2488 Common Fan-foot *Pechipogo strigilata* 20mm DGG (ADULT: P. 267)

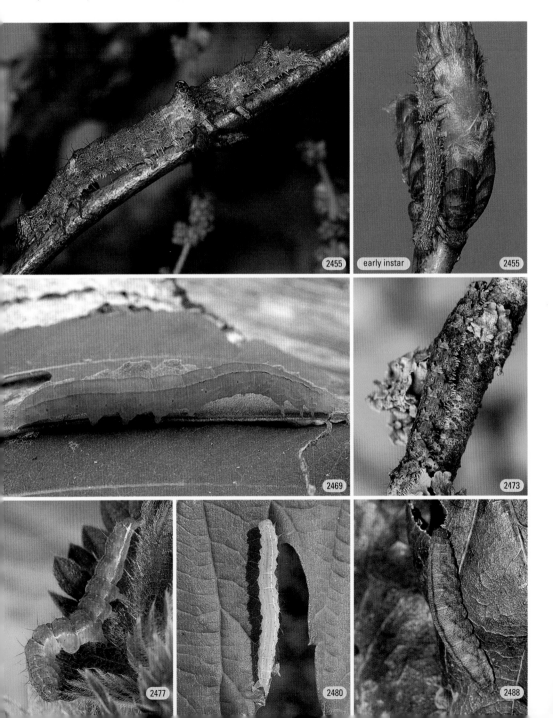

2455 | early instar 2455
2469 | 2473
2477 | 2480 | 2488

APPENDIX: VAGRANT AND ACCIDENTAL BUTTERFLIES AND MACRO MOTHS

The following is a list of extremely rare vagrant and accidental butterflies and macro moths that have been recorded in Britain, but which are not included in the photographic section of the book.

1530 Fiery Skipper *Hylephhilla phyleus* Recorded Devon 1820. North American species.
1533 Mallow Skipper *Carcharodus alceae* Surrey, 1923. Southern European species.
1535 Oberthur's Grizzled Skipper *Pyrgus armoricanus* Norfolk, 1820. European.
1536 Apollo *Parnassius apollo* Alpine European species.
1537 Small Apollo *Parnassius phoebus* 50mm North Wales 1887.
1538 Spanish Festoon *Zerynthia rumina* Sussex 1887. Southern European species.
1542 Moorland Clouded Yellow *Colias palaeno* Central Europe.
1547 Cleopatra *Gonepteryx cleopatra* Probable import from southern Europe, North Africa.
1554 Dappled White *Euchloe simplonia* Probable import from southern Europe, North Africa.
1560 Slate Flash *Rapala schistacea* Wiltshire 1922. From India.
1563 Scarce Copper *Lycaena virgaureae* Extinct, possible former resident.
1564 Sooty Copper *Lycaena tityus* European species, seen Devon 1887, Sussex 1958.
1565 Purple-shot Copper *Lycaena alciphron* European species, Suffolk 1886.
1566 Purple-edged Copper *Lycaena hippothoe* European species. Dubious 18th-century records from East Anglia.
1568 Lang's Short-tailed Blue *Leptotes pirithous* European species, seen Bloxworth, Dorset, 1938.
1577 Turquoise Blue *Plebicula dorylas* A few 18th- and 19th-century records.
1579 Green-underside Blue *Glaucopsyche alexis* Devon 1936. European species.
1583 Julia *Dryas julia* London 1937, on bananas from Jamaica.
1586 Albin's Hampstead Eye *Junonia villida* Hampstead, London, 1800s. Indian species.
1587 Blue Pansy *Junonia oenone* Surrey 1950. Tropical species.
1588 Zebra *Colobura dirce* Sussex 1933, on bananas from South America.
1589 Small Brown Shoemaker *Hypanartia lethe* London 1935, Weymouth, Dorset 1970. South American species.
1592 American Painted Lady *Vanessa virginiensis* North American species.
1595 Scarce Tortoiseshell *Nymphalis xanthomelas* Recorded Sevenoaks, Kent, 1953.
1602 Weaver's Fritillary *Boloria dia* European species. Old records.

1604 Aphrodite Fritillary *Issoria aphrodite* Warwickshire, 1833. North American species.
1605 Niobe Fritillary *Argynnis niobe* Dubious 19th-century records. European species.
1609 Mediterranean Fritillary *Argynnis pandora* Cornwall 1911, Dorset 1969. Southern European species.
1611 Spotted Fritillary *Melitaea didyma* Dumfries 1886, Essex 1986. European species.
1616 Large Wall *Lasiommata maera* Very scarce European migrant.
1622 Woodland Grayling *Hipparchia fagi* Surrey 1946. European species.
1623 Hermit *Chazara briseis* Southern England 1938. Southern European species.
1624 False Grayling *Arethusana arethusa* Surrey 1974. European species.
1671 Blackberry Looper *Chlorochlamys chloroleucaria* 35mm North American species. One dubious 19th-century record.
1695 Large Lace Border *Scopula limboundata* Dubious record from 1820. North American species.
1700 Strange Wave *Idaea laevigata* Import. Once reared from larva found in imported coconut fibre.
1703 Rusty Wave *Idaea inquinata* Import. Imported on dried flowers from southern Europe and North Africa.
1717 Purple-barred Yellow *Lythria purpuraria* Dubious 19th-century records only.
1729 Fortified Carpet *Scotopteryx moeniata* Old unconfirmed records.
1741a Traveller *Costaconvexa centrostrigaria* Possible import from North America.
1783 Cumbrian Umber *Horisme aquata* Unconfirmed record from Cumberland, 1882.
1829 Doubleday's Pug *Eupithecia cauchiata* Only once recorded in Britain by Henry Doubleday in mid-19th century.
1869 Purple Treble-bar *Aplocera praeformata* European species, only seen twice in the UK in 1919 and 1946.
1886 Light Magpie *Abraxas pantaria* Unconfirmed. European species, no genuine British record.
1888b Ringed Border *Stegania cararia* Very rare migrant from Europe, one recorded from Jersey in 1981.
1892 Dingy Angle *Macaria bicolorata* Unconfirmed. Dubious record from around 1800. North American species.
1898 White Spot *Hypagyrtis unipunctata* Unconfirmed. Dubious record from around 1800. North American species.
1900 Bordered Chequer *Nematocampa limbata* Unconfirmed. Dubious record from around 1800. North American species.
1916a *Ennomos subsignaria* Pupa found in Covent Garden 1984. North American species.
1921a Dusky Scalloped Oak *Crocallis dardoinaria* Has been recorded from Guernsey.
1953 Dusky Carpet *Tephronia sepiaria* Only one record, from Wales in early 19th century.
1971 Pink-spotted Hawk-moth *Agrius cingulata* Import. Imported from North America with sweet potatoes in the 18th and 19th centuries.

1974 Five-spotted Hawk-moth *Manduca quinquemaculatus* Import. Imported from North America with potatoes in the 19th century.

1975a Rustic Sphinx *Manduca rustica* Import. North American species. One record from Aberdeen docks in 1983.

1977 Wild Cherry Sphinx *Sphinx drupiferarum* North American species. One record from Somerset in 1970.

1988 Mediterranean Hawk-moth *Hyles nicaea* One UK record only of larvae in Devon, 1964.

1989 Seathorn Hawk-moth *Hyles hippophaes* One UK record only of larvae in Devon, 1857.

1990a White-lined Hawk-moth *Hyles lineata* North American species, similar to 1990 Striped Hawk-moth but six stripes on thorax. One record from 1897.

2023 Long-tailed Satin *Trichocercus sparshalli* One record only, in 1829. Australian moth.

2055 Beautiful Utetheisa *Utetheisa bella* North American species, similar to 2054 Crimson Speckled, recorded once in Wales, 1948.

2065 Isabelline Tiger *Pyrrharctia isabella* North American species, twice imported with oak timber, in 1906 and 1970.

2066 *Halysidota moeschleri* Imported from West Indies in 1961.

2069a *Hypercompe scribonia* Import. Imported to Aberdeen with timber from North America, 1969.

2072 Basker *Euchromia lethe* Import. African species, imported with bananas.

2073 *Antichloris viridis* Import. Imported with bananas from West Indies.

2074 Docker *Antichloris caca* Import. Unconfirmed, from South America.

2074a Banana Stowaway *Antichloris eriphia* Import. Imported with bananas.

2086 Gregson's Dart *Agrotis spinifera* African species. One record from Isle of Man in 1869.

2094a *Agrotis deprivata* Import. From Chile, larvae found in onions in 1977.

2095 Gothic Dart *Feltia subgothica* Unconfirmed North American species, imported with timber in 1800.

2096 Tawny Shoulder *Feltia subterranea* Unconfirmed. North American species, dubious 19th-century records.

2100 Eversmann's Rustic *Actebia fennica* Very scarce migrant from northern Europe and Russia, where it seems to be decreasing. FP Bilberry.

2146 Kidney-spotted Minor *Lacinipolia renigera* Unconfirmed. North American species. Dubious 19th-century record.

2146a *Lacinipolia laudabilis* North American species. One record from Cheshire, 1936.

2161 Stranger *Lacanobia blenna* Migrant. Records from 19th century only. Mediterranean species.

2179a Spanish Moth *Xanthopastis timais* South American import, 1946.

2180 Kew Arches *Brithys crini pancratii* Import. Larvae found in Kew Gardens, London, in 1933. Mediterranean species.

2207 *Mythimna commoides* Import. North American species recorded once in Kent in 1897.

2210 Maori *Graphania dives* New Zealand moth. One British record in 1950.

2212 Green Silver-spangled Shark *Cucullia argentea* Unconfirmed. Only two dubious records, from around 1800 and 1932.

2213 Scarce Wormwood *Cucullia artemisiae* Rare migrant. Two larvae found in 1885, one in 1971. FP Mugwort.

2215 Lettuce Shark *Cucullia lactucae* Unconfirmed. Old dubious records.

2220 Water Betony *Shargacucullia scrophulariae* May–Jun. Very scarce migrant that cannot be distinguished from Mullein except by genitalia dissection. Two British records only. FP Flowers and seeds of mulleins, figworts.

2222 False Water Betony *Shargacucullia prenanthis* Unconfirmed. Dubious record from around 1840. From alpine Europe.

2222a *Shargacucullia caninae* Unconfirmed. Dubious record from 1867.

2224 Antirrhinum Brocade *Calophasia platyptera* One record from Sussex, 1896. European species.

2234 Ash Shoulder-knot *Scotochrosta pulla* Unconfirmed. One record from Essex, 1917.

2234a *Copipanolis styracis* Import. North American species imported on asparagus to London in 1980.

2239 Nonconformist *Lithophane lamda* Rare migrant. Extremely scarce migrant from Denmark and Scandinavia. Similar to 2238 Conformist.

2244 Double-spot Brocade *Meganephra bimaculosa* Two British records from 1815 and 1949.

2246 Green-brindled Dot *Valeria oleagina* Unconfirmed. Dubious 19th-century records.

2250a Bedrule Brocade *Blepharita solieri* One record, from Scotland in 1976.

2282 Large Dagger *Acronicta cuspis* Unconfirmed. Dubious 19th-century record.

2307 Berber *Pseudenargia ulicis* Mediterranean species. One record from Hampshire in 1935. FP Gorse.

2332 Union Rustic *Eremobina pabulatricula* Extinct. Jul–Aug. Last seen in Hertfordshire, 1935. FP Grasses.

2356 Scarce Arches *Luperina zollikoferi* Migrant. Rare migrant from eastern Europe and Asia.

2386a Asian Cotton Leaf Worm *Spodoptera litura* Import. On aquatic plants from Singapore. Manchester, 1978.

2386b Southern Army Worm *Spodoptera eridania* Import. On pot-plants from America. Essex, 1977

2390 African *Perigea capensis* Occurs widely in Africa. One British record from Cornwall in 1958.

2395 Goldwing *Synthymia fixa* Mediterranean species. One British record from Devon, 1937.

2398 Pease Blossom *Periphanes delphinii* Extinct. Twelve British records from the 19th century, but not seen since 1893.

2406 Scarce Meal-moth *Schinia rivulosa* Unconfirmed. North American species. One dubious record from 1909.

2409 Scarce Marbled *Eublemma minutata* European species recorded on Isle of Wight in 1872.

2416 Nun *Acontia aprica* Unconfirmed. North American species. Dubious record from 1809.

2417 Brixton Beauty *Acontia nitidula* Unconfirmed. Asian species. Dubious record from 1805.

2419 Spiny Bollworm *Earias biplaga* Import. From sub-Saharan Africa, Asia. Cotton.

2420 Egyptian Bollworm *Earias insulana* Import. From Africa, Asia, Australia.

2423a Eastern Nycteoline *Nycteola asiatica* Migrant. One record from Yorkshire in 2002. Very similar to 2423 Oak Nycteoline.

2424 Sallow Nycteoline *Nycteola degenerana* Unconfirmed. Two British records, latest 1905.

2424a Grey Square *Pardasena virgulana* Probable African import, 1992.

2426 Marbled Tuffet *Charadra deridens* Import. Probable import from North America, 1952.

2427 Brother *Raphia frater* Import. Probable import from North America, 1949.

2431 Accent Gem *Ctenoplusia accentifera* African species. One British record form Kent in 1969.

2432a Streaked Plusia *Trichoplusia vittata* Similar to other Plusias but with white streak in centre of forewing. One British record, Sussex, 1995. African species.

2435a Soybean Looper *Pseudoplusia includens* Import. North American species, imported once on asparagus from Florida to London in 1978.

2446 Double-spotted Spangle *Megalographa bimaculata* Unconfirmed. Dubiously British. North American species.

2453a French Red Underwing *Catocala elocata* One record from Jersey, 1903.

2457 Trent Double-stripe *Clytie illunaris* Single larva found in Lincolnshire in 1964.

2458 Double-barred *Caenurgina crassiuscula* Unconfirmed. North American species. Dubious early 19th-century records.

2459 Triple-barred *Mocis trifasciata* Unconfirmed. North American species. Dubious early 19th-century records.

2465a *Diphthera festiva* Probable import, London docks, 1867, from Central America. Bright yellow with black and blue spots. **FP** Sweet Potato, Pecan.

2468 Great Kidney *Synedoida grandirena* Dubious record from Bristol about 1900. North American species.

2471 Angled Gem *Anomis sabulifera* Probable import. One record from Kent in 1935. Native to Africa, India, Australia.

2475a *Orodesma apicina* Import. South American species. Two early 19th-century records.

2481 Black Snout *Plathypena scabra* One record from Kent in 1956. Probably imported. North American species.

2486 Waved Tabby *Idia aemula* Unconfirmed. Dubious 19th-century record. North American species.

2487 Twin-striped Tabby *Idia lubricalis* Unconfirmed. Dubious 19th-century record. North American species.

2496 *Eudryas staejohannis* Central American species, once reputedly recorded in London, presumed import.

MACRO MOTH AND BUTTERFLY LARVAL FOODPLANTS

The following is a list of foodplants and the vernacular (English) names of the Macro moths and butterflies that feed on them. It is only the larvae (caterpillars) that eat these plants. Some adults may feed by sipping nectar or sap to provide energy, but they do not grow any larger after emergence. Macro moths are given first; butterfly species are shown after the 'B'. Many species have more than one foodplant so will appear more than once, and many plants are food for more than one species.

Alder *Alnus glutinosa*
Alder Kitten, Autumnal Moth, Blue-bordered Carpet, Brindled Beauty, Canary-shouldered Thorn, Common Lutestring, Common White Wave, Conformist, Coronet, Dingy Shell, Dusky Hook-tip, Early Thorn, Early Tooth-striped, Grey Birch, Iron Prominent, Kentish Glory, Large Emerald, Lime Hawk-moth, May Highflyer, Miller, Northern Winter Moth, Pale Brindled Beauty, Pebble Hook-tip, Purple Thorn, Sharp-angled Peacock, Small Fan-foot, Small Yellow Wave, Waved Carpet, White-barred Clearwing

Algae
Buff Footman, Common Footman, Dingy Footman, Dotted Footman, Four-dotted Footman, Four-spotted Footman, Hoary Footman, Northern Footman, Orange Footman, Pigmy Footman, Red-necked Footman, Rosy Footman, Round-winged Muslin, Scarce Footman, Small Dotted Footman

Alyssum, Garden *Alyssum* spp.
Least Carpet

Angelica, Wild *Angelica sylvestris*
Brindled Ochre (stems/roots), Triple-spotted Pug, White-spotted Pug (seeds)

Apple *Malus* spp.
Blue-bordered Carpet, Chinese Character, Clouded Silver, Dark Dagger, Eyed Hawk-moth, Figure of Eight, Green Pug (flowers), Grey Dagger, Gypsy Moth, Lackey, Lappet, Northern Winter Moth, November Moth, Pinion-spotted Pug, Red-belted Clearwing, Satellite, Short-cloaked Moth, Spring Usher, Winter Moth, **B** Black-veined White

Ash *Fraxinus excelsior*
Ash Pug, Barred Tooth-striped, Brick, Centre-barred Sallow, Copper Underwing, Coronet, Dusky Thorn, Lilac Beauty, Lunar Thorn, Privet Hawk-moth, Purple Thorn, Tawny Pinion

Aspen *Populus tremula*
Chevron, Chocolate-tip, Clifden Nonpareil, Clouded Border, Clouded Silver, Common Wave, Dark Bordered Beauty, Dusky Clearwing, Dusky Marbled Brown, Engrailed, Eyed Hawk-moth, Figure of Eighty, Herald, Large Dark Prominent, Lead-coloured Drab, Lesser Belle, Light Orange Underwing, Minor Shoulder-knot, Oak Beauty, Olive, Pale Prominent, Pebble Prominent, Poplar Grey, Poplar Hawk-moth, Poplar Kitten, Poplar Lutestring, Puss Moth, Red Underwing, Sallow Kitten, Satellite, Scallop Shell, Scarce Chocolate-tip, Seraphim, Small Chocolate-tip, Swallow Prominent, Three-humped Prominent, Twin-spotted Quaker, White Satin, **B** Large Tortoiseshell

Asphodel, Bog *Narthecium ossifragum*
Shoulder-striped Clover (seeds)

Aster, Sea *Aster tripolium*
Star-wort (flowers)

Balsam, Orange *Impatiens capensis*
Balsam Carpet

Barberry *Berberis vulgaris*
Barberry Carpet, Scarce Tissue

Bartsia, Red *Odontites venus*
Barred Rivulet (seeds)

Bearberry *Arctostaphylos uva-ursi*
Broad-barred White Underwing, Netted Mountain Moth, Saxon, Small Dark Yellow Underwing

Bedstraw *Galium* spp.
BedstrawHawk-moth, Beech-green Carpet, Common Carpet, Dark-barred Twin-spot Carpet, Elephant Hawk-moth, Galium Carpet, Green Carpet, Large Twin-spot Carpet, Many-lined, Mottled Grey, Oblique Carpet, Oblique-striped, Purple Bar, Royal Mantle, Ruddy Carpet, Silver-ground Carpet, Silver-striped Hawk-moth, Slender-striped Rufous, Small Elephant Hawk-moth, Small Scallop, Striped Hawk-moth, Striped Twin-spot Carpet, Water Carpet

Bedstraw, Fen *Galium uliginosum*
Devon Carpet

Bedstraw, Heath *Galium saxatile*
Beech-green Carpet, Mottled Grey, Oblique Carpet, Small Argent and Sable, Striped Twin-spot Carpet, Water Carpet

Bedstraw, Hedge *Galium mollugo*
Beech-green Carpet, Common Carpet, Galium Carpet, Green Carpet, Hummingbird Hawk-moth, Purple Bar, Royal Mantle, Ruddy Carpet, Water Carpet, Wood Carpet

Bedstraw, Lady's *Galium verum*
Beech-green Carpet, Common Carpet, Galium Carpet, Green Carpet, Hummingbird Hawk-moth, Mottled Grey, Oblique Striped, Red Twin-spot Carpet, Royal Mantle, Ruddy Carpet, Water Carpet, Wood Carpet

Bedstraw, Marsh *Galium palustre*
Devon Carpet, Oblique Carpet, Purple Bar

Beech *Fagus sylvatica*
August Thorn, Barred Hook-tip, Barred Sallow, Clay Triple Lines, Fan-foot (withered leaves), Festoon, Green Silver-lines, Large Emerald, Light Emerald, Lobster Moth, Nut-tree Tussock, Olive Crescent (withered leaves), Pale November Moth, Scarce Umber, Scorched Wing, Small Engrailed, Sprawler, Square Spot, Tawny Prominent, Triangle, Yellow-line Quaker

Beet, Sea *Beta vulgaris*
Rosy Wave, Stranger

Bellflower, Giant *Campanula latifolia*
Campanula Pug/Jasione Pug

Bellflower, Nettle-leaved *Campanula trachelium*
Campanula Pug/Jasione Pug

Bilberry *Vaccinium myrtillus*
Arran Carpet, Beautiful Snout, Black Mountain Moth, Broad-bordered White Underwing, Common Marbled Carpet, Common Pug, Cousin German, Dark Marbled Carpet, Flounced Chestnut, Fox Moth, Glaucous Shears, Gold Spangle, Golden-rod Brindle, Green Arches, Grey Mountain Carpet, Hebrew Character, July Highflyer, Light Knot Grass, Little Emerald, Little Thorn, Manchester Treble-bar, Mottled Beauty, Northern Deep-brown Dart, Northern Spinach, Oak Eggar, Pale Eggar, Rannoch Looper, Ringed Carpet, Scallop Shell, Scalloped Oak, Scarce Silver Y, Scotch Burnet, Small Autumnal Moth, Small Lappet, Smoky Wave, Twin-spot Carpet, Vapourer, **B** Green Hairstreak

Bilberry, Bog *Vaccinium uliginosum*
Nonconformist

Bindweed, Field *Convolvulus arvensis*
Convulvulus Hawk-moth, Four-spotted, Pale Shoulder, Spotted Sulphur

Birch *Betula* spp.
Alder Kitten, Alder Moth, Angle Shades, Angle-striped Sallow, Argent and Sable, August Thorn, Autumn Green Carpet, Autumnal Moth, Barred Umber, Birch Mocha, Blue-bordered Carpet, Brindled Beauty, Brindled White-spot, Broken-barred Carpet, Canary-shouldered Thorn, Chestnut, Chevron, Clouded Drab, Common Emerald, Common Lutestring, Common Marbled Carpet, Common Quaker, Common White Wave, Conformist, Cousin German, Coxcomb Prominent, Dark Chestnut, Dark Marbled Carpet, December Moth, Dotted Border, Dun-bar, Dusky Hook-tip, Early Thorn, Early Tooth-striped, Engrailed, Feathered Thorn, Flounced Chestnut, Golden-rod Brindle, Great Brocade, Green Silver-lines, Grey Birch, Grey Dagger, Hebrew Character, Iron Prominent, Kentish Glory, Large Dark Prominent, Large Emerald, Large Red-belted Clearwing, Large Thorn, Lesser Swallow Prominent, Light Emerald, Light Knot Grass,

Lime Hawk-moth, Little Emerald, Lobster Moth, Lunar Thorn, Lydd Beauty, March Moth, Miller, Mottled Beauty, Mottled Umber, Northern Winter Moth, November Moth, Nut-tree Tussock, Old Lady, Orange Moth, Orange Underwing, Pale Brindled Beauty, Pale Eggar, Pale Oak Beauty, Pale Pinion, Pale Tussock, Peacock Moth, Pebble Hook-tip, Peppered Moth, Purple Thorn, Rannoch Sprawler, Red-green Carpet, Ringed Carpet, Satellite, Satin Beauty, Satin Lutestring, Scalloped Hazel, Scalloped Hook-tip, Scarce Prominent, Scarce Silver-lines, Scarce Umber, Scorched Wing, September Thorn, Small Angle Shades, Small Engrailed, Small Grass Emerald, Small Lappet, Small White Wave, Sprawler, Square Spot, Suspected, Svensson's Copper Underwing, Sweet Gale Moth, Sycamore, Twin-spotted Quaker, Vapourer, Waved Carpet, Welsh Clearwing, White-barred Clearwing, White Prominent, Willow Beauty, Winter Moth, Yellow Horned, **B** Large Tortoiseshell

Blackthorn *Prunus spinosa*
August Thorn, Blue-bordered Carpet, Brimstone Moth, Broken-barred Carpet, Brown-tail, Chinese Character, Clouded Drab, Clouded Silver, Common Emerald, Common Quaker, Dark Chestnut, Dark Dagger, December Moth, Deep-brown Dart, Dotted Border, Dun-bar, Early Moth, Early Thorn, Emperor Moth, Feathered Thorn, Figure of Eight, Grass Eggar, Green-brindled Crescent, Green Pug (flowers), Grey Dagger, Hebrew Character, Lackey, Lappet, Leopard Moth, Lunar-spotted Pinion, Lydd Beauty, Magpie, March Moth, Marsh Dagger, Mottled Beauty, Mottled Pug, Mottled Umber, November Moth, Oak Eggar, Old Lady, Orange Moth, Pale Brindled Beauty, Pale Eggar, Pale November Moth, Pale Tussock, Satellite, Scalloped Hazel, Scalloped Oak, Scarce Umber, Sharp-angled Peacock, Short-cloaked Moth, Sloe Carpet, Sloe Pug (flowers), Small Eggar, Sprawler, Swallow-tailed Moth, Twin-spotted Quaker, Vapourer, White-pinion Spotted, Winter Moth, Yellow-tail, **B** Brown Hairstreak, Black Hairstreak, Black-veined White

Borage *Borago officinalis*
Angle Shades

Bracken *Pteridium aquilinum*
Brown Silver-line, Small Angle Shades

Bramble *Rubus fruticosus*
Angle Shades, Beautiful Carpet, Brown Rustic, Brown-spot Pinion, Brown-tail, Buff Arches, Chinese Character, Common Marbled Carpet, Dark Tussock, Dotted Border Wave, Dwarf Cream Wave, Emperor Moth, Feathered Brindle, Fox Moth, Garden Tiger, Grass Eggar, Green Arches, Kent Black Arches, Knot Grass, Lackey, Little Thorn, Mottled Beauty, Oak Eggar, Passenger, Pale Eggar, Peach Blossom, Rosy Marbled (flowers), Saxon, Scarce Vapourer, Scarlet Tiger, Shaded Fan-foot (withered leaves), Small Fan-foot, Small Fan-footed Wave, V-Pug (flowers), **B** Grizzled Skipper

Brassicas *Brassica* spp.
Cabbage Moth, **B** Large/Cabbage White, Small White

Bristle Bent *Agrostis curtisii*
Speckled Footman, **B** Grayling

Broom *Cytisus scoparius*
Broom-tip, Dark Tussock, Deep-brown Dart, Frosted
Yellow, Grass Eggar, Grass Emerald, Grass Wave, Lead
Belle, Oak Eggar, Rosy Marbled (flowers), Spanish
Carpet, Streak, **B** Green Hairstreak

Buckthorn *Rhamnus cathartica*
Brown Scallop, Dark Umber, Irish Annulet, Lappet,
Tissue, **B** Brimstone, Green Hairstreak

Buckthorn, Alder *Frangula alnus*
Tissue, **B** Brimstone

Buckthorn, Sea *Hippophae rhamnoides*
Ash Pug, Sharp-angled Peacock

Bugloss, Viper's *Echium vulgare*
Golden Twin-spot, **B** Painted Lady

Bulrush *Typha latifolia*
Bulrush Wainscot (stems), Rush Wainscot (stems),
Webb's Wainscot (stems)

Bulrush, Lesser *Typha angustifolia*
Bulrush Wainscot (stems), Webb's Wainscot (stems)

Bur-reed, Branched *Sparganium erectum*
Reed Tussock, Webb's Wainscot (stems)

Burdock *Arctium* spp.
Beautiful Golden Y, Frosted Orange (root/stems), Rosy
Rustic (root/stems)

Butterbur *Petasites hybridus*
Butterbur

Buttercup *Ranunculus* spp.
Beaded Chestnut, Fern

Cabbage *Brassica* spp.
Flame Carpet, Cabbage Moth, **B** Large/Cabbage White,
Small White

Campion *Silene* spp.
Campion, Lychnis (seeds)

Campion, Bladder *Silene vulgaris*
Marbled Clover, Marbled Coronet (seeds), Netted Pug,
Sandy Carpet (seeds), Tawny Shears (seeds)

Campion, Red *Silene dioica*
Marbled Coronet (seeds), Rivulet (flowers/seed
capsules), Sandy Carpet (seeds), Lychnis (seeds)

Campion, Sea *Silene uniflora*
Barret's Marbled Coronet, Feathered Brindle, Grey,
Netted Pug, Tawny Shears (seeds)

Campion, White *Silene latifolia*
Marbled Clover, Sandy Carpet (seeds)

Canary-grass, Reed *Phalaris arundincaea*
Double Lobed (stems), Marbled Minor, Southern
Wainscot, Striped Wainscot

Carrot, Wild *Daucus carota*
Sussex Emerald, Yellow Belle

Catchfly, Nottingham *Silene nutans*
Tawny Shears (seeds), White Spot (seeds)

Catchfly, Spanish *Silene otites*
Viper's Bugloss

Chamomile *Chamaemelum nobile*
Chamomile Shark

Cherry *Prunus* spp.
Green Pug

Chestnut, Horse *Aesculus hippocastanum*
Sycamore

Chestnut, Sweet *Castanea sativa*
Waved Carpet

Chickweed *Stellaria* spp.
Angle Shades, Beaded Chestnut, Black Rustic, Brown-
spot Pinion, Cloaked Carpet, Large Twin-spot Carpet,
Mottled Rustic, Muslin Moth, Pale Pinion, Riband
Wave, Ruby Tiger, Sharp-angled Carpet, Silver-ground
Carpet, Small Blood-vein, Uncertain, Vine's Rustic,
White-marked, Yellow Shell

Chrysanthemum *Chrysanthemum* spp.
Golden Twin-spot, Slender Burnished Brass

Cinquefoil *Potentilla* spp.
Annulet, Straw Belle, **B** Grizzled Skipper

Cinquefoil, Marsh *Potentilla palustris*
Purple-bordered Gold, Rosy Marbled (flowers)

Clematis, Wild *Clematis vitalba*
Haworth's Pug, Small Emerald

Clover *Trifolium* spp.
Belted Beauty, Black Rustic, Burnet Companion, Chalk
Carpet, Common Heath, Hebrew Character, Latticed
Heath, Marbled Clover, Mother Shipton, Narrow-
bordered Five-spot Burnet, Scarce Black Arches,
Shaded Broad-bar, Silver Y, Stephen's Gem,
B Clouded Yellow, Pale Clouded Yellow

Clover, Red *Trifolium pratense*
Narrow-bordered Five-spot Burnet

Club-rush *Schoenoplectus lacustris*
Haworth's Minor (stems), Rush Wainscot (stems),
Webb's Wainscot (stems)

Cock's-foot *Dactylis glomerata*
Clouded Brindle, Clouded-bordered Brindle, Drinker
Moth, Marbled Minor, Rufous Minor, Striped Wainscot,
Tawny Marbled Minor

Colt's-foot *Tussilago farfara*
Cinnabar

Comfrey *Symphytum officinale*
Scarlet Tiger

Compositae
Broad-barred White

Cotton *Gossipium herbaceum*
Egyptian Bollworm, Spiny Bollworm

Cotton-grass *Eriophorum* spp.
Haworth's Minor (stems), Large Ear (root/stems),
B Large Heath

Couch, Sand *Elytrigia juncea*
Coast Dart

Cow Parsley *Anthriscus sylvestris*
Single-dotted Wave, White-spotted Pug (seeds)

Cow-wheat, Common *Melampyrum pratense*
Lead-coloured Pug (flowers), **B** Heath Fritillary

Cowberry *Vaccinium vitis-idaea*
Black Mountain Moth, Broad-bordered White
Underwing, Manchester Treble-bar, Scotch Burnet

Cowslip *Primula veris*
B Duke of Burgundy

Cranberry *Vaccinium oxycoccos*
Manchester Treble-bar

Crowberry *Empetrum nigrum*
Black Mountain Moth, Broad-bordered White Underwing, Northern Dart, Scotch Burnet, Weaver's Wave

Cruciferae
Garden Carpet, **B** Bath White

Cuckooflower (Lady's Smock) *Cardamine pratensis*
B Green-veined White, Orange-tip

Currant, Black *Ribes nigrum*
Currant Clearwing, Currant Pug, Magpie, Phoenix,
Spinach, V-Moth

Currant, Red *Ribes rubrum*
Currant Pug, Magpie, Phoenix, Spinach, V-Moth

Cypress *Cupressus* spp.
Blair's Shoulder-knot, Freyer's Pug/Edinburgh
Pug/Mere's Pug, Ochreous Pug (shoots)

Cypress, Monterey *Cupressus macrocarpa*
Blair's Shoulder-knot, Cypress Carpet, Cypress Pug

Dandelion *Taraxacum officinale*
Angle Shades, Beaded Chestnut, Bird's Wing, Black
Rustic, Brown Rustic, Chestnut, Dark Chestnut, Dark-
barred Twin-spot Carpet, Dotted Border Wave,
Feathered Footman, Feathered Ranunculus, Garden
Tiger, Grey Chi, Jersey Tiger, Knot Grass, Large
Ranunculus, Lewes Wave, Mottled Rustic, Mullein
Wave, Muslin Moth, Nutmeg, Plain Golden Y, Plain
Wave, Porter's Rustic, Portland Ribbon Wave,
Powdered Rustic, Riband Wave, Rosy Rustic
(root/stems), Ruby Tiger, Rustic, Satin Wave, Silver Y,
Slender Burnished Brass, Speckled Footman, Treble
Brown-spot, Treble Lines, Uncertain, Vine's Rustic,
Wood Tiger

Delphinium *Delphinium* spp.
Golden Plusia

Dewberry *Rubus caesius*
Kent Black Arches

Dock *Rumex* spp.
Beaded Chestnut, Black Rustic, Blood-vein, Brown-spot
Pinion, Chestnut, Common Marbled Carpet, Cream
wave, Dark-barred Twin-spot Carpet, Dark Chestnut,
Feathered Ranunculus, Garden Tiger, Gem, Green
Arches, Grey Chi, Isle of Wight Wave, Large
Ranunculus, Large Twin-spot Carpet, Lewes Wave,
Mottled Beauty, Muslin Moth, Nutmeg, Pale Pinion,
Portland Ribbon Wave, Red Sword-grass, Riband Wave,
Ruby Tiger, Satin Wave, Striped Hawk-moth, Sword-
grass, Twin-spot Carpet, White-marked, Wood Tiger,
Yellow Shell

Dock, Water *Rumex hydrolapathum*
Water Ermine, **B** Large Copper

Dogwood *Cornus sanguinea*
Mottled Pug, Yellow-barred Brindle, **B** Green
Hairstreak, Holly Blue

Dried herbs/Withered plants
Rusty Wave

Dyer's Greenweed *Genista tinctoria*
Lead Belle, Scotch Annulet

Elder *Sambucus nigra*
White-spotted Pug (flowers)

Elm *Ulmus* spp.
Alder Moth, Black V, Brindled Beauty, Buff-tip,
Chestnut, Clouded Drab, Dark Chestnut, December
Moth, Dun-bar, Flounced Chestnut, Grey Dagger, Large
Thorn, Light Emerald, November Moth, Oak Beauty,
Old Lady, Satellite, Sprawler, Twin-spotted Quaker,
B Camberwell Beauty, Large Tortoiseshell, White-letter
Hairstreak

Elm, English *Ulmus procera*
Clouded Magpie, Dusky-lemon Sallow, Lesser-spotted Pinion, Lime Hawk-moth, Lunar-spotted Pinion, White-spotted Pinion

Elm, Wych *Ulmus glabra*
Blomer's Rivulet, Clouded Magpie, Dusky-lemon Sallow, Lesser-spotted Pinion, Lunar-spotted Pinion, Brick, White-spotted Pinion

Euonymus
Magpie

Eyebright *Euphrasia officinalis*
Heath Rivulet (seeds), Pretty Pinion (flowers/seeds)

False-brome *Brachypodium sylvaticum*
Marbled White-spot

False Oat-grass *Arrhenatherum elatius*
Grass Eggar

Fennel, Hog's *Peucedanum officinale*
Fisher's Estuarine Moth

Fescue, Sheep's & Red *Festuca ovina, rubra*
B Grayling, Marbled White

Fescue, Tall *Festuca arundinacea*
Morris's Wainscot

Feverfew *Tanacetum parthenium*
Chamomile Shark

Figwort *Scrophularia* spp.
Mullein, Water Betony (flowers/seeds)

Fir *Abies* spp.
Grey Pine Carpet

Fir, Douglas *Pseudotsuga menziesii*
Barred Red, Dwarf Pug, Satin Beauty, Spruce Carpet

Fleabane, Common *Pulicaria dysenterica*
Small Marbled

Flixweed *Descurainia sophia*
Grey Carpet

Foxglove *Digitalis purpurea*
Ashworth's Rustic, Foxglove Pug, Frosted Orange (stem/roots), B Heath Fritillary (Exmoor)

Fuchsia
Elephant Hawk-moth, Silver-striped Hawk-moth, Striped Hawk-moth

Fungi
Waved Black

Garlic Mustard *Alliaria petiolata*
B Green-veined White, Orange-tip, Small White

Genista
Passenger

Godetia
Bedstraw Hawk-moth

Golden Rod *Solidago virguarea*
Bleached Pug (flowers), Cudweed, Golden-rod Pug, Grey Pug, Lime-speck Pug (flowers), Star-wort (flowers), V-Pug (flowers), White-spotted Pug (seeds), Wormwood Pug (flowers)

Gooseberry *Ribes uva-crispa*
Magpie, Phoenix, V-Moth

Goosefoot *Chenopodium* spp.
Dark Spinach, Goosefoot Pug (flowers/seeds), Nutmeg, Orache Moth, Plain Pug (seeds), Spotted Clover, Wormwood Pug (flowers)

Goosegrass *Galium aparine*
Barred Straw, Common Carpet, Red Twin-spot Carpet, Water Carpet

Gorse *Ulex europaeus*
Grass Emerald, Grass Wave, July Belle, Lead Belle, Spanish Carpet, Willow Beauty, B Green Hairstreak, Silver-studded Blue

Grape-vine *Vitis vinifera*
Silver-striped Hawk-moth, Striped Hawk-moth

Grasses
Anomalous, Antler, Beaded Chestnut, Beautiful Gothic, Brighton Wainscot (stems), Brown-line Bright-eye, Clay, Cloaked Minor, Clouded-bordered Brindle, Clouded Brindle, Common Rustic, Common Wainscot, Confused (root/stems), Cosmopolitan, Crescent-striped (root/stems), Dark Arches (root/stems), Dark Brocade, Dark Mottled Willow, Deep-brown Dart, Delicate, Devonshire Wainscot, Double Line, Drinker Moth, Dumeril's Rustic (root), Dusky Brocade, Dusky Sallow, Ear Moth (root/stems), Exile (root/stems), Feathered Brindle, Feathered Ear, Feathered Gothic, Flounced Rustic (root/stems), Gold Spot, Hedge Rustic, L-album Wainscot, Large Nutmeg, Lesser Common Rustic, Light Arches (root/stems), Lunar Underwing, Marbled Minor, Middle-barred Minor, Northern Deep-brown Dart, Pale Mottled Willow (seeds), Pretty Marbled, Reddish Light Arches (root/stems), Rosy Minor (root/stems), Rufous Minor, Rustic Shoulder-knot, Saltern Ear (root/stems), Sandhill Rustic (root/stems), Scarce Arches, Scarce Brindle (roots), Shoulder-striped Wainscot, Silver Barred, Slender Brindle, Slender-striped Rufous, Small Clouded Brindle, Small Dotted Buff, Small Wainscot, Smoky Wainscot, Straw Dot, Straw Underwing, Tawny Marbled Minor, Union Rustic, White-point, White-speck, B Chequered Skipper, Essex Skipper, Gatekeeper, Large Skipper, Lulworth Skipper, Meadow Brown, Mountain Ringlet, Ringlet, Small Heath, Small Skipper, Silver-spotted Skipper, Speckled Wood, Wall

Groundsel *Senecio vulgaris*
Beautiful Golden Y, Brown Rustic, Cinnabar, Gem, Least Carpet, Plain Golden Y, Silver-ground Carpet, Wood Tiger

Groundsel, Sticky *Senecio viscosus*
Bordered Straw (flowers)

Hair-grass, Tufted *Deschampsia cespitosa*
Silver Hook, Small Dotted Buff

Hair-grass, Wavy *Deschampsia flexuosa*
Anomalous

Hawkweed *Hieracium* spp.
Shark

Hawk's Beard *Crepis* spp.
Marbled Clover, Shaded Pug, Shark

Hawthorn *Crateagus* spp.
Alder Moth, August Thorn, Beaded Chestnut, Brimstone Moth, Brindled Beauty, Brindled Green, Brindled Pug, Broken-barred Carpet, Brown-tail, Chestnut, Chinese Character, Clouded Drab, Clouded Silver, Common Emerald, Common Pug, Common Quaker, Dark Chestnut, Dark Dagger, December Moth, Deep-brown Dart, Dotted Border, Dun-bar, Early Moth, Early Thorn, Emperor Moth, Feathered Thorn, Figure of Eight, Flounced Chestnut, Green-brindled Crescent, Grey Dagger, Grey Pug, Hebrew Character, Knot Grass, Lackey, Lappet, Large Thorn, Light Emerald, Little Emerald, Lunar-spotted Pinion, Magpie, March Moth, Marsh Dagger, Mottled Pug, Mottled Umber, Mouse Moth, November Moth, Oak Eggar, Oak-tree Pug, Old Lady, Orange Moth, Pale Brindled Beauty, Pale Eggar, Pale November Moth, Peppered Moth, Pinion-spotted Pug, Satellite, Scalloped Hazel, Scalloped Oak, Scarce Vapourer, Short-cloaked Moth, Small Eggar, Sprawler, Swallow-tailed Moth, Vapourer, White-pinion Spotted, Willow Beauty, Winter Moth, Yellow-line Quaker, Yellow-tail, **B** Black-veined White

Hazel *Corylus avellana*
Barred Umber, Clouded Border, Clouded Magpie, Coronet, Coxcomb Prominent, Dun-bar, Emperor Moth, Green Silver-lines, Iron Prominent, July Highflyer, Large Emerald, Lobster Moth, Magpie, Mottled Umber, Nut-tree Tussock, Oak Beauty, Pale November Moth, Scarce Umber, Small White Wave, Winter Moth

Heath *Erica* spp.
Common Heath, Grass Wave, Grey Scalloped Bar, Scotch Annulet

Heath, Cross-leaved *Erica tetralix*
Neglected Rustic, Rannoch Brindled Beauty, Shoulder-striped Clover, Southern Chestnut

Heather *Calluna vulgaris*
Annulet, Arran Carpet, Ashworth's Rustic, Beautiful

Snout, Beautiful Yellow Underwing, Black Mountain Moth, Black Rustic, Bordered Grey, Clouded Buff, Common Heath, Cousin German, Dark Tussock, Emperor Moth, Flounced Chestnut, Fox Moth, Glaucous Shears, Golden-rod Brindle, Grass Eggar, Grass Wave, Grey Mountain Carpet, Grey Scalloped Bar, Heath Rustic, Horse Chestnut, July Highflyer, Knot Grass, Lackey, Light Knot Grass, Ling Pug (flowers), Mottled Beauty, Narrow-winged Pug (flowers), Neglected Rustic, Northern Dart, Northern Deep-brown Dart, Oak Eggar, Pale Eggar, Rannoch Brindled Beauty, Red Sword-grass, Ringed Carpet, Ruby Tiger, Rustic, Scalloped Oak, Scarce Silver Y, Scotch Annulet, Shoulder-striped Clover, Small Autumnal Moth, Small Grass Emerald, Smoky Wave, Sweet Gale Moth, True Lover's Knot, Twin-spot Carpet, Weaver's Wave, Yellow-line Quaker, **B** Silver-studded Blue

Heather, Bell *Erica cinerea*
Beautiful Yellow Underwing, Neglected Rustic, Rannoch Belted Beauty, Shoulder-striped Clover, Southern Chestnut, True Lover's Knot

Hemlock, Western *Tsuga heterophylla*
Dwarf Pug, Spruce Carpet, Tawny-barred Angle

Hemp Agrimony *Eupatorium cannabinum*
Frosted Orange (stem/roots), Scarce Burnished Brass, V-Pug (flowers), **B** Grizzled Skipper

Hogweed *Heracleum sphondylium*
Brindled Ochre (stems/roots)

Holly *Ilex aquifolium*
Yellow-barred Brindle, **B** Holly Blue

Hollyhock, Garden *Althaea* spp.
Mallow

Honesty *Lunaria annua*
B Orange-tip, Large White

Honeysuckle *Lonicera* spp.
Barred Tooth-striped, Beautiful Golden Y, Broad-bordered Bee Hawk-moth, Copper Underwing, Early Grey, Early Tooth-striped, Green Arches, Lilac Beauty, Mottled Beauty, Orange Moth, Plain Golden Y, Svensson's Copper Underwing, Twin-spotted Quaker, **B** White Admiral

Hop, Wild *Humulus lupulus*
Angle Shades, Buttoned Snout, Currant Pug, Dark Spectacle, **B** Comma

Hornbeam *Carpinus betulus*
Pale November Moth, Small White Wave

Horse Chestnut *Aesculus hippocastanum*
Sycamore

Horsetail *Equisetum* spp.
Rosy Rustic (root/stems)

Iris, Yellow *Iris pseudacorus*
Belted Beauty, Crescent (stem), Crinan Ear (stem), Red Sword-grass, Rush Wainscot (stem), Water Ermine, Webb's Wainscot (stem)

Ivy *Hedera helix*
Least Carpet, Oak Eggar, Old Lady, Swallow-tailed Moth, Treble Brown-spot, Willow Beauty, Yellow-barred Brindle, **B** Holly Blue

Ivy, Ground *Glechoma hederacea*
Jersey Tiger

Juniper *Juniperus communis*
Blair's Shoulder-knot, Freyer's Pug/Edinburgh Pug/Mere's Pug, Juniper Carpet, Juniper Pug, Ochreous Pug (shoots)

Knapweed *Centaurea* spp.
Grey Pug, Lime-speck Pug (flowers), Satyr Pug (flowers)

Knapweed, Common *Centaurea nigra*
Scarce Forester, Treble Lines

Knapweed, Greater *Centaurea scabiosa*
Scarce Forester

Knotgrass *Polygonum aviculare*
Barred Straw, Bird's Wing, Blood-vein, Bright Wave, Cream Wave, Dotted Border Wave, Dwarf Cream Wave, Feathered Footman, Gem, Isle of Wight Wave, Knot Grass, Lewes Wave, Mottled Rustic, Mullein Wave, Plain Wave, Portland Ribbon Wave, Red Twin-spot Carpet, Riband Wave, Rustic, Satin Wave, Small Blood-vein, Small Fan-footed Wave, Striped Hawk-moth, Tawny Wave, Treble Brown-spot, Treble Lines, Vestal, Vine's Rustic

Lady's Mantle *Alchemilla* spp.
Red Carpet, **B** Orange Tip

Larch *Larix* spp.
Larch Pug, Ochreous Pug (shoots), Small Engrailed

Larkspur *Consolida ajacis*
Pease Blossom, Purple-shaded Gem

Lavender, Sea *Limonium vulgare*
Ground Lackey

Lettuce *Lactuca*
Small Ranunculus, Stephen's Gem

Lettuce, Wild *Lactuca serriola*
Shark

Lichen, Beard *Usnea* spp.
Dotted Carpet

Lichen, Dog *Peltigera canina*
Round-winged Muslin

Lichens *Usnae* spp., *Peltigera* spp.
Beautiful Hook-tip, Brussels Lace, Buff Footman, Common Footman, Dew Moth, Dingy Footman, Dotted Carpet, Dotted Footman, Four-dotted Footman, Four-spotted Footman, Hoary Footman, Marbled Beauty, Marbled Green, Marbled Grey, Muslin Footman, Northern Footman, Orange Footman, Pigmy Footman, Red-necked Footman, Rosy Footman, Round-winged Muslin, Scarce Footman, Small Dotted Footman, Speckled Beauty

Lilac *Syringa vulgaris*
Privet Hawk-moth, Waved Umber

Lime *Tilia* spp.
Black V, Brindled Beauty, Brindled White-spot, Buff-tip, Copper Underwing, Grey Dagger, Least Black Arches, Lime Hawk-moth, Orange Sallow, Pale Brindled Beauty, Pale Tussock, Peppered Moth, Satellite, Scalloped Hazel, September Thorn, Svensson's Copper Underwing, Vapourer

Lime, Small-leaved *Tilia cordata*
Pauper Pug, Scarce Hook-tip

Lime, Large-leaved *Tilia platyphyllos*
Pauper Pug

Loosestrife, Purple *Lythrum salicaria*
Willowherb Hawk-moth

Loosestrife, Yellow *Lysimachia vulgaris*
Dentated Pug (in shade), Reed Dagger

Lucerne *Medicago sativa*
Levant Blackneck, Mother Shipton

Lyme-grass *Elymus arenarius*
Lyme Grass

Madder, Wild *Rubia peregrina*
Hummingbird Hawk-moth

Mallow, Common *Malva sylvestris*
Mallow, Pale Shoulder, **B** Painted Lady

Mallow, Marsh *Althaea officinalis*
Mallow, Marsh Mallow Moth (root/stems), Pale Shoulder

Maple *Acer* spp.
Barred Sallow, Mocha, Pale November Moth, Small Yellow Wave

Maple, Field *Acer campestre*
Maple Prominent, Maple Pug, Nut-tree Tussock, Plumed Prominent, Sycamore

Marigold, Common/Garden *Calendula officinalis*
Bordered Straw (flowers), Ni Moth

Marjoram *Origanum vulgare*
Black-veined Moth, Lace Border

Marram *Ammophila arenaria*
Shore Wainscot

Mayweed *Matricaria* spp., *Tripleurospermum* spp.
Chamomile Shark, Dewick's Plusia

Meadow-grass, Smooth *Poa pratensis*
Silver Barred

Meadow-rue, Common *Thalictrum flavum*
Marsh Carpet (seeds)

Meadow Sweet *Filipendula ilmaria*
Emperor Moth, Hebrew Character, Lesser Cream
Wave, Powdered Quaker, Satyr Pug (flowers), Scarlet
Tiger

Medick, Black *Medicago lupulina*
Mother Shipton, **B** Common Blue

Milkwort, Common *Polygala vulgaris*
Small Purple-barred

Mint, Garden *Mentha* spp.
Large Ranunculus

Mint, Water/Wild *Mentha aquatica*
Water Ermine

Monk's Hood *Aconitum napellus*
Golden Plusia, Pease Blossom, Purple-shaded Gem

Moor-grass, Blue *Sesleria caerulea*
Burren Green (root/stems), **B** Scotch Argus (England)

Moor-grass, Purple *Molinia caerulea*
Large Ear (root/stems), Marbled White-spot, Silver-
barred, Striped Wainscot, **B** Scotch Argus (Scotland)

Mosses
Rosy Footman, Round-winged Muslin

Mouse-ear, Common *Cerastium fontanum*
Small Yellow Underwing

Mouse-ear, Field *Cerastium arvense*
Marsh Pug (flowers/seed capsules)

Mugwort *Artemesia vulgaris*
Bordered Pug, Grey Pug, Lime-speck Pug (flowers),
Mullein Wave, Scarce Wormwood, V-Pug (flowers),
Wormwood, Wormwood Pug (flowers)

Mullein *Verbascum* spp.
Mullein, Water Betony (flowers/seed)

Mullein, Black/Dark *Verbascum nigrum*
Mullein, Striped Lychnis (flowers/seeds)

Mullein, Great *Verbascum thapsus*
Mullein

Mullein, White *Verbascum lychnitis*
Striped Lychnis (flowers/seeds)

Myrtle, Bog *Myrica gale*
Glaucous Shears, Golden-rod Brindle, Great Brocade,
Light Knot Grass, Nonconformist, Powdered Quaker,
Rannoch Brindled Beauty, Red Sword-grass, Ringed
Carpet, Rosy Marsh Moth, Sweet Gale Moth,
Sword-grass

Nettle, Common *Urtica dioica*
Angle Shades, Beautiful Golden Y, Bloxworth Snout,
Burnished Brass, Dark Spectacle, Dewick's Plusia,
Frosted Orange (root/stems), Golden Spangle, Hebrew
Character, Jersey Tiger, Paignton Snout, Plain Golden
Y, Silver Y, Snout, Spectacle, **B** Comma, Painted Lady,
Peacock (in sunlight), Red Admiral, Small Tortoiseshell
(in sunlight)

Nettle, Dead *Lamium* spp.
Burnished Brass, Golden Spangle, Jersey Tiger, Plain
Golden Y, Speckled Yellow

Nettle, White Dead *Lamium album*
Beautiful Golden Y

Nettle, Hemp *Galeopsis* spp.
Small Rivulet (flowers/seeds)

Oak *Quercus* spp.
Alchymist (shoots), Alder Moth, Angle Shades, August
Thorn, Black Arches, Blair's Mocha, Blossom
Underwing, Blotched Emerald, Brindled Beauty,
Brindled Green, Brindled Pug, Brindled White-spot,
Broken-barred Carpet, Brown-spot Pinion, Buff-tip,
Chestnut, Clay Fan-foot (withered leaves), Clouded
Drab, Common Emerald, Common Fan-foot (withered
leaves), Common Lutestring, Common Quaker,
Common White Wave, Copper Underwing, Coxcomb
Prominent, Dark Chestnut, Dark Crimson Underwing,
December Moth, Dotted Border, Dun-bar, Dusky Hook-
tip, Engrailed, False Mocha, Fan-foot (withered leaves),
Feathered Thorn, Festoon, Flounced Chestnut, Frosted
Green, Goat Moth, Great Oak Beauty, Great
Prominent, Green Silver-lines, Grey Dagger, Grey
Shoulder-knot, Heart Moth, Hebrew Character, Iron
Prominent, Lackey, Large Thorn, Least Black Arches,
Light Crimson Underwing, Light Emerald, Little
Emerald, Lobster Moth, Lunar Double-stripe, Lunar
Marbled Brown, Lunar Thorn, Lydd Beauty, Maiden's
Blush, Marbled Brown, Marbled Pug, March Moth,
Merveille du Jour, Mottled Umber, November Moth,
Oak Beauty, Oak Hook-tip, Oak Lutestring, Oak
Nycteoline, Oak Processionary, Oak-tree Pug, Oak
Yellow Underwing, Olive Crescent (withered leaves),
Orange Upperwing, Pale Brindled Beauty, Pale
November Moth, Pale Oak Beauty, Pale Tussock,
Peppered Moth, Purple Thorn, Red-green Carpet,
Satellite, Satin Beauty, Scalloped Hazel, Scalloped Oak,
Scarce Dagger, Scarce Merveille du Jour, Scarce Silver-
lines, Scarce Umber, Scarce Vapourer, Scorched Wing,
September Thorn, Small Angle Shades, Small Black

Arches, Small Brindled Beauty, Small Fan-foot, Sprawler, Spring Usher, Square Spot, Svensson's Copper Underwing, Sycamore, Tawny Prominent, Triangle, Twin-spotted Quaker, Vapourer, Winter Moth, Yellow-legged Clearwing (stumps), Yellow-line Quaker, Yellow-tail, **B** Purple Hairstreak

Oak, Evergreen/Holm *Quercus ilex*
Blair's Mocha, Least Black Arches, Lunar Double-stripe, Oak-tree Pug, Tawny Prominent

Old Man's Beard/Traveller's Joy *Clematis vitalba*
Fern, Haworth's Pug, Least Carpet, Lime-speck Pug (flowers), Pretty Chalk Carpet, Small Emerald, Small Waved Umber, Sub-angled Wave

Oleander *Nerium oleander*
Oleander Hawk-moth

Orache *Atriplex* spp.
Blood-vein, Dark Spinach, Nutmeg, Orache Moth, Plain Pug (seeds)

Osier *Salix viminalis*
Cream-bordered Green Pea, Red-tipped Clearwing

Pansy, Wild *Viola tricolor*
B Queen of Spain Fritillary

Parsley, Cow *Anthriscus sylvestris*
Single-dotted Wave, White-spotted Pug (seeds)

Parsley, Milk *Peudecanum pulustre*
B Swallowtail

Parsnip, Wild *Pastinica sativa*
Straw Belle, White-spotted Pug

Pear *Pyrus* spp.
Chinese Character, Green Pug (flowers)

Pellitory-of-the-wall *Parietaria judaica*
Bloxworth Snout, **B** Red Admiral

Periwinkle *Vinca* spp.
Oleander Hawk-moth

Persicaria *Polygonum* spp.
Cream Wave, Plain Wave

Pignut *Conopodium majus*
Chimney Sweeper

Pine *Pinus* spp.
Bordered White, Pine Beauty, Pine Carpet, Satin Beauty, Scalloped Hazel, Square Spot

Pine, Scots *Pinus sylvestris*
Barred Red, Bordered White, Dusky Peacock, Grey Pine Carpet, Ochreous Pug (shoots), Pine Beauty, Pine Carpet, Pine Hawk-moth, Tawny-barred Angle

Plantain *Plantago* spp.
Belted Beauty, Brown Rustic, Deep-brown Dart, Dotted Border Wave, Feathered Ranunculus, Garden Tiger, Jersey Tiger, Knot Grass, Large Ranunculus, Lewes Wave, Marsh Moth, Mottled Rustic, Mullein Wave, Muslin Moth, Powdered Rustic, Rosy Rustic (root/stems), Ruby Tiger, Rustic, Satin Wave, Treble Brown-spot, Treble Lines, Uncertain, Wood Tiger, Yellow Belle, **B** Glanville Fritillary, Heath Fritillary

Plaintain, Sea *Plantago maritima*
Black-banded, Ground Lackey

Plum *Prunus* spp.
Blue-bordered Carpet, Clouded Silver, Green-brindled Crescent, Gypsy Moth, Lappet, Short-cloaked Moth, White-pinion Spotted

Pond-sedge, Lesser *Carex acutiformis*
Blair's Wainscot (stems)

Poplar *Populus* spp.
Black V, Brick, Chocolate-tip, Clouded Border, Conformist, December Moth, Dingy Shears, Dusky Clearwing, Dusky Marbled Brown, Eyed Hawk-moth, Figure of Eighty, Herald, Large Dark Prominent, Lead-coloured Drab, Miller, Pale Prominent, Pebble Prominent, Pink-barred Sallow, Poplar Grey, Poplar Hawk-moth, Poplar Kitten, Poplar Lutestring, Puss Moth, Red Underwing, Rosy Underwing, Sallow, Sallow Kitten, Satellite, Scarce Chocolate-tip, Seraphim, Swallow Prominent, Three-humped Prominent, Twin-spotted Quaker, White Satin, Yellow-line Quaker, **B** Camberwell Beauty, Large Tortoiseshell

Poplar, Black *Populus nigra*
Hornet Moth, Pale-lemon Sallow

Potato *Solanum tuberosum*
Death's Head Hawk-moth, Slender Burnished Brass

Pretty Whin *Genista anglica*
Grass Emerald, July Belle, Lead Belle

Primrose *Primula vulgaris*
Green Arches, Silver-ground Carpet, **B** Duke of Burgundy

Primrose, Evening *Oenothera biennis*
Willowherb Hawk-moth

Privet *Ligustrum* spp.
Barred Tooth-striped, Copper Underwing, Coronet, Dusky Thorn, Lilac Beauty, Lydd Beauty, Privet Hawk-moth, Scalloped Hazel, Small Blood-vein, Swallow-tailed Moth, Waved Umber, Willow Beauty, Yellow-barred Brindle

Ragwort *Senecio* spp.
Cinnabar, Common Pug, Feathered Ranunculus, Golden Rod Pug, Grey Pug, Large Ranunculus, Lime-speck Pug (flowers), Shaded Pug, Sussex Emerald, Wormwood Pug (flowers)

Raspberry *Rubus idaeus*
Beautiful Carpet, Kent Black Arches

Rattle, Yellow *Rhinanthus minor*
Grass Rivulet (seeds), Lead-coloured Pug (flowers)

Reed, Common *Phragmites australis*
Brown-veined Wainscot (stems), Drinker Moth, Fen Wainscot (stems), Fenn's Wainscot, Flame Wainscot, Large Wainscot (stems), Obscure Wainscot, Reed Dagger, Reed Leopard, Reed Tussock, Silky Wainscot (stems), Southern Wainscot, Striped Wainscot, Twin-spotted Wainscot (stems), White-mantled Wainscot (stems)

Reed Canary Grass *Phalaris arundinacea*
Drinker Moth

Reedmace *Typha latifolia*
Bulrush Wainscot (stems), Rush Wainscot (stems), Webb's Wainscot (stems)

Reedmace, Lesser *Typha angustifolia*
Bulrush Wainscot (stems), Webb's Wainscot (stems)

Restharrow, Common *Ononis repens*
Bordered Sallow (flowers/seeds), Bordered Straw (flowers), Marbled Clover, Rest Harrow, Yellow Belle, **B** Common Blue

Restharrow, Spiny *Ononis spinosa*
Bordered Sallow

Rock-rose, Common *Heliathemum mummularium*
Annulet, Cistus Forester, Silky Wave, **B** Brown Argus, Green Hairstreak, Northern Brown Argus, Silver-studded Blue

Rocket, Sea *Cakile maratima*
Ni Moth, Sand Dart

Roots
Common Swift, Ghost Moth, Gold Swift, Great Dart, Map-winged Swift, Orange Swift, Turnip Moth (and lower stems)

Rose, Burnet *Rosa pimpinellifolia*
Belted Beauty

Rose, Wild/Dog *Rosa canina*
Barred Yellow, Dark Dagger, Grey Dagger, Little Thorn, Peppered Moth, Shoulder Stripe, Small Eggar, Streamer, V-Pug (flowers)

Roseroot *Sedum rosea*
Yellow-ringed Carpet

Rowan *Sorbus aucuparia*
Brimstone Moth, Grey Dagger, Mottled Pug, Orange Underwing, Red-green Carpet, Welsh Wave

Rush *Juncus* spp.
Haworth's Minor (stems)

Rush, Jointed *Juncus articulatus*
Small Rufous (stems)

Rush, Soft *Juncus effusus*
Small Rufous (stems)

Sage, Wood *Teucrium scorodonia*
Feathered Brindle, Golden Twin-spot, Speckled Yellow

Sallow *Salix* spp.
Angle Shades, Autumn Green Carpet, Barred Umber, Black V, Bordered Beauty, Brick, Brindled Beauty, Brown-spot Pinion, Brown-tail, Buff-tip, Canary-shouldered Thorn, Chevron, Clouded Border, Clouded Drab, Common Emerald, Common Marbled Carpet, Common Pug, Common Quaker, Common Wave, Common White Wave, Conformist, Copper Underwing, Coxcomb Prominent, Cream-bordered Green Pea, Dark Dagger, Dark Marbled Carpet, Dark Tussock, Dingy Mocha, Dingy Shears, Dotted Border, Double Kidney, Dun-bar, Early Thorn, Early Tooth-striped, Emperor Moth, Engrailed, Eyed Hawk-moth, Feathered Thorn, Flounced Chestnut, Fox Moth, Glaucous Shears, Goat Moth, Golden-rod Brindle, Grass Eggar, Great Brocade, Grey Dagger, Grey Pug, Gypsy Moth, Hebrew Character, Herald, July Highflyer, Knot Grass, Lackey, Lappet, Large Thorn, Light Knot Grass, Lunar Hornet Moth, Magpie, Miller, Minor Shoulder-knot, Mottled Umber, Mouse Moth, Oak Eggar, Old Lady, Pale Brindled Beauty, Pale Eggar, Pale November Moth, Pale Oak Beauty, Pale Pinion, Pale Prominent, Passenger, Peacock Moth, Pebble Prominent, Peppered Moth, Pink-barred Sallow, Poplar Hawk-moth, Powdered Quaker, Puss Moth, Red-line Quaker, Reed Dagger, Rosy Underwing, Ruddy Highflyer, Sallow, Sallow Clearwing, Sallow Kitten, Satellite, Saxon, Scallop Shell, Scalloped Hazel, Scalloped Oak, Scarce Chocolate-tip, Scarce Vapourer, Scorched Wing, Sharp-angled Peacock, Slender Pug, Small Angle Shades, Small Chocolate-tip, Small Engrailed, Small Lappet, Small Seraphim, Sprawler, Suspected, Svensson's Copper Underwing, Swallow Prominent, Sweet Gale Moth, Twin-spot Carpet, Twin-spotted Quaker, Waved Carpet, White-marked, White Satin, Winter Moth, Yellow-line Quaker, Yellow-tail, **B** Purple Emperor

Saltmarsh-grass, Common *Puccinellia maritima*
Mathew's Wainscot

Saltwort, Prickly *Salsola kali*
Sand Dart, Strayer

Sandwort, Sea *Honckenya peploides*
Coast Dart

Saw-wort *Serratula tinctoria*
Reddish Buff

Saxifrage *Saxifraga* spp.
Scotch Annulet, Yellow-ringed Carpet

Saxifrage, Burnet *Pimpinella saxifraga*
Lime-speck Pug (flowers), Pimpinel Pug (seeds), Single-dotted Wave

Scabious *Scabiosa columbaria*
Lime-speck Pug (flowers), Shaded Pug

Scabious, Devil's Bit *Succisa pratensis*
Narrow-bordered Bee Hawk-moth, **B** Marsh Fritillary

Sea-spurrey, Rock *Spergularia rupicola*
Barret's Marbled Coronet

Sedge *Carex* spp.
Antler, Gold Spot, Red Sword-grass

Sedge, Glaucous *Carex flacca*
Least Minor

Sedge, Great Fen *Cladium mariscus*
Reed Tussock

Sedge, Tufted *Carex elata*
Reed Dagger

Sheep's-bit *Jasione montana*
Campanula Pug/Jasione Pug

Small-reed, Purple *Calamagrostis canescens*
Concolorous

Small-reed, Wood *Calamagrostis epigejos*
Lempke's Gold Spot, Mere Wainscot, Concolorous

Snapdragon *Antirrhinum majus*
Striped Hawk-moth

Sneezewort *Anthemis ptarmica*
Tawny-speckled Pug

Sorrel, Common *Rumex acetosa*
Bird's Wing, Blood-vein, Bordered Grey, Feathered Brindle, Fiery Clearwing, Forester, Grey Chi, **B** Small Copper

Sorrel, Sheep's *Rumex acetosella*
Forester, **B** Small Copper

Speedwell, Germander *Veronica chamaedrys*
B Heath Fritillary

Spikenard, Ploughman's *Inula conyzae*
Small Marbled

Spindle *Euonymus europaeus*
Scorched Carpet, **B** Holly Blue

Spruce *Picea* spp.
Grey Pine Carpet

Spruce, Norway *Picea abies*
Barred Red, Cloaked Pug (cones), Dusky Peacock,

Dwarf Pug, Feathered Beauty, Satin Beauty, Spruce Carpet, Tawny-barred Angle

Spruce, Sitka *Pivea sitchensis*
Spruce Carpet

Spurge *Euphorbia*
Spurge Hawk-moth

Spurge, Wood *Euphorbia amygdaloides*
Drab Looper

St John's Wort *Hypericum* spp.
Lesser Treble-bar, Purple Cloud, Treble Bar

Stitchwort *Stellaria* spp.
Cloaked Carpet, Sharp-angled Carpet

Stonecrop *Sedum* spp.
Scotch Annulet, Yellow-ringed Carpet

Stonecrop, Biting *Sedum acre*
Feathered Ranunculus

Stork's Bill, Common *Erodium cicutarium*
Satyr Pug (flowers), **B** Brown Argus

Strawberry, Wild *Fragaria vesca*
Dark Marbled Carpet, Kent Black Arches, **B** Grizzled Skipper

Sweet Briar *Rosa rubiginosa*
Shoulder Stripe

Sweet William *Dianthus barbatus*
Varied Coronet (seeds)

Sycamore *Acer pseudoplatanus*
Alder Moth, Mocha, Mottled Umber, Pale Oak Beauty, Sycamore

Tamarisk *Tamarix gallica*
Channel Islands Pug, Vapourer

Thistle *Carduus* and *Cirsium* spp.
Frosted Orange (root/stems), Purple Marbled (flowers/seeds), **B** Painted Lady

Thistle, Sow *Sonchus arvensis*
Shark

Thrift *Armeria maritima*
Black-banded, Feathered Ranunculus, Thrift Clearwing

Thyme, Wild *Thymus polytrichus*
Ashworth's Rustic, Lace Border, Satyr Pug (flowers), Straw Belle, Thyme Pug (flowers), Transparent Burnet, **B** Large Blue

Toadflax *Linaria* spp.
Toadflax Pug, Yellow Belle

Toadflax, Common *Linaria vulgaris*
Silver Y, Toadflax Brocade

Toadflax, Pale *Linaria repens*
Toadflax Brocade

Toadflax, Purple *Linaria purpurea*
Toadflax Brocade

Tormentil *Potentilla erecta*
Rosy Marbled (flowers)

Touch-me-not *Impatiens noli-tangere*
Netted Carpet

Traveller's Joy/Old Man's Beard *Clematis vitalba*
Fern, Haworth's Pug, Least Carpet, Lime-speck Pug
(flowers), Pretty Chalk Carpet, Small Emerald, Small
Waved Umber, Sub-angled Wave

Treacle Mustard *Erysimum cheiranthoides*
Grey Carpet

Tree Indigo *Indigofera tinctoria*
Levant Blackneck

Tree Lupin *Lupinus arboreus*
Feathered Ranunculus, Grass Eggar, Portland Moth

Trees
Alder Moth, Copper Underwing, Dark Dagger,
Dun-bar, Grey Dagger, Hebrew Character, Small
Quaker, Sprawler, Svensson's Copper Underwing,
Sycamore

Trefoil *Lotus* and *Trifolium* spp.
Annulet, Chalk Carpet, Common Heath, Latticed
Heath, Narrow-bordered Five-spot Burnet, Northern
Deep-brown Dart, Scarce Black Arches

Trefoil, Bird's Foot *Lotus corniculatus*
Belted Beauty, Bordered Grey, Burnet Companion,
Five-spot Burnet, Grass Eggar, Mother Shipton, New
Forest Burnet, Six-belted Clearwing, Six-spot Burnet,
Slender Scotch Burnet, **B** Clouded Yellow, Common
Blue, Dingy Skipper, Green Hairstreak

Trefoil, Greater Bird's Foot *Lotus pedunculatus*
Five-spot Burnet, **B** Dingy Skipper, Wood White

Valerian, Common *Valeriana officinalis*
Lesser Cream Wave, Valerian Pug

Valerian, Red *Centranthus ruber*
Large Ranunculus

Vetch *Vicia* spp.
Common Heath, Narrow-bordered Five-spot Burnet,
Scarce Black Arches, Shaded Broad-bar, Six-belted
Clearwing, **B** Dingy Skipper, Small Blue, Wood White

Vetch, Horseshoe *Hippocrepis comosa*
B Adonis Blue, Berger's Clouded Yellow, Chalkhill
Blue, Silver-studded Blue

Vetch, Tufted *Vicia cracca*
Blackneck

Vetch, Wood *Vicia sylvatica*
Scarce Blackneck

Vetchling, Meadow *Lathyrus pratensis*
Narrow-bordered Five-spot Burnet, New Forest Burnet,
B Wood White

Violet, Common Dog *Viola riviniana*
B Dark Green Fritillary, High-brown Fritillary, Pearl-
bordered Fritillary, Silver-washed Fritillary, Small Pearl-
bordered Fritillary

Violet, Marsh *Viola palustris*
B Small Pearl-bordered Fritillary

Virginia Creeper *Parthenocissus quinquefolia*
Silver-striped Hawk-moth

Wallflower *Erysimum cheiri*
Flame Carpet

Wayfaring Tree *Viburnum lantana*
Orange-tailed Clearwing

Willow *Salix* spp.
Chocolate-tip, Cream-bordered Green Pea, Dingy
Shears, Double Kidney, Eyed Hawk-moth, Flounced
Chestnut, Goat Moth, Herald, Lunar Hornet Moth,
Minor Shoulder-knot, Pebble Prominent, Poplar Grey,
Poplar Hawk-moth, Puss Moth, Red Underwing, Red-
tipped Clearwing, Red Underwing, Rosy Underwing,
Sallow Kitten, Scarce Chocolate-tip, Sharp-angled
Peacock, Small Chocolate-tip, Swallow Prominent,
White Satin, **B** Large Tortoiseshell

Willow, Creeping *Salix repens*
Belted Beauty, Chevron, Dark Bordered Beauty,
Nonconformist, Portland Moth, Small Grass Emerald

Willowherb *Epilobium* spp.
Bedstraw Hawk-moth, Elephant Hawk-moth,
Eversmann's Rustic, Silver-striped Hawk-moth, Small
Angle Shades, Small Phoenix, Twin-spot Carpet,
Willowherb Hawk-moth

Willowherb, Broad-leaved *Epilobium montanum*
Small Phoenix

Willowherb, Rosebay *Chamerion angustifolium*
Small Phoenix, White-banded Carpet

Wood borers
Clearwings, Goat Moth, Hornet Moth, Leopard Moth,
Lunar Hornet Moth

Wood-sedge *Carex sylvatica*
Silver Hook

Wormwood *Artemesia* spp.
Scarce Wormwood, Wormwood

Wormwood, Field *Artemesia campestris*
Dewick's Plusia, Spotted Clover

Wormwood, Sea *Seriphidium maritima*
Essex Emerald, Ground Lackey, Scarce Pug, Star-wort (flowers), Wormwood Pug (flowers)

Yarrow *Achillia millefolium*
Common Pug, Dewick's Plusia, Grey Pug, Lime-speck Pug (flowers), Mullein Wave, Sussex Emerald, Tawny-speckled Pug, V-Pug (flowers), Wormwood Pug (flowers), Yarrow Pug (seeds)

Yew *Taxus baccata*
Satin Beauty, Square Spot, Willow Beauty

Yorkshire-fog *Holcus lanatus*
Lempke's Gold Spot

Many moths are **polyphagous** (eat many different foods) and they are listed here:
Angle Shades, Archers Dart, Autumnal Rustic, Barred Chestnut, Beaded Chestnut, Beautiful Brocade, Beautiful Golden Y, Bird's Wing, Black Rustic, Blossom Underwing, Bright-line Brown-eye, Broad-bordered Yellow Underwing, Broom Moth, Brown Rustic, Brown-spot Pinion, Brown-tail, Buff Ermine, Chestnut, Clouded Buff, Coast Dart, Common Emerald, Cream-spot Tiger, Crescent Dart, Crimson Speckled, Dark Brocade, Dark Chestnut, Dark Sword-grass, Dark Tussock, Dog's Tooth, Dot Moth, Dotted Clay, Double Dart, Double Square-spot, Double-striped Pug (flowers), Feathered Footman, Feathered Ranunculus, Fen Square-spot, Flame, Flame Shoulder, Fox Moth, Garden Dart, Garden Tiger, Gold Spot, Golden Spangle, Gothic, Grass Eggar, Green Arches, Grey Arches, Grey Chi, Ground Lackey, Gypsy Moth, Heart and Club, Heart and Dart, Hebrew Character, Ingrailed Clay, Jersey Tiger, Jubilee Fan-foot (withered leaves), Knot Grass, Large Ranunculus, Large Yellow Underwing, Least Yellow Underwing, Lesser Broad-bordered Yellow Underwing, Lesser Yellow Underwing, Light Brocade, Light Feathered Rustic, Little Emerald, Lunar Yellow Underwing, March Moth, Mediterranean Brocade, Mottled Rustic, Mouse Moth, Muslin Moth, Northern Drab, Northern Rustic, Oak Eggar, Old Lady, Orache Moth, Pale Shining Brown, Pale-shouldered Brocade, Pearly Underwing, Plain Clay, Plain Golden Y, Porter's Rustic, Powdered Rustic, Purple Clay, Radford's Flame Shoulder, Red Chestnut, Red Sword-grass, Ruby Tiger, Rustic, Scarce Bordered Straw, Scarce Vapourer, Scarlet Tiger, Setaceous Hebrew Character, Shears, Shuttle Shaped Dart, Silurian, Silver Y, Silvery Arches, Six-striped Rustic, Small Angle Shades, Small Mottled Willow, Small Square-spot, Speckled Footman, Square-spot Dart, Square-spot Rustic, Square-spotted Clay, Sword-grass, Treble Lines, Triple-spotted Clay, Twin-spot Carpet, Uncertain, Vine's Rustic, Water Ermine, White Colon, White Ermine, White-line Dart, Wood Tiger, Yellow Shell

BIBLIOGRAPHY

These publications and websites were either consulted in the preparation of this book or are of interest generally. This is not, of course, a complete list of books, sites or organisations and in no way implies that only these would be useful.

Many county moth groups and individuals have published books and/or run their own websites, packed with information. Your own county site is often the place to start if you would like to attend a moth-watching evening or have found a moth that you cannot identify, or just want to tell someone about your exciting find! Each county has its own recorder who will be pleased to check identifications and receive records.

Next time you see a moth sitting on a window pane, try to identify it. It is bound to be interesting. If you find a caterpillar in your exotic fruit or vegetables, don't complain, keep it. It might turn out to be a new record for Britain.

Photographs and descriptions of larvae of all known British macro-moths and butterflies.

Razowski, J. (2002/3). *Tortricidae of Europe*, Vols 1 & 2. Frantisek Slamka, Bratislava.
Very clear photographs of set adults, description and distribution details, genitalia drawings.

Skinner, B. (1998). *Moths of the British Isles*. Viking.
Standard text book covering all known resident and migrant Macro moths. Life size set specimens.

Thomas, J.A. (1986). *RSNC Guide to Butterflies of the British Isles*. Country Life Books.
Descriptions, distribution maps, drawings and photographs.

Waring, P. and Townsend, M. (2003). *Field Guide to the Moths of Great Britain & Ireland*. British Wildlife Publishing.
Comprehensive information, with 1,600 superb illustrations by Richard Lewington.

BOOKS

Bradley, J.D. (2000). *Checklist of Lepidoptera Recorded from the British Isles*. Bradley & Bradley.
The complete systematic arrangement of British species with Log numbers.

Emmet, A.M. (ed.) (2007). *The Moths and Butterflies of Great Britain and Ireland*. Harley Books.
Nine volumes available (2007) covering most British species with illustrations, descriptions, distribution maps, genitalia, lifestyle and habitat.

McGavin, G.C. (2005). *Pocket Nature: Insects & Spiders*. Dorling Kindersley.
Photographic guide to a wide range of insects and spiders of Britain and Europe.

Goater, B. (1986). *British Pyralid Moths*. Harley Books.
Similar to Skinner (1998), but for pyrales.

Leverton, R. (2001). *Enjoying Moths*. Poyser.
Lavishly illustrated with stunning photographs and fascinating text – lives up to its title.

Lewington, R. (2003). *Pocket Guide to the Butterflies of Great Britain and Ireland*. British Wildlife Publishing.
All life-cycle stages beautifully illustrated by the author, with informative text.

Manley, C. (2006). *Moths of Trigon*. Pavonia Print.
An introduction to moths and mothing on a Dorset country estate. 500 species illustrated.

Manley, W.B.L. (1973). *A Guide to* Acleris cristana *in Britain*. (Denis & Schiffermueller, 1775, reprinted from *Entomologist's Gazette*, Vol. 24). 119 forms illustrated and described.

Porter, J. (1997). *Caterpillars of the British Isles*. Viking.

WEBSITES

www.atropos.info
Editor: Mark Tunmore, 36 Tinker Lane, Meltham, Holmfirth, West Yorkshire HD9 4EX
Atropos is the only independent journal devoted to the Lepidoptera and Odonata of the British Isles, and concentrates mainly on migrant moths, with plenty of illustrations.

www.david.element.ukgateway.net
Wide selection of photographs of insects, spiders, beetles, birds, reptiles and mammals.

www.dorsetmothgroup.org.uk
Moth sightings and events in Dorset.

www.kendall-bioresearch.co.uk
Clearly explains the taxonomy of insects and other classes, along with anatomical illustrations.

www.leps.it
Moths and butterflies of Europe and North Africa. Based in Italy, and good for unusual migrants.

www.mothshots.com
Moth photographs by Keith Tailby.

www.nationalmothnight.info
This annual event is run jointly by Atropos and Butterfly Conservation. The aim is to record moths throughout Britain from as many different participants and localities as possible on one particular night in a year. This provides a good snapshot of what is on the wing at the time. The date varies from year to year.

www.portlandbirdobs.btinternet.co.uk
Martin Cade runs moth lights on Portland most nights and posts stunning photographs of migrant moths and birds on a daily basis.

WEBSITES (cont.)

www.simplybirdsandmoths.co.uk
Descriptive title, with images and information by Tony Davison.

www.suffolkmoths.org.uk
Hugely informative county moth site.

www.ukbutterflies.co.uk
Site run by Pete Eeles, with information on, and images of, all British species of butterfly.

www.uklepidoptera.co.uk
Photographs and text by Jeff Higgott.

www.ukmoths.org.uk
A brilliant website run by Ian Kimber, aiming to show photographs of all UK moths. At the end of 2007 it featured 1,800 species.

EQUIPMENT SUPPLIERS

www.angleps.com
Anglian Lepidopterist Supplies, Station Road, Hindolveston, Norfolk NR20 5DE
Entomology supplies, moth light traps, etc. A very informative site.

www.bioquip.net
Bioquip, 1 Clive Cottage, London Road, Allostock, Knutsford, Cheshire WA16 9LT
Moth traps, nets, pheromones, generators, etc.

www.watdon.com
Watkins & Doncaster, P.O. Box 5, Cranbrook, Kent TN18 5EZ
Entomological equipment, traps, books, etc. Established in 1874, the founder of London Zoo insect house.

FURTHER INFORMATION

THE WILDLIFE AND COUNTRYSIDE ACT, 1981

The following species of Lepidoptera are protected by law from being taken, interfered with or disturbed in England, Scotland and Wales. The Act also covers all other plants and animals. These species are considered at risk of extinction. The list is administered by the statutory body, the **Joint Nature Conservation Committee** (www.jncc.gov.uk) and reviewed every 5 years.

0168 New Forest Burnet
0384 Fiery Clearwing
1539 Swallowtail Butterfly
1581 Large Blue
1606 High Brown Fritillary
1610 Marsh Fritillary
1613 Heath Fritillary
1668 Essex Emerald
1672 Sussex Emerald
1785 Barberry Carpet
1966 Black-veined Moth
2168 Viper's Bugloss (presumed extinct)
2365 Fisher's Estuarine Moth
2393 Reddish Buff

OTHER ORGANISATIONS

Amateur Entomologists' Society
P.O. Box 8774, London SW7 5ZG
www.amentsoc.org
Publishes *The Bulletin* magazine and many useful handbooks and guides. Also runs field meetings, online forums and the AES Bug Club for younger members. Holds a large annual exhibition at Kempton Park, London, in October.

British Entomological & Natural History Society
Dinton Pastures Country Park, Davis Street, Hurst, Reading, Berks RG10 0TH
www.benhs.org.uk
Publishes the *British Journal of Entomology and Natural History*. Maintains a library and invertebrate collections that are open to members. Arranges lectures and runs a programme of field meetings in the summer. Holds an annual exhibition in London.

Butterfly Conservation
Manor Yard, East Lulworth, Wareham, Dorset BH20 5QP
Tel: 0870 774 4309
www.butterfly-conservation.org
Nationwide, with local branches. Works for the interests of Britain's moths and butterflies. Publishes *Butterfly* magazine. Administers the UK Biodiversity Action Plans for Lepidoptera covering 81 species of moth worthy of particular recording and conservation effort. It also runs the **National Moth Recording Scheme**, which aims to increase public awareness of moths and create a national database for all moth records (www.mothscount.org). This is administered from Butterfly Conservation headquarters.

Royal Entomological Society
41 Queen's Gate, London SW7 5HR
www.royensoc.co.uk
Founded in 1833, Charles Darwin was a Fellow. Publishes members' journal and many other handbooks and guides.

INDEX

Page numbers in *italic* refer to the Caterpillars, Eggs and Pupae section.